General Class

FCC License Preparation
for
Element 3
General Class Theory

by
Gordon West
WB6NOA

---

with Technical Editor
Eric P. Nichols
KL7AJ

Ninth Edition

Master Publishing, Inc.

Also by Gordon West, WB6NOA
with
Eric P. Nichols, KL7AJ

Technician Class
FCC License Preparation for
Element 2 Technician Class Theory
Also available as an audio book on CD
and with W5YI Ham Study software

Extra Class
FCC License Preparation for
Element 4 Extra Class Theory
Also available as an audio book on CD
and with W5YI Ham Study software

GROL + RADAR
General Radiotelephone Operator License
Plus Ship Radar Endorsement
with Pete Trotter, KB9SMG and Eric P. Nichols, KL7AJ
FCC Commercial Radio License Preparation for
Element 1, Element 3, and Element 8 Question Pools
Also available with
W5YI Comm Study Software

For more information visit
www.W5YI.org
or call 800-669-9594

About the Author

Gordon West, WB6NOA

Gordon West has been a ham radio operator for more than 50 years, holding the top Extra Class license, call sign WB6NOA. He also holds the highest FCC commercial operator license, the First Class General Radiotelephone Certificate with Radar Endorsement.

Gordon teaches evening ham radio classes and offers weekend ham radio licensing seminars on a monthly schedule. These seminars cover entry-level and upgrade licenses in ham radio. He has served on the faculty of Coastline College and Orange Coast College. Gordon is a regular contributor to amateur radio, marine, and general two-way radio magazines. He is a fellow of the Radio Club of America, and a life member of the American Radio Relay League. The ARRL presented Gordon with its "Instructor of the Year" award. The Dayton Amateur Radio Association named Gordon their "2006 Amateur of the Year" for his efforts in recruiting and training new amateurs, in addition to his lifelong involvement in ham radio. Through his Gordon West Radio School, he has trained eight out of ten newly-licensed hams with his classes, books and audio courses over the past 35 years.

Eric P. Nichols, KL7AJ
Technical Editor

Joining author Gordon West for this new Ninth Edition of his General Class study manual as Technical Editor is Eric P. Nichols, KL7AJ. Eric has been a licensed amateur operator since 1972, holding the top Extra Class license, as well as the FCC GROL commercial license. He has spent his adult career in various aspects of radio research, broadcast communications, and teaching.

A prolific author, he has written many articles for *QST, QEX,* and a number of other ham radio magazines, as well as professional journals. In 2010 and again in 2014 he was the recipient of the William Orr, W6SAI, Technical Writing Award conferred by the American Radio Relay League for articles he authored for QST magazine. He is the author of *Radio Science for the Radio Amateur*, and *The Opus of Amateur Radio Knowledge and Lore*. Along with Gordon West, WB6NOA he is Technical Editor of the *GROL+RADAR* study manual for the FCC commercial radio licenses.

Eric lives in North Pole, AK. He has operated just about every mode available to the radio amateur, but always returns to CW on the lower HF bands as his "default" mode. He enjoys restoring vintage "boat anchor" radio equipment as well as designing cutting edge radio instrumentation with Arduino, his latest obsession. Being in interior Alaska, he gets a lot of requests from new hams (and some older ones) for a first-time Alaskan radio contact, and is always willing to try a "sked" on any HF band or mode!

This book was developed and published by:
Master Publishing, Inc.
Niles, Illinois

Editing by:
Pete Trotter, KB9SMG and Karin Thompson, K0RTX

Photograph Credit:
All photographs that do not have a source identification are either from the author,
or Master Publishing, Inc. originals.

Cartoons by:
Carson Haring, AC0BU

*Thanks to the following for their assistance with this book: Suzy West, N6GLF; Don
Arnold, W6GPS; Chip Margelli, K7JA; Dennis Gonya, K6LIG; Tracy Lenocker,
WA6ERA; Marilynn Jordan, W6MCJ; Larry Wilson, K6SCH; Jim Ford, N6JF; Dave
Forbes, W5FUZ; Dave Mitchell, AJ5F; Jim Colwell, KG5GIF; Dave Stites, W6TUX;
and California Rescue Net members.*

Ninth Edition
    5   4   3   2

Table of Contents

QUESTION POOL NOMENCLATURE

The latest nomenclature changes and question pool numbering system recommended by the Volunteer Examiner Coordinator's Question Pool Committee (QPC) have been incorporated in this book. The General Class (Element 3) question pool has been rewritten at the high-school reading level. This question pool is valid from July 1, 2015 through June 30, 2019.

FCC RULES, REGULATIONS AND POLICIES

The NCVEC QPC releases revised question pools on a regular cycle, and issues deletions as necessary. The FCC releases changes to FCC rules, regulations and policies as they are implemented. This book includes the most recent information released by the FCC at the time this copy was printed.

Preface

Welcome to General Class amateur radio!

The General Class license gives you privileges on all of the worldwide amateur radio bands for long-range skywave communications. These new bands will add to your Technician Class HF, VHF and UHF privileges. With a General Class license, you will receive operating privileges on every ham radio band for voice, data, video, and CW.

As a General Class operator, you'll be able to travel the world and always stay in touch using skywave communications. Whether you sail the international waters of the South Seas, or cruise the highways of North America or Europe, you can stay in touch. More good news – recent international agreements allow you to operate in many foreign ports and countries without having to officially sign-up for a reciprocal license.

You'll be able to help our hobby grow with your General Class license! We encourage you to join an all-General Volunteer Examination team to conduct Element 2 Technician Class written exams. As you gain experience with your new license, you can actively recruit new ham radio operators to our hobby and service.

This new Ninth Edition of our book covers everything you need to know to pass the General Class Element 3 written examination. There is no longer a Morse code test required for any class of ham license! The Federal Communications Commission eliminated the Morse code test requirement effective February 23, 2007.

The question pool in this book is effective July 1, 2015 through June 30, 2019. The only prerequisite to take the exam for your new General Class license is a valid Technician Class license or a recently-earned CSCE for Technician Element 2.

This new edition of *General Class* will make your test preparation a breeze. We've reorganized the entire, new Element 3 General Class question pool to improve your learning experience and cut down on the study time required to pass the exam.

We are on the air daily and hope to talk to you soon on the General Class bands!

73

Gordon West, WB6NOA

Eric P. Nichols, KL7AJ

About This Book

Our book provides you with all of the study material you need to prepare yourself to pass the Element 3 General Class examination. The test questions and 4 distracters are presented in this book exactly as you'll see them on the exam. We have reorganized the questions and answers into common subject groups for more logical learning. This will cut down on your study time and improve your knowledge of how to operate as a General Class ham!

The Federal Communications Commission completely eliminated Morse code testing as a requirement for any amateur radio license effective February 23, 2007. We always encourage our students to know the code, so this book has a complete chapter on fun ways to begin learning Morse code once you are on the air as a new General Class operator. Chapter 5 gives you sound advice on how to learn the Morse code. Even though there is no more code test, knowing the dots and dashes will help you become a better General Class operator.

Our book also provides you with valuable information you need to be an active ham on the HF worldwide bands. To help you get the most out of *General Class*, here's a look at how the book is organized:

- *Chapter 1* explains in detail the new HF operating privileges you'll earn by passing your Element 3 General Class written examination.

- *Chapter 2* provides a look at the history of amateur radio licensing in the U.S., and the current status of all license classes.

- *Chapter 3* contains all 462 Element 3 General Class questions, 35 of which will be on your upcoming exam. You'll notice that the questions and answers have been reorganized to follow the syllabus Gordo uses to teach General Class at his Radio School weekend sessions. It makes your learning experience easier and more meaningful.

- *Chapter 4* tells you how to find an exam site, what to do before you get to the site, what required papers to bring with you, and what to check for when you pass your exam.

- *Chapter 5* gives solid advice on how to learn Morse code at 5 wpm.

- *The Appendix* contains a list of VECs, a Glossary of important ham radio terms, and other useful information.

If you need additional study materials, we've recorded an audio course that follows this book, and W5YI also has interactive software to allow you to study for upcoming exams on your PC. In addition, Gordo also has recorded audio courses for learning Morse code.

Need additional study materials?
Call W5YI at 800-669-9594 or go to www.w5yi.org

General Class Privileges

The General Class amateur license permits you to use segments of every amateur band for worldwide, long-distance voice, data, and video communications. These new privileges add to those you now enjoy with your current amateur license.

The General Class license has always been considered "the big one" because of the almost unlimited skywave privileges this license provides on each of the worldwide ham bands. Although the older, grandfathered Novice and Technician-Plus licenses offer slivers of worldwide band privileges, it is the General Class license that gives you major operating "elbow room" on segments of all the worldwide bands. Whether it's day or night, summer or winter, these worldwide bands will always offer skywave communications for thousands of miles of range.

Gordo at the controls of the United Nations Station, 4U1UN, in New York.

Never in the history of amateur radio has it been easier than now to obtain the General Class license. There is no more Morse code test. The Federal Communications Commission concluded "…this change (eliminating the code test) eliminates an unnecessary burden that may discourage current amateur radio operators from advancing their skills and participating more fully in the benefits of amateur radio." Most other countries have dropped their Morse code test requirements, too.

The Element 3 theory exam has been dramatically improved in content, better reflecting General Class worldwide radio equipment and antennas. Simple math questions deal with modern, high frequency equipment. No longer will you need to memorize "far out" formulas that you would rarely use as a licensed ham radio operator. There is more emphasis on General Class operating, band plans, data modes, and high frequency simple antennas to build. Although this new question pool is more comprehensive in entire content, your upcoming exam remains at 35 multiple choice questions, 74% passing grade.

WORLDWIDE SPECTRUM

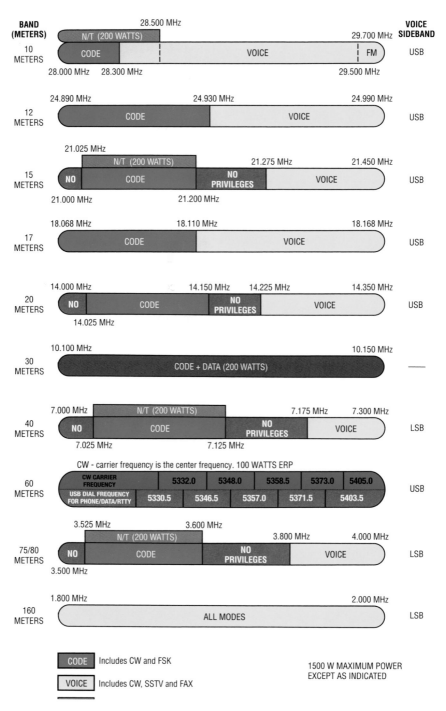

Figure 1-1. General Class HF License Privileges

GENERAL CLASS LICENSE PRIVILEGES

Figure 1-1 graphically illustrates your new General Class code, data, and voice privileges on the medium frequency (MF) (300 kHz-3 MHz) and high frequency (HF) (3 MHz-30 MHz) bands. Code and data privileges are in the designated areas on the left side of each band. Voice privileges are on the right side of each band. Designated areas between the code and voice privileges have "no privileges" for the General Class operator. These are reserved for grandfathered Advanced Class and current Extra Class operators.

As you can see, grandfathered Advanced and Extra Class operators have the same band privileges that you will enjoy as a General Class operator, they just have a little bit more elbow room. But don't worry – there is plenty of room throughout the General Class voice spectrum for working the world!

160 METERS, 1.8 MHZ - 2.0 MHZ

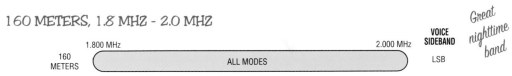

General Class privileges let you operate voice and code from one end to the other of the 160-meter band. These are the same privileges enjoyed by Advanced and Extra Class operators. The 160-meter band is great for long-distance, nighttime communications. At night, 160 meters lets you work the world!

75/80 METERS, 3.500 MHZ - 4.000 MHZ

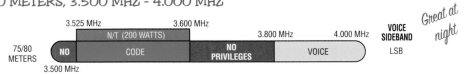

On 75/80 meters, General Class code, data, and radioteletype (RTTY) privileges are from 3.525 to 3.600 MHz. Single sideband voice privileges were recently expanded to 3.800 to 4.000 MHz.

60 METERS – 5 CHANNELS

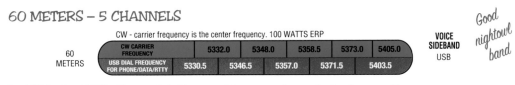

In 2003, the FCC allocated 5 discrete 60 meter channels for ham radio use on a non-interference basis with Government and Military stations, which are primary on this band. We are permitted 100 watts effective radiated power, referenced to a unity gain half-wave dipole. On upper side band (USB), tune your radio dial to read the carrier frequency shown on the lower bar. Voice emissions may not occupy more than 2.8 kHz, common for most ham transceivers. In the data modes, tune to this same carrier frequency and your data signal occupies up 1.5 kHz, in channel center. For CW, select the CW mode and tune to the channel CENTER frequency shown in the upper bar. On newer rigs, these 5 channels are pre-memorized for different modes of operation so no VFO tuning is required! More details for operating on 60 meters are on page 234 in the Appendix.

40 METERS, 7.000 MHZ - 7.300 MHZ

Good day & night

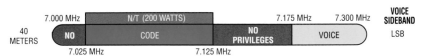

On 40 meters, General Class code, data, and RTTY privileges are enjoyed from 7.025 to 7.125 MHz. Single sideband voice privileges recently were expanded to 7.175 to 7.300 MHz. During daylight hours, 40 meters is a great band for base station and mobile contacts up to 500 miles away. At night, 40 meters skips all over the country, and many times all over the world!

30 METERS, 10.100 MHZ - 10.150 MHZ

Hot band for CW & data

Only code, data, and RTTY are permitted on this band. Thirty meters is located just above the 10-MHz WWV time broadcasts on shortwave radio. Voice is not allowed on this band by any class of amateur operator. Power is limited to 200 watts PEP.

20 METERS, 14.000 MHZ - 14.350 MHZ

Long-range day & evening contact

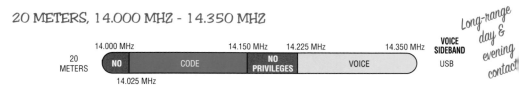

This is the best DX worldwide band there is, day or night! Morse code, data, and radioteletype (RTTY) privileges extend from 14.025 to 14.150 MHz. General Class voice privileges extend from 14.225 to 14.350 MHz. This is where the real DX activity takes place. Almost 24 hours a day, you should be able to work stations in excess of 5000 miles away on the 20-meter band with only a modest antenna setup. If you are a mariner, most of the long range maritime mobile bands are within your privileges as a General Class operator. If you are into recreational vehicles (RVs), there are nets on the 20 meter band all over the country especially for you. The "where it's at" band is 20 meters when you want to work the world from your car, boat, RV, or home shack!

17 METERS, 18.068 MHZ - 18.168 MHZ

Best during the day

All emission types are authorized on this newer Amateur Radio band. There is plenty of elbow room here with lots of foreign DX coming in day and night. Most new base antennas have 17 meters included.

15 METERS, 21.000 MHZ - 21.450 MHZ

Daytime band

15 meter General Class CW, data and RTTY privileges extend from 21.025 to 21.200 MHz. Single sideband voice privileges recently were expanded on 15 meters to 21.275 to 21.450 MHz. The 15 meter band is great for daytime skywave contacts. This is a popular band for mobile operators because antenna requirements are relatively small. We've worked all over the world on the 15 meter band with mobile equipment.

12 METERS, 24.890 MHZ - 24.990 MHZ

Best in daytime

Code, data, and RTTY privileges on the 12-meter band extend from 24.890 to 24.930 MHz. Voice privileges are from 24.930 to 24.990 MHz. Although this is a very narrow band, expect excellent daytime range throughout the world. At night, range is limited to groundwave coverage because the ionosphere is not receiving sunlight to produce skywave coverage on this band.

10 METERS, 28.000 MHZ - 29.700 MHZ

Daytime band that may or may not be open for "skip"

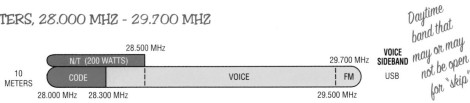

General Class CW, data, and RTTY privileges begin at the very bottom of the band, 28.000 MHz, and extend up to 28.300 MHz. Voice privileges begin at 28.300 MHz and extend up to 29.700 MHz. This expands your voice privileges on this band from those you enjoy as a Technician Class operator. And wait until you try the full fidelity of frequency modulation (FM) on 29.600 MHz! There are even FM repeaters at the top of 10 meters, too.

Don't forget your handheld!
When you upgrade to
General, you keep your VHF/
UHF/SHF privileges.

6 METERS AND UP

Your General Class license allows you unlimited band privileges and unlimited emission privileges on several higher-frequency bands, as shown in *Table 1-1*.

Table 1-1. 6 Meter and Higher Band Privileges

Frequency	Meters
50-54 MHz	6 meters
144-148 MHz	2 meters
222-225 MHz	1.25 meters
420-450 MHz	0.70 meters (70 cm)
902-928 MHz	0.35 meters (35 cm)
1240-1300 MHz	0.23 meters (23 cm)

MICROWAVE BANDS

Your General Class license allows you unlimited band privileges and unlimited emission privileges in the microwave bands, as indicated in *Table 1-2*. These VHF, UHF, and SHF frequencies are the same ones for which you received privileges when you passed your Technician or Technician-Plus Class examinations.

Table 1-2. Microwave Band Frequency Privileges

Frequency	Frequency
2300-2310 MHz	47.0-47.2 GHz
2390-2450 MHz	75.5-1.0 GHz
3.3-3.5 GHz	119.98-20.02 GHz
5.65-5.925 GHz	142-49 GHz
10.0-10.5 GHz	241-50 GHz
24.0-24.25 GHz	All above 300 GHz

Our first book, *Technician Class*, for Element 2, provides a detailed explanation of the VHF, UHF, and SHF bands and presents the specific ARRL-recommended band plans for these frequencies. *Technician Class* is available from your local amateur radio dealer, at hamfests, or by calling The W5YI Group at 800/669-9594, or visit **www.w5yi.org**.

THE CONSIDERATE OPERATOR'S FREQUENCY GUIDE

Nothing in the FCC rules recognizes special privileges on any specific frequency for a net, group, or individual. No one "owns" a frequency. Rather, amateur operators rely on "gentlemen's agreements," good amateur practice, and common sense for all ham operators to check to see if the frequency is in use prior to transmitting – regardless of mode.

That said, here's a handy listing of frequencies that are generally recognized for certain modes or activities. Our thanks to our friends at *ARRL*, who gave us permission to reprint it here.

160 Meters (1.8 – 2.0 MHz)

1.800-2.000	CW
1.800-1.810	Digital Modes
1.810	CW QRP calling frequency
1.843-2.000	SSB, SSTV and other wideband modes
1.910	SSB QRP
1.995-2.000	Experimental
1.999-2.000	Beacons

80 Meters (3.5 – 4.0 MHz)

3.500-3.510	CW DX window
3.560	QRP CW calling frequency
3.570-3.600	RTTY/Data
3.585-3.600	Automatically controlled data stations
3.590	RTTY/Data DX
3.790-3.800	DX window
3.845	SSTV
3.885	AM calling frequency
3.985	QRP SSB calling frequency

40 Meters (7.0 – 7.3 MHz)

7.030	QRP CW calling frequency
7.040	RTTY/Data DX
7.070-7.125	RTTY/Data
7.100-7.105	Automatically controlled data stations
7.171	SSTV
7.173	D-SSTV
7.285	QRP SSB calling frequency
7.290	AM calling frequency

30 Meters (10.1 – 10.15 MHz)

10.130-10.140	RTTY/Data
10.140-10.150	Automatically controlled data stations

20 Meters (14.0 – 14.35 MHz)

14.060	QRP CW calling frequency
14.070-14.095	RTTY/Data
14.095-14.0995	Automatically controlled data stations
14.100	IBP/NCDXF beacons
14.1005-14.112	Automatically controlled data stations
14.230	SSTV
14.233	D-SSTV
14.236	Digital Voice
14.285	QRP SSB calling frequency
14.286	AM calling frequency

17 Meters (18.068 – 18.168 MHz)

18.100-18.105	RTTY/Data
18.105-18.110	Automatically controlled data stations
18.110	IBP/NCDXF beacons
18.162.5	Digital Voice

15 Meters (21.0 – 21.45 MHz)

21.060	QRP CW calling frequency
21.070-21.110	RTTY/Data
21.090-21.100	Automatically controlled data stations
21.150	IBP/NCDXF beacons
21.340	SSTV
21.385	QRP SSB calling frequency

12 Meters (24.89 – 24.99 MHz)

24.920-24.925	RTTY/Data
24.925-24.930	Automatically controlled data stations
24.930	IBP/NCDXF beacons

10 Meters (28.0 – 29.7 MHz)

28.060	QRP CW calling frequency
28.070-28.120	RTTY/Data
28.120-28.189	Automatically controlled data stations
28.190-28.225	Beacons
28.200	IBP/NCDXF beacons
28.385	QRP SSB calling frequency
28.680	SSTV
29.000-29.200	AM
29.300-29.510	Satellite downlinks
29.520-29.580	Repeater inputs
29.600	FM simplex
29.620-29.680	Repeater outputs

TECHNICIAN EXAM ADMINISTRATION

There is one more very important privilege you gain when you achieve General Class status. As a General Class licensee, you may take part in the administration of Element 2 Technician Class written examinations, once you become accredited as a volunteer examiner at the General Class level by a VEC.

So, if you wish to see the amateur service grow in your local area, find 2 other General Class operators, then contact your local or national VEC for accreditation, and start your own testing team for newcomers to our hobby.

To become an accredited Volunteer Examiner as a General Class licensee call the W5YI VEC at 800-669-9594.

SUMMARY

In late 2006, the FCC "refarmed" code, data, and voice privileges for General, Advanced, and Extra Class operators. All of the band charts in this new book have been updated to reflect the added privileges for high frequency voice operation. The FCC tightened up the code spectrum, and added more elbow room to the voice spectrum. General Class operators gained:

- 50 kHz of voice spectrum on 75 meters
- 50 kHz of voice spectrum on 40 meters
- 25 kHz of voice spectrum on 15 meters

With the elimination of the Morse code test on February 23, 2007, and the addition of all of this voice spectrum, General Class is the place to be!

Are you ready to prepare for the General Class Element 3 written examination? We sure hope so. Welcome – in advance – to the worldwide bands! We hope to hear you on the high frequency bands very soon.

2

A Little Ham History!

Ham radio has changed a lot in the 100-plus years since radio's inception. In the past 25 years, we have seen some monumental changes! So, before we get started preparing for the exam, we're going to give you a little refresher lesson about our hobby, its history, and an overview of how you'll progress through the amateur ranks to the top amateur ticket – the Extra Class license.

In this chapter you'll learn all of the licensing requirements under the FCC rules that became effective April 15, 2000. And you'll learn about the six classes of license that were in effect *prior* to those rules changes. That way, when you run into a Novice, Technician Plus or Advanced Class operator on the air, you'll have some understanding of their skill level, experience, and frequency privileges.

WHAT IS THE AMATEUR SERVICE?

There are more than 743,000 Americans who are licensed amateur radio operators in the U.S. today. The Federal Communications Commission, the Federal agency responsible for licensing amateur operators, defines our radio service this way:

"The amateur service is for qualified persons of all ages who are interested in radio technique solely with a personal aim and without pecuniary interest."

Ham radio is first and foremost a fun hobby! In addition, it is a service. And note the word "qualified" in the FCC's definition – that's the reason why you're studying for an exam; so when you pass the exam, you prove that you are qualified to get on the air.

Millions of operators around the world exchange ham radio greetings and messages by voice, radioteletype, telegraphy, facsimile, and television worldwide. Japan, alone, has more than a million hams! It is very commonplace for U.S. amateurs to communicate with Russian amateurs. China is just getting started with its amateur service. Being a ham operator is a great way to promote international good will.

The benefits of ham radio are countless! Ham operators are probably known best for their contributions during times of disaster. In recent years, many recreational sailors in the Caribbean who have been attacked by modern-day pirates have had their lives saved by hams directing rescue efforts. Following the 9/11 terrorist attacks on the World Trade Center and the Pentagon, literally thousands of local hams assisted with emergency communications. After Katrina blew through New Orleans, ham radio operators were the first to report the levee breach and to warn that flood waters were rushing into the city.

The ham community knows no geographic, political or social barrier. If you study hard and make the effort, you are going to earn your upgrade to General Class and get on the HF worldwide bands. Follow the suggestions in our book and your chances of passing the written exam are excellent, and learning will be easy and fun!

A BRIEF HISTORY OF AMATEUR RADIO LICENSING

Before government licensing of radio stations and amateur operators was instituted in 1912, hams could operate on any wavelength they chose and could even select their own call letters. The Radio Act of 1912 mandated the first Federal licensing of all radio stations and assigned amateurs to the short wavelengths of less than 200 meters. These "new" requirements didn't deter them, and within a few years there were thousands of licensed ham operators in the United States.

Since electromagnetic signals do not respect national boundaries, radio is international in scope. National governments enact and enforce radio laws within a framework of international agreements that are overseen by the International Telecommunications Union. The ITU is a worldwide United Nations agency headquartered in Geneva, Switzerland. The ITU divides the radio spectrum into a number of frequency bands, with each band reserved for a particular use. Amateur radio is fortunate to have many bands allocated to it all across the radio spectrum.

In the U.S., the Federal Communications Commission is the government agency responsible for the regulation of wire and radio communications. The FCC allocates frequency bands in accordance with the ITU plan to the various services – including the amateur service – and regulates stations and operators.

By international agreement, in 1927 the alphabet was apportioned among various nations for basic call sign use. The prefix letters K, N and W were assigned solely to the United States. The letter A is shared by the United States and other countries.

In the early years of amateur radio licensing in the U.S., the classes of licenses were designated by the letters "A," "B," and "C." The highest license class with the most privileges was "A." In 1951, the FCC dropped the letter designations and gave the license classes names – names that are familiar to us today. Class A became Advanced; Class B became General; and Class C became Conditional. At the same time, the FCC also created the Extra Class, and Technician Class licenses. They also added a new Novice Class – a one-year, non-renewable license for beginners that required a 5-wpm Morse code speed proficiency test and a 20-question written examination on elementary theory and regulations, with both tests taken before one licensed ham.

The General exam required 13-wpm code speed, and Extra required 20-wpm. Each of the five written exams was progressively more comprehensive and formed what came to be known as the *Incentive Licensing System.*

In the '70s, the Technician Class license became very popular because of the number of repeater stations appearing on the air that extended the range of VHF and UHF mobile and handheld radios. It also was very fashionable to be able to patch your mobile radio into the telephone system, which allowed hams to make telephone calls from their automobiles long before the advent of cell phones.

In 1979, the international amateur service regulations were changed to permit all countries to waive the manual Morse code proficiency requirement for "...stations making use exclusively of frequencies above 30 MHz." This set the stage for creation of the Technician "no-code" license in 1991, when the 5-wpm Morse code requirement was eliminated. New "no-code" Technician licensees were permitted to operate on all amateur bands above 30 MHz. Applicants for the no-code Technician license had to pass the 35-question Novice and 30-question Technician Class written examinations but no Morse code test.

"No-code" Technician Class amateurs who passed a 5-wpm code test were awarded a Technician-Plus license. Besides their 30 MHz and higher no-code frequency privileges, Tech-Plus licensees gained the Novice CW privileges and a sliver of the 10 meter voice spectrum.

With these changes in 1991, there were six amateur service license classes – Novice, Technician, Technician-Plus, General, Advanced, and Extra – along with five written exams and three Morse code tests used to qualify hams for their various licenses.

The Amateur Service is Restructured

As you can see, through the years the ham radio licensing and privileges underwent a myriad of changes. In 1998, the FCC began working with the ham radio community to restructure our amateur radio service to make it more effective. The objective of this restructuring was to streamline the license process, eliminate unnecessary and duplicated rules, and reduce the emphasis on the Morse code test. The result of this review was a complete restructuring of the U.S. amateur service, which became effective April 15, 2000. The restructuring included a change in the Morse code requirement for General and Extra classes to 5-wpm and the reduction from six to three amateur radio license classes. Since 2000 there have been only 3 amateur radio license classes:

- Technician Class, the HF/VHF/UHF entry level license.
- General Class, the HF entry level license, which required a 5-wpm code test.
- Amateur Extra Class, a technically oriented senior license, based on-5wpm code credit.

The next major change to FCC Amateur Radio rules occurred on February 23, 2007, when the FCC completely eliminated the Morse code examination for all amateur radio licenses! The FCC action was based on 6,200 written comments, with most supporting the elimination of all code tests. At the same time, the FCC also "upgraded" No-code Technician Class operators, awarding them use of the Novice and Technician-Plus high frequency privileges on 80, 40, 15, and 10 meters.

In its public notice announcing elimination of the Morse code test requirement, the FCC Commissioners wrote: "We believe that because the international requirement for telegraphy proficiency has been eliminated, we should treat Morse code telegraphy no differently than other amateur service communication techniques. This change eliminates an unnecessary regulatory burden that may discourage current amateur radio operators from advancing their skills and participating more fully in the benefits of amateur radio."

Eliminating the Morse code test in no way diminishes the enthusiasm many ham operators have for the technique of sending dits and dahs over the air. In fact, we believe we will have more General Class hams learning the code than ever before, now that they can do it on high frequency where practicing code with other hams is fun!

Self-Testing in the Amateur Service

Prior to 1984, all amateur radio exams were administered by FCC personnel at FCC Field Offices around the country. In 1984, the FCC adopted a two-tier system beneath it called the Volunteer Examiner Coordinator (VEC) system to handle amateur radio license exams. The VEC System was formed after Congress passed laws that allowed the FCC to accept the services of Volunteer Examiners (VEs) to prepare and administer amateur service license examinations. The testing activity of VEs is managed by Volunteer Examiner Coordinators (or VECs). A VEC acts as the administrative liaison between the VEs, who administer the various ham examinations, and the FCC, which grants the license.

Also in 1984, the length of term for amateur radio licenses was increased from five to ten years.

A team of three VEs, who must be accredited by a VEC, is required to conduct amateur radio examinations. General Class amateurs may serve as examiners for the Technician class. Advanced Class amateurs may administer exams for Technician and General class. The Extra Class exam may only be administered by VEs who hold an Extra Class license.

In 1986, the FCC turned over responsibility for maintenance of the examination question pools for amateur radio licenses to the National Conference of Volunteer Examiner Coordinators (NCVEC). The Conference appoints a Question Pool Committee (QPC) to develop and revise the various question pools according to a schedule. As a rule, each of the 3 question pools is changed once every 4 years. The FCC requires at least ten times as many questions in each of the pools as may appear on an examination. Both the Technician Class Element 2 and General Class Element 3 written examinations contain 35 multiple-choice questions. The Extra Class Element 4 written examination has 50 questions.

OPERATOR LICENSE CLASSES AND EXAM REQUIREMENTS

Anyone is eligible to become a U.S. licensed amateur operator (including foreign nationals, if they are not a representative of a foreign government). There is no age limitation – if you can pass the examinations, you can become a ham!

Today, there are three amateur operator licenses issued by the FCC – Technician, General, and Extra. Each license requires progressively higher levels of learning and proficiency, and each gives you additional operating privileges. This is known as incentive licensing – a method of strengthening the amateur service by offering more radio spectrum privileges in exchange for more operating and electronic knowledge.

There is no waiting time required to upgrade from one amateur license class to another. Similarly, there is no required waiting time to retake a failed exam. You can even take all three examinations at one sitting if you're really brave! *Table 2-1* details the amateur service license structure and required examinations.

Table 2-1: Current Amateur License Classes and Exam Requirements

License Class	Exam Element	Type of Examination
Technician Class	2	35-question, multiple-choice written examination. Minimum passing score is 26 questions answered correctly (74%).
General Class	3	35-question, multiple-choice written examination. Minimum passing score is 26 questions answered correctly (74%).
Extra Class	4	50-question, multiple-choice written examination. Minimum passing score is 37 questions answered correctly (74%).

ABOUT THE WRITTEN EXAMS

What is the focus of each of the written examinations, and how does it relate to gaining expanding amateur radio privileges as you move up the ladder toward your Extra Class license? *Table 2-2* summarizes the subjects covered in each written examination element.

Table 2-2. Question Element Subjects

Exam Element	License Class	Subjects
Element 2	Technician	Elementary operating procedures, radio regulations, and a smattering of beginning electronics. Emphasis is on VHF and UHF operating.
Element 3	General	HF (high-frequency) operating privileges, amateur practices, radio regulations, and a little more electronics. Emphasis is on HF bands.
Element 4	Extra	Basically a technical examination. Covers specialized operating procedures, more radio regulations, formulas and heavy math. Also covers the specifics on amateur testing procedures.

No Jumping Allowed

You cannot skip over a license class or by-pass a required examination as you upgrade from Technician to General to Extra. For example, to obtain a General Class license, you must first take and pass the Element 2 written examination for the Technician Class license then take and pass the Element 3 written examination. To obtain an Extra Class license, you must first pass the Element 2 (Technician) and Element 3 (General) written examinations and then successfully pass the Element 4 (Extra) written examination.

TAKING THE ELEMENT 3 EXAM

Here's a summary of what you can expect when you go to the session to take the Element 3 written examination for your General Class license. Detailed information about how to find an exam session, what to expect at the session, what to bring to the session, and more is included in Chapter 4.

Examination Administration

All amateur radio examinations are administered by a team of at least three Volunteer Examiners (VEs) who have been accredited by a Volunteer Examiner

Coordinator (VEC). The VEs are licensed hams who volunteer their time to help our hobby grow.

How to Find an Exam Session

Examination sessions are organized under the auspices of an approved VEC. A list of VECs is located in the Appendix on page 224. The W5YI-VEC and the ARRL-VEC are the 2 largest examination groups in the country. These organizations test in all 50 states. Their 3-member, accredited examination teams are just about everywhere. So when you call the VEC, you can be assured they probably have an examination team only a few miles from where you are reading this book right now!

> *Want to find a test site fast?*
> Visit the W5YI-VEC website at **www.w5yi.org**, or call 800-669-9594.

Taking the Exam

The Element 3 written exam is a multiple-choice format. The VEs will give you a test paper that contains the 35 questions and multiple choice answers and an answer sheet for you to complete. Take your time! Make sure you read each question carefully and select the correct answer. Once you're finished, double check your work before handing in your exam papers.

The VEs will score your exam immediately. You'll know before you leave the exam site whether you've passed. Chances are very good that, if you've studied hard, you'll get that passing grade!

GETTING/KEEPING YOUR CALL SIGN

Once the VE team scores your exam and you've passed, the process of upgrading your official FCC Amateur Radio License begins – usually that same day.

At the exam site, you will complete NCVEC Form 605, which is your application to the FCC for your license. If you pass the exam, the VE team will send on the required paperwork to their VEC. The VEC reviews the paperwork then files your application with the FCC. This filing is done electronically and your license upgrade will be granted and posted on the FCC's website within a few days.

If you didn't check the "Change Call Sign" box on your NCVEC Form 605 application, you will simply keep your current call sign. However, if you do check the "Change Call Sign" box, you will receive an entry-level "Group D" call sign as if you were a newly-licensed amateur. We suggest that you don't check the "Change Call Sign" box and stick with your present call sign. If you have been operating for any period of time, your call sign is familiar to you and in some ways a part of your on-the-air identity. It can be a little difficult to become accustomed to a new call sign.

As soon as you pass your exam and have the CSCE, you are permitted to go on the air with your General Class HF privileges – even before your license upgrade appears on the FCC's Universal License System database. See Chapter 4 for more details on this process.

Vanity Call Signs

If you checked the "Change Call Sign" box on the Form 605, your call sign is assigned by the FCC's computer. Once you have that call sign, you can apply for a Vanity Call Sign if you would prefer a different letter combination. This process is explained in more detail In Chapter 4.

HOW MANY CLASSES OF LICENSES?

Once you've passed your Element 3 exam and go on the air as a new General Class operator, you'll be talking to fellow hams throughout the U.S. and around the world. Here's a summary of the new and "grandfathered" licenses that your fellow amateurs may hold and a recap of the level of expertise they have demonstrated in order to gain their licenses.

New License Classes

Following the FCC's restructuring of Amateur Radio licensing that took effect April 15, 2000, there are just three written exams and three license classes – Technician, General, and Extra. Persons who hold licenses issued prior to April 15, 2000 may continue to hold onto their license class and renew it every 10 years for as long as they wish.

"Grandfathered" Licensees

Once you get on the air with your new General Class privileges, every now and then you might meet a Novice operator while yakking on 10 meters, or sending CW on 15, 40, or 80 meters. And then there are the Advanced Class operators who may continue to hold onto their license class designation until they finally decide to move up to Extra Class. When you meet an operator holding an Advanced Class license, you know without a doubt that he had to successfully complete a 13 word per minute Morse code test along with the written exam to earn that license.

When you look at the Frequency Charts in this book, you'll see that we have updated them to reflect the expanded privileges on many high frequency bands for General Class and higher operators. We also list the sub-band privileges for Extra Class, Advanced Class, General Class, Technician Class and even the Novice.

"Paper Upgrade" to General

The FCC Rules (Part 97.505) provides credit for General Class Element 3, without examination, to those applicants who can prove they held an unexpired Technician Class license granted before March 21, 1987. No other class of license receives this element credit. You can submit a copy of your old Technician license and receive credit for the Element 3 exam to qualify for your General Class upgrade. To do so, you must attend a VE testing session, pay the exam fee and submit your documentation and application through the normal VE to VEC session process to receive what is commonly referred to as a General Class "paper upgrade."

To see if you qualify for any of these opportunities to regain your former license privileges, or for a "paper upgrade" to General Class, contact the W5YI VEC at 800-669-9594.

Element Credit for Prior Licenses

Recent rule changes by the FCC make it possible for hams whose licenses have expired to regain their priviliges simply by taking and passing the Element 2 Technician Class written exam. If you were licensed as a General, passing the Tech exam will earn you a new General Class license. If you were Advanced, passing the Tech exam will also get you a new General Class license. And if you were an Extra, passing the Tech exam will earn you a new Extra Class license!

This rule applies to those with expired General, Advanced, and Extra Class licenses that are beyond the two-year grace period. In order to take advantage of this, you must show proof of holding your expired license. If you do not have a copy of your old license, one resource to help verify your former status is to e-mail call sign historian Pete Varounis, NL7XM, at twelveVDC@aol.com.

Paperless Licenses

Effective February 17, 2015 the FCC no longer routinely issues/mails a paper license document to Amateur Radio licensees and other WTB licensed services. The Commission maintains that the official Amateur Radio license authorization is the electronic record that exists in its Universal Licensing System Database. Licensees may access their current, official authorization, and print out an unofficial "reference copy" of their license, using the FCC ULS License Search feature at: **http://wireless.fcc.gov/uls.**

The FCC will provide a paper license to those who notify the Commission that they prefer to receive one. To notify the FCC that you want a license mailed to you, contact the FCC at 877-480-3201 between 8:00 a.m. to 6:00 p.m. Eastern time Monday through Friday (except Federal holidays). You can also request a paper license by logging into the ULS license record using your FRN and CORES password and selecting to receive a paper copy by mail. If you do not know your CORES password, you can reset it on the FCC website: **https://apps.fcc.gov/coresWeb**

IT'S EASY!

The primary pre-requisite for passing any amateur radio operator license exam is the "will" to do it. If you follow our suggestions in this book, your chances of passing the General Class exam are excellent.

The 2007 FCC rule changes that eliminated the Morse code test requirement for General Class make it even easier for you to earn your General Class license and enjoy voice privileges on the high frequency bands that were expanded in those same changes.

When you become a General Class operator, GET ON THE AIR! Operating is an important step to becoming a good ham and ultimately a candidate for the highest license – Amateur Extra Class. But, GET ON THE AIR and enjoy your new General Class worldwide HF privileges!

Gordo and Chip work the Hawaii tropo duct, 2500 mile DX on VHF and UHF!

3

Getting Ready for the Exam

Your General Class written examination will consist of 35 multiple-choice questions taken from the 462 questions that make up the 2015-19 Element 3 question pool. Each question on your examination and the multiple-choice answer will be identical to those contained in this book.

This chapter contains the official, complete 462-question FCC Element 3 General Class question pool from which your examination will be taken. Of the 35 questions, you must get 74% of the questions correct – which means you must answer 26 questions correctly in order to pass.

Your examination will be administered by a team of 3 or more Volunteer Examiners (VEs) – amateur radio operators who are accredited by a Volunteer Examiner Coordinator (VEC). You will receive a Certificate of Successful Completion of Examination (CSCE) when you pass the examination. This is official proof that you have passed the exam and it will be given to you before you leave the exam center.

With this completed form in hand, you can begin operating with General Class privileges immediately using your current call sign with "temporary AG."

THE 2015-19 QUESTION POOL

The Element 3 General Class question pool contained in this book is valid from July 1, 2015, through June 30, 2019.

The 462 questions and distracters in the new General Class question pool were developed by the National Conference of Volunteer Examiner Coordinators' Question Pool Committee (NCVEC-QPC). The QPC Chairman is Roland Anders, K3RA, and the QPC members are Perry Green, WY1O, Michael Matson, N6OPH, Larry Pollock, NB5X, and Jim Wiley, KL7CC.

The QPC encourages amateur radio operators throughout the country to submit revised questions for the amateur radio pools to the committee. If you have any suggestions for new or revised questions, you can send them to Gordo, and he'll be happy to forward them on to the QPC. Gordo's address is on page 213.

WHAT THE EXAMINATION CONTAINS

The examination questions and the multiple-choice answers (one correct answer and three "distracters") for all license class levels are public information. They are widely published and are identical to those in this book. *There are no "secret" questions.* FCC rules prohibit any examiner or examination team from making any changes to any questions, including any numerical values. No numbers, words, letters, or punctuation marks can be altered from the published question pool. By studying all 462 Element 3 questions in this book, you will be reading the same exact questions that will appear on your 35-question Element 3 written examination. But which 35 out of the 462 total questions?

Table 3-1. FCC Element 3 General Class Question Pool

Subelement	Topic	Total Questions	Exam Questions
G1	Commission's Rules	60	5
G2	Operating Procedures	59	5
G3	Radio Wave Propagation	41	3
G4	Amateur Radio Practices	65	5
G5	Electrical Principles	44	3
G6	Circuit Components	37	2
G7	Practical Circuits	38	3
G8	Signals and Emissions	33	3
G9	Antennas and Feedlines	58	4
G0	Electrical and RF Safety	27	2
TOTALS		462	35

Table 3-1 shows how the 35 question examination for Element 3 will be compiled from the question pool. For example, for the Element 3 examination, three questions from the 35 total exam questions will be taken from subelement G8, Signals and Emissions (one from each of the three topics in subelement G8). On subelement G1, Commission's Rules, you will have 5 exam questions on your test. Rusty on electrical principles? Your test will have only 3 questions from subelement G5.

The question pool is divided into 10 subelements which are each divided into topics. Each subelement covers a different subject with each topic covering a part of that subject. You can review the complete list of subelement topics in the Question Pool Syllabus found on page 230 of this book.

All Volunteer Examination teams use the same question pool. This uniformity in material ensures common examinations throughout the country. Most exams are computer-generated so that while the specific questions will vary, the combination of questions will not. The computer selects one question from each topic within each subelement for your Element 3 exam.

Trust us, every question on your Element 3 exam will look very familiar to you by the time you finish studying this book

QUESTION CODING

Each and every question in the 462 question Element 3, General Class pool is numbered using a **code**. *The coded numbers and letters reveal important facts about each question!*

The numbering code always contains 5 alphanumeric characters to identify each question. Here's how to read the question number so you know the subelement and topic that it is from and you can see exactly how the computer selects one question out of each topic for your exam. Once you know this information, you can increase your odds of achieving a "max" score on the exam, especially if there is a specific group of questions which seems impossible for you to understand.

Let's pick a typical question out of the pool – G1A04 – and let me show you how this numbering code works:

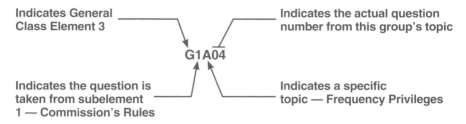

Figure 3-1. Examination Question Coding

- The first character "G" identifies the license class question pool from which the question is taken. "T" would be for Technician. "G" is for General, and "E" would be for Extra.

- The second digit, a "1", identifies the subelement number, 1 through 0. General subelement 1 deals with FCC Rules.

- The third character, "A", indicates the topic area within the subelement. Topic "A" deals with your General Class frequency privileges.

- The fourth and fifth digits indicate the actual question number within the subelement topic's group. The "04" indicates this is the fourth question about frequency privileges, and within the topic area of Commission's Rules. There are 14 individual questions in topic area G1A, *but only one question out of this topic group will appear on the test.*

Here's the Secret Study Hint

Only one exam question will be taken from any single group! A computer-generated test is set up to take only one question from each topic. It cannot skip a topic, nor can it take any more than one question from that topic.

If you decide to skip a topic completely because you are having trouble understanding the subject, guess what – how many questions out of any one topic? That's right, only one per topic. This means you are not going to get hammered on any Element 3 test with a whole bunch of questions dealing with a specific topic. Great secret, huh?

Study Time

How long will it take you to prepare for your upcoming exam?

The General Class question pool in this book is valid from July 1, 2015, through June 30, 2019. It contains a total of 462 questions – but don't panic! Most questions are repeated several different ways, and these "repeats" reinforce what you already learned. It is probably going to take about 30 days to work through this book and prepare for your General Class exam.

QUESTIONS REARRANGED FOR SMARTER LEARNING

The first thing you'll notice when you look at how the Element 3 question pool is presented in this book is that we have completely rearranged the entire General Class question pool to precisely follow Gordo's weekend ham radio training classes. This rearrangement will take you logically through each and every one of the 462 questions with their answers exactly as you will see them on an Element 3 exam. The questions are arranged here into 18 subjects in a way that eliminates the need for you to jump back and forth between topics or subelements to match up questions on similar subjects

For example, we have taken all of the questions in the pool about where you can operate your ham radio and grouped them together into one section that allows you to better understand all of the material that relates to this subject. This arrangement of the questions follows a natural learning process

Trust us, the reorganization of all of the test questions in the pool has been tested and finely-tuned in hundreds of Gordo's weekend classes. This method of learning WORKS! You will probably cut your study time in half simply by following the questions as presented here in our book!

Each and every Element 3 question is in this book. A cross-reference of all 462 questions is found on pages 231 to 232 of the book.

This book – and our General Class audio course – contain all 462 General Class questions, 4 possible answers, the noted correct answer, and our upbeat description of how the correct answer works into the real world of amateur radio. We highlight **KEY WORDS** that will help you remember the correct answer and provide you with a fast review of the entire question pool just before you sit for the big General Class exam.

We also include many web addresses that can provide you with hours of fascinating study on selected "hot topics" that will help you really understand the real world of ham radio. You can visit a site while you study, or visit after you've earned your General Class license and are on the air.

When you visit some of these websites, it may not be immediately apparent why we are suggesting that you go there. Some addresses take you to the sites of local ham clubs. Most of these are specialty clubs, and they contain lots of information on how to operate on repeaters, or satellites, or provide educational resources on learning about electronics or antennas or how radios work.

And a disclaimer – while we have worked hard to make sure all of these addresses are current at the time of publication, websites move, addresses change, or sites simply go away. If you find an address that doesn't work, feel free to drop us an e-mail so we can update it for the next printing of this book. And if you know of a website that you think is a gem, send us that information and we'll consider it for our next printing.

Here's our e-mail address:
masterpubl@aol.com

How to Read the Questions

Using an actual question from page 27, here is a guide to explain what it is you will be studying as you go through all of the Q&As in the book:

Official Q&A

G1C05 Which of the following is a limitation on transmitter power on the 28 MHz band for a General Class control operator?
A. 100 watts PEP output.   C. 1500 watts PEP output.
B. 1000 watts PEP output.   D. 2000 watts PEP output.
Novice and Technician Class operators are restricted to 200 watts on high frequency bands; however, as a General Class operator you can run up to *1500 watts PEP* (Peak Envelope Power) output. [97.313] **ANSWER C.**

FCC Part 97 Rule Citation

Correct Answer

Key Words To Remember

Topic Areas

Here is a list of our 18 topic areas showing the page where it starts in the book. Again, there is a complete cross reference list of the Q&As in numerical order on pages 231 to 232 in the Appendix, along with the official Question Pool Syllabus.

STUDY SUGGESTIONS

Finally, as you get ready to start studying the questions, here are some suggestions to make your learning easier:

1. Read over each multiple-choice answer carefully. Some answers start out looking good, but turn bad during the last 2 or 3 words. If you speed read the answers, you could very easily go for a wrong answer because you didn't read them all the way through. Also, don't count on the multiple-choice answers always appearing in the exact same A-B-C-D order on your actual computer-generated test. While they won't change any words in the answers, they will sometimes scramble the A-B-C-D order.

2. Give this book to a friend, and ask him or her to read you the correct answer. You then reply with the question wording.

3. Mark the heck out of your book! When the pages begin to fall out, you're probably ready for the exam!

4. Our book is available on audio CDs, too. So if you'd like to listen to Gordo and Eric read the questions and answers to you while you're driving your car, riding your bike, or laying on the beach, we can do that for you. The CD symbol, disk number, and track number at the beginning of each topic section keys this book to the audio book. You can get this book on audio CD where you purchased this book, or by calling 800-669-9594, or by visiting www.w5yi.org.

CD 1 **TRACK 2**

5. Highlight the keywords one week before the test. Then speed read the brightly highlighted keywords twice a day before the exam.

Are you ready to work through the 462 Q & A's? Put a check mark by the easy ones that you may already know the answer for, and put a little circle by any question that needs a little bit more study. Save your highlighting work until a few days before your upcoming test. Work the Q & A's for about 30 minutes at a time. We'll drop in a little bit of humor to keep you on track; and if you actually need Gordo's live words of encouragement, you can call him on the phone Monday through Thursday, 10:00 a.m. to 4:00 p.m. (California time), 714-549-5000.

THE QUESTION POOL, PLEASE

Okay, this is the big moment – your General Class, Element 3, question pool. Don't freak out and get overwhelmed with the prospect of learning 462 Q & A's. You will find that the topic content is repeated many times, so you're really going to breeze through this test without any problem!

G1D09 How long is a Certificate of Successful Completion of Examination (CSCE) valid for exam element credit?
- A. 30 days.
- B. 180 days.
- C. 365 days.
- D. For as long as your current license is valid.

When you pass your exam, your examiners will all sign a Certificate of Successful Completion of Examination (CSCE). With the signed CSCE in hand, you are good to go on the air immediately with your new privileges! This CSCE is proof-positive that you passed the exam just in case there is a paperwork error down the line. Your license usually is upgraded within two weeks, so the *365-day* period of this *CSCE* applies only in rare cases where paperwork gets lost. [97.9(b)] **ANSWER C.**

When you pass your exam, you'll receive
your CSCE and lots of congratulations!

G1D06 When must you add the special identifier "AG" after your call sign if you are a Technician Class licensee and have a CSCE for General Class operator privileges, but the FCC has not yet posted your upgrade on its website?

A. Whenever you operate using General Class frequency privileges.
B. Whenever you operate on any amateur frequency.
C. Whenever you operate using Technician frequency privileges.
D. A special identifier is not required as long as your General Class license application has been filed with the FCC.

Until your call sign appears on the Universal Licensing System data base, *add the special identifier "AG"* when you operate using General Class privileges. You don't need to append this identifier when operating within Technician frequency privileges, just when using your new General Class frequencies. [97.119(f)(2)] **ANSWER A.**

G1D01 Who may receive credit for the elements represented by an expired amateur radio license?

A. Any person who can demonstrate that they once held an FCC issued General, Advanced, or Amateur Extra class license that was not revoked by the FCC.
B. Anyone who held an FCC issued amateur radio license that has been expired for not less than 5 years and not more than 15 years.
C. Any person that previously held an amateur license issued by another country, but only if that country has a current reciprocal licensing agreement with the FCC.
D. Only persons who once held an FCC issued Novice, Technician, or Technician Plus license.

In 2014, the FCC issued a new rule that allows *General, Advanced, and Extra Class* hams who have let their license expire by more than 2 years to *regain their original license level* by simply taking and passing the Technician Class Element 2 exam. This means that granddad, who had an Extra Class license back in the '50s can now get back to that Extra Class level just by studying up on the current Element 2 using our book and passing the Technician exam "entry level test" to become an Extra Class again! [97.501, 97.505(a)] **ANSWER A.**

G1D11 If a person has an expired FCC issued amateur radio license of General Class or higher, what is required before they can receive a new license?

A. They must have a letter from the FCC showing they once held an amateur or commercial license.
B. There are no requirements other than being able to show a copy of the expired license.
C. The applicant must be able to produce a copy of a page from a call book published in the USA showing his or her name and address.
D. The applicant must pass the current Element 2 exam.

A previously-licensed amateur radio operator may get back to their expired General Class or higher license simply by *passing the current Element 2 Technician Class exam*. The applicant will need to document his or her original license. This could be the old license itself, an old Callbook listing, or proof of an old license from a look-up service, such as that provided by call sign historian Pete Varounis, NL7XM. Email him at **twelveVDC@aol.com. ANSWER D.**

G1D03 On which of the following band segments may you operate if you are a Technician Class operator and have a CSCE for General Class privileges?

    A. Only the Technician band segments until your upgrade is posted in the FCC database.

    B. Only on the Technician band segments until your license arrives in the mail.

    C. On any General or Technician Class band segment.

    D. On any General or Technician Class band segment except 30-meters and 60-meters.

Once you pass your General Class written examination, you are good to *go on the air on all* of the *General Class* segments of the worldwide *bands plus your present Technician frequencies*. Keep our book handy to reference the frequencies for General Class operations on each band. [97.9(b)] **ANSWER C.**

Ham operator, Dick Bruno, N6ISY, veteran West Coast public service communicator, works new upgrades on High Frequency.

Your New General Bands

Elmer Point: Here are the formulas that you need to convert frequency to wavelength, and wavelength to frequency:

Converting Frequency to Wavelength

To find wavelength (λ) in meters if you know frequency (f) in megahertz (MHz), Solve:

$$\lambda(\text{meters}) = \frac{300}{f(\text{MHz})}$$

Converting Wavelength to Frequency

To find frequency (f) in megahertz (MHz) if you know wavelength (λ) in meters, Solve:

$$f(\text{MHz}) = \frac{300}{\lambda(\text{meters})}$$

G1A01 On which of the following bands is a General Class license holder granted all amateur frequency privileges?

    A. 60, 20, 17, and 12 meters.
    B. 160, 80, 40, and 10 meters.
    C. 160, 60, 30, 17, 12, and 10 meters.
    D. 160, 30, 17, 15, 12, and 10 meters.

As a new General, you will gain high frequency privileges on each and every ham band. But until you upgrade to Extra, you don't get all of the frequency privileges on every amateur band. Extra and Advanced operators have some exclusive room on 80, 40, 20, and 15 meters. Not to worry – *General Class has all frequency privileges on 160, 30, 17, 12, and 10 meters*, and the five channel privileges on *60 meters*. [97.301(d)] **ANSWER C.**

G1A10 Which of the following frequencies is available to a control operator holding a General Class license?
A. 28.020 MHz.
B. 28.350 MHz.
C. 28.550 MHz.
D. All of these choices are correct.

As a General Class operator, you receive all privileges from 28.000 to 29.700 MHz on the 10 meter band. *All of the choices are correct.* [97.301(d)] **ANSWER D.**

G1C05 Which of the following is a limitation on transmitter power on the 28 MHz band for a General Class control operator?
A. 100 watts PEP output.
B. 1000 watts PEP output.
C. 1500 watts PEP output.
D. 2000 watts PEP output.

Novice and Technician Class operators are restricted to 200 watts on high frequency bands; however, as a General Class operator you can run up to *1500 watts PEP* (Peak Envelope Power) output. [97.313(c)(2)] **ANSWER C.**

G1E02 When may a 10-meter repeater retransmit the 2-meter signal from a station having a Technician Class control operator?
A. Under no circumstances.
B. Only if the station on 10-meters is operating under a Special Temporary Authorization allowing such retransmission.
C. Only during an FCC declared general state of communications emergency.
D. Only if the 10-meter repeater control operator holds at least a General Class license.

Technician Class operators have no privileges between 29.500 to 29.700 MHz where 10 meter repeaters operate. As a General Class operator, you can set up a home station as a cross-band relay system. This could allow a Technician on the 2-meter band to end up transmitting and receiving on the 10-meter band. Think of all the excitement you could give Technician Class operators on 2 meters when the 10 meter FM segment of the band is open for worldwide skywave communications. This is perfectly legal to do, provided a *General Class, or higher, control operator* stays at the control point of your station. [97.205(b)] **ANSWER D.**

G1C02 What is the maximum transmitting power an amateur station may use on the 12-meter band?
A. 50 watts PEP output.
B. 200 watts PEP output.
C. 1500 watts PEP output.
D. An effective radiated power equivalent to 100 watts from a half-wave dipole.

On the *12 meter band*, you can run the legal limit of *1500 watts* PEP output. [97.313(a),(b)] **ANSWER C.**

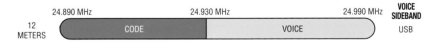

G1A09 Which of the following frequencies is within the General Class portion of the 15-meter band?

A. 14250 kHz.
B. 18155 kHz.
C. 21300 kHz.
D. 24900 kHz.

The *15 meter band* is at 21 MHz (21000 kHz), so *21300 kHz* is a great frequency for voice operations to regularly work the world in the morning and afternoon. [97.301(d)] **ANSWER C.**

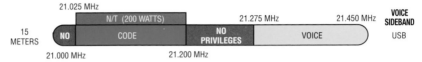

G1A07 Which of the following frequencies is within the General Class portion of the 20-meter phone band?

A. 14005 kHz.
B. 14105 kHz.
C. 14305 kHz.
D. 14405 kHz.

Remember that phone privileges for high frequency General Class operation are those at the top of the band. Your *20 meter band* voice privileges extend from 14225 up to 14350 kHz, so *14305 kHz* is within General Class voice privileges. [97.301(d)] **ANSWER C.**

G1C04 Which of the following limitations apply to transmitter power on every amateur band?

A. Only the minimum power necessary to carry out the desired communications should be used.
B. Power must be limited to 200 watts when transmitting between 14.100 MHz and 14.150 MHz.
C. Power should be limited as necessary to avoid interference to another radio service on the frequency.
D. Effective radiated power cannot exceed 1500 watts.

Although you might be permitted to run an amplifier with 1500 watts output, always try to run the *minimum power necessary to make contact* with the other station. This will help keep you out of your neighbors TV and HiFi systems. [97.313(a)] **ANSWER A.**

G1A02 On which of the following bands is phone operation prohibited?

A. 160 meters.
B. 30 meters.
C. 17 meters.
D. 12 meters.

As a new General, you can operate throughout the entire 30 meter band using CW and DATA emissions with power output limited to 200 watts. *No phone (voice) activity is allowed on 30 meters*. [97.305] **ANSWER B.**

G1A03 On which of the following bands is image transmission prohibited?

A. 160 meters.   C. 20 meters.
B. 30 meters.   D. 12 meters.

Image transmissions include popular slow scan television and facsimile. On *30 meters, image transmissions are prohibited.* [97.305] **ANSWER B.**

G1C01 What is the maximum transmitting power an amateur station may use on 10.140 MHz?

A. 200 watts PEP output.   C. 1500 watts PEP output.
B. 1000 watts PEP output.   D. 2000 watts PEP output.

On the *30 meter* CW and Data *band*, only *200 watts* peak envelope power output is allowed in accordance with FCC rules. [97.313(c)(1)] **ANSWER A.**

G1A05 Which of the following frequencies is in the General Class portion of the 40-meter band?

A. 7.250 MHz.   C. 40.200 MHz.
B. 7.500 MHz.   D. 40.500 MHz.

Welcome to *40 meters*, where we recently gained an additional 50 kHz of voice spectrum, from 7175 to 7300 kHz, lower sideband. Listen for Gordo most weekday mornings on *7.250 MHz*, within the General Class portion of the 40 meter band. [97.301(d)] **ANSWER A.**

G1A14 In what ITU region is operation in the 7.175 to 7.300 MHz band permitted for a control operator holding an FCC issued General Class license?

A. Region 1.   C. Region 3.
B. Region 2.   D. All three regions.

Here in the US, including Hawaii, we are in *ITU Region 2.* This allows voice privileges, as well as data and CW, from 7.175 to 7.300 MHz (7175 to 7300 kHz) for General Class operators. But these privileges are available only in ITU Region 2. If you head off to the South Seas in ITU Region 3, your 40 meter privileges will be different. [97.301(d)] **ANSWER B.**

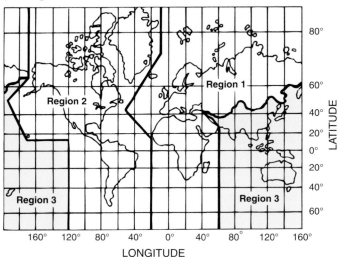

ITU Regions

G1A04 Which of the following amateur bands is restricted to communication on only specific channels, rather than frequency ranges?
A. 11 meters.
B. 12 meters.
C. 30 meters.
D. 60 meters.

The new 60 meter ham band is shared with a few government stations on a non-interference basis – they can interfere with us, but we cannot interfere with them! Ham operators are authorized *5 discrete channels*, which are great frequencies for passing regional radio traffic. *60 meters* is the only band where we have been assigned specific channel allocations, and we may now use digital and voice on each of these channels. [97.303(s)] **ANSWER D.**

CW - carrier frequency is the center frequency. 100 WATTS ERP

60 METERS	CW CARRIER FREQUENCY	5332.0	5348.0	5358.5	5373.0	5405.0	VOICE SIDEBAND USB
	USB DIAL FREQUENCY FOR PHONE/DATA/RTTY	5330.5	5346.5	5357.0	5371.5	5403.5	

G1C03 What is the maximum bandwidth permitted by FCC rules for Amateur Radio stations transmitting on USB frequencies in the 60 meter band?
A. 2.8 kHz.
B. 5.6 kHz.
C. 1.8 kHz.
D. 3 kHz.

On the *60 meter band*, there are five channels allocated on specific frequencies, with a maximum bandwidth of *2.8 kHz*. [97.303(h)(1)] **ANSWER A.**

G2D07 Which of the following is required by the FCC rules when operating in the 60-meter band?
A. If you are using other than a dipole antenna, you must keep a record of the gain of your antenna.
B. You must keep a record of the date, time, frequency, power level and stations worked.
C. You must keep a record of all third party traffic.
D. You must keep a record of the manufacturer of your equipment and the antenna used.

FCC rules require 60 meter band, 5-channel operation not to exceed 100 watts effective radiated power out as measured on a dipole antenna. On a dipole, gain is zero, so 100 watts into the dipole from your transmitter will not exceed 100 watts effective radiated power output. However, *if you're transmitting using a beam antenna*, you will need to turn your power output down to correspond with the amount of gain the beam exhibits. If the beam offers 3 dB gain in the forward direction, this 2 times increase in effective radiated power will require you to reduce your transmitter power output 3 dB down, to half of 100 watts. You then must *note this in a station logbook* and keep it as a permanent part of your station's written files. [97.303(i)] **ANSWER A.**

G1A13 What is the appropriate action if, when operating on either the 30-meter or 60-meter bands, a station in the primary service interferes with your contact?
A. Notify the FCC's regional Engineer in Charge of the interference.
B. Increase your transmitter's power to overcome the interference.
C. Attempt to contact the station and request that it stop the interference.
D. Move to a clear frequency or stop transmitting.

Both our 30 meter and 60 meter bands are shared, and authorized government users always have priority. So *change frequency or stop transmitting.* [97.303(h)(2)(j)] **ANSWER D.**

G1A12 Which of the following applies when the FCC rules designate the Amateur Service as a secondary user on a band?
- A. Amateur stations must record the call sign of the primary service station before operating on a frequency assigned to that station.
- B. Amateur stations are allowed to use the band only during emergencies.
- C. Amateur stations are allowed to use the band only if they do not cause harmful interference to primary users.
- D. Amateur stations may only operate during specific hours of the day, while primary users are permitted 24 hour use of the band.

Both our 30 meter and 60 meter bands are shared, and authorized government users always have priority. They are primary on the band, which means *we must not cause harmful interference to government users.* [97.303] **ANSWER C.**

G1A06 Which of the following frequencies is within the General Class portion of the 75-meter phone band?

A. 1875 kHz.	C. 3900 kHz.
B. 3750 kHz.	D. 4005 kHz.

The 75/80 meter ham band is a good one for short-range, daytime communications and long-range, nighttime skywave signals. 80 meters refers to the bottom of the band for CW and data, and *75 meters* refers to the top of the band for phone. 300 divided by 75 = 4.000 MHz. To convert MHz to kHz, move the decimal point 3 places to the right. *3900 kHz* is within the phone privileges for General Class. [97.301(d)] **ANSWER C.**

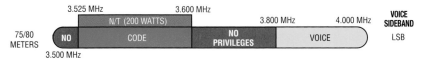

G1A08 Which of the following frequencies is within the General Class portion of the 80-meter band?

A. 1855 kHz.	C. 3560 kHz.
B. 2560 kHz.	D. 3650 kHz.

General Class CW and data privileges for the *80 meter band* extend from 3525 kHz through 3600 kHz. *3560 kHz* is a good frequency for CW, RTTY and data. [97.301(d)] **ANSWER C.**

G1C06 Which of the following is a limitation on transmitter power on the 1.8 MHz band?

A. 200 watts PEP output.	C. 1200 watts PEP output.
B. 1000 watts PEP output.	D. 1500 watts PEP output.

As a new General Class operator, you are permitted to run up to *1500 watts* of Peak Envelope Power (PEP) output on all bands other than 60 meters and 30 meters. However, by FCC rules, you should always run the minimum power necessary to make the contact. [97.313] **ANSWER D.**

G1A11 When General Class licensees are not permitted to use the entire voice portion of a particular band, which portion of the voice segment is generally available to them?
    A. The lower frequency end.
    B. The upper frequency end.
    C. The lower frequency end on frequencies below 7.3 MHz and the upper end on frequencies above 14.150 MHz.
    D. The upper frequency end on frequencies below 7.3 MHz and the lower end on frequencies above 14.150 MHz.

Study our band plan charts and see where your privileges begin and end. *Voice privileges*, or "phone," on all bands are always at the *top of the band*. [97.301]
ANSWER B.

Voice (phone) privileges are always at the top end of the bands.

G2B08 What is the "DX window" in a voluntary band plan?
    A. A portion of the band that should not be used for contacts between stations within the 48 contiguous United States.
    B. An FCC rule that prohibits contacts between stations within the United States and possessions in that portion of the band.
    C. An FCC rule that allows only digital contacts in that portion of the band.
    D. A portion of the band that has been voluntarily set aside for digital contacts only.

It is important to begin your General Class worldwide band operations in accordance with both the FCC rules and voluntary band plans. Most high frequency bands have a spot where stateside hams will *call and listen only for foreign country DX stations*. For example, 1830 to 1850 kHz in the 160 meter band has long been recognized as the DX window for that band – no idle chit-chatting here! Use the high frequency DX window as a great spot to listen for worldwide DX. **ANSWER A.**
☞ **www.arrl.org/band-plan-1**

Elmer Point: As a brand new General, spend a few days on the air LISTENING before you go on the air. Look at this band plan, and then tune in to hear how everything has its place on the radio dial. One of the best ways to complete your first transmission using your new General Class privileges is to answer an upbeat CQ call. Double-check to make sure you are within your General Class privileges, and check the band plan to make sure you are not answering a station looking only for foreign DX.

160 Meters (1.8 - 2.0 MHz)

1.800-2.000	CW
1.800-1.810	Digital Modes
1.810	CW QRP calling frequency
1.843-2.000	SSB, SSTV and other wideband modes
1.910	SSB QRP
1.995-2.000	Experimental
1.999-2.000	Beacons

80 Meters (3.5 - 4.0 MHz)

3.500-3.510	CW DX window
3.560	QRP CW calling frequency
3.570-3.600	RTTY/Data
3.585-3.600	Automatically controlled data stations
3.590	RTTY/Data DX
3.790-3.800	DX window
3.845	SSTV
3.885	AM calling frequency
3.985	QRP SSB calling frequency

40 Meters (7.0 - 7.3 MHz)

7.030	QRP CW calling frequency
7.040	RTTY/Data DX
7.070-7.125	RTTY/Data
7.100-7.105	Automatically controlled data stations
7.171	SSTV
7.173	D-SSTV
7.285	QRP SSB calling frequency
7.290	AM calling frequency

30 Meters (10.1 - 10.15 MHz)

10.130-10.140	RTTY/Data
10.140-10.150	Automatically controlled data stations

20 Meters (14.0 - 14.35 MHz)

14.060	QRP CW calling frequency
14.070-14.095	RTTY/Data
14.095-14.0995	Automatically controlled data stations
14.100	IBP/NCDXF beacons
14.1005-14.112	Automatically controlled data stations
14.230	SSTV
14.233	D-SSTV
14.236	Digital Voice
14.285	QRP SSB calling frequency
14.286	AM calling frequency

17 Meters (18.068 - 18.168 MHz)

18.100-18.105	RTTY/Data
18.105-18.110	Automatically controlled data stations
18.110	IBP/NCDXF beacons
18.162.5	Digital Voice

15 Meters (21.0 - 21.45 MHz)

21.060	QRP CW calling frequency
21.070-21.110	RTTY/Data
21.090-21.100	Automatically controlled data stations
21.150	IBP/NCDXF beacons
21.340	SSTV
21.385	QRP SSB calling frequency

12 Meters (24.89 - 24.99 MHz)

24.920-24.925	RTTY/Data
24.925-24.930	Automatically controlled data stations
24.930	IBP/NCDXF beacons

10 Meters (28.0 - 29.7 MHz)

28.060	QRP CW calling frequency
28.070-28.120	RTTY/Data
28.120-28.189	Automatically controlled data stations
28.190-28.225	Beacons
28.200	IBP/NCDXF beacons
28.385	QRP SSB calling frequency
28.680	SSTV
29.000-29.200	AM
29.300-29.510	Satellite downlinks
29.520-29.580	Repeater inputs
29.600	FM simplex
29.620-29.680	Repeater outputs

Wider digital bandwidths may be found above parts of the RTTY / data sub-bands.

G2D08 What is a reason why many amateurs keep a station log?

A. The ITU requires a log of all international contacts.

B. The ITU requires a log of all international third party traffic.

C. The log provides evidence of operation needed to renew a license without retest.

D. To help with a reply if the FCC requests information.

Whenever Gordo lets a guest ham operate his equipment, he writes down details of who the other operator was in his *station log*. This way, *if the FCC should ask* who was the control operator or third party during a transmission on a given date and time, he will be able to look it up and have solid information about what went out over the airwaves!

ANSWER D.

☞ **www.w3beinformed.org**

While the FCC doesn't require it, keeping a log of your station operation is a good idea.

---

ham apps As a radio amateur, you should not only know where you are, but also when you are. You need an accurate clock in your shack. The Precise-Time app gives your logbook accurate time and your choice of time zones includes Greenwich (UTC) time. https://itunes.apple.com/us/app/precise-time/id391343043?mt=8

G2D09 What information is traditionally contained in a station log?
  A. Date and time of contact.
  B. Band and/or frequency of the contact.
  C. Call sign of station contacted and the signal report given.
  D. All of these choices are correct.

To keep accurate records of transmissions from his station, Gordo records all these details and sometimes more in his station's log book. If operating mobile, he includes latitude and longitude. *All of these details* help him respond accurately to any QSL card he receives. **ANSWER D.**

G2D01 What is the Amateur Auxiliary to the FCC?
  A. Amateur volunteers who are formally enlisted to monitor the airwaves for rules violations.
  B. Amateur volunteers who conduct amateur licensing examinations.
  C. Amateur volunteers who conduct frequency coordination for amateur VHF repeaters.
  D. Amateur volunteers who use their station equipment to help civil defense organizations in times of emergency.

The *Amateur Auxiliary* is made up of *volunteer hams* who are formally *enlisted to monitor the airwaves for rule violations,* and who report violations to their local Official Observer Coordinator (OOC) to take action. **ANSWER A.**

G2D02 Which of the following are objectives of the Amateur Auxiliary?
  A. To conduct efficient and orderly amateur licensing examinations.
  B. To encourage self-regulation and compliance with the rules by radio amateur operators.
  C. To coordinate repeaters for efficient and orderly spectrum usage.
  D. To provide emergency and public safety communications.

The benchmark of the amateur service is *self-regulation and compliance* with the rules. All hams help other hams stay on the straight and narrow. The Amateur Auxiliary volunteers help further by reporting those who don't respond to the help others offer. **ANSWER B.**

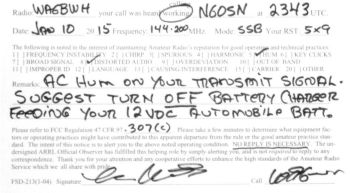

Nothing causes fear and trepidation like an "Official Notice." But you needn't fear an OO notice; it's far better that a friendly fellow ham catches you in error than the FCC! An OO report has no legal authority, but does serve as a friendly reminder to pay attention to the rules.

G2D03 What skills learned during hidden transmitter hunts are of help to the Amateur Auxiliary?

A. Identification of out of band operation.
B. Direction finding used to locate stations violating FCC Rules.
C. Identification of different call signs.
D. Hunters have an opportunity to transmit on non-amateur frequencies.

On a transmitter hunt, portable, mobile, and base station beam antennas are used to triangulate and home-in on a specific signal. It takes 3 or more stations to triangulate. Homing-in on a signal requires techniques in using attenuators, directional antennas and other specialized *direction finding* equipment. You can foxhunt with almost any simple transceiver.
ANSWER B.

Kids and adults love fox hunt direction-finding exercises!

G1B11 How does the FCC require an amateur station to be operated in all respects not specifically covered by the Part 97 rules?

A. In conformance with the rules of the IARU.
B. In conformance with Amateur Radio custom.
C. In conformance with good engineering and good amateur practice.
D. All of these choices are correct.

When hams come up with a new radio signaling technique, it might not be specified in the FCC rules. As long as this new signaling technique conforms to *good engineering and good amateur practice* you can begin operating even though the rules may not specifically authorize this new particular type of radio emission. [97.101(a)] **ANSWER C.**

G1B12 Who or what determines "good engineering and good amateur practice" as applied to the operation of an amateur station in all respects not covered by the Part 97 rules?

A. The FCC.
B. The Control Operator.
C. The IEEE.
D. The ITU.

Only *the Federal Communications Commission (FCC)* can decide what meets "good engineering and good amateur practice." [97.101(a)] **ANSWER A.**

Elmer Point: Amateur Auxiliary operators know the Part 97 Rules and Regulations inside and out. You should, too! The FCC rules are written in plain language providing fun reading to see all that the FCC encourages you to do on the air. Call 800-669-9594, and tell them Gordo and Eric want you to read the FCC Part 97 Rule book.

G1B08 When choosing a transmitting frequency, what should you do to comply with good amateur practice?

    A. Insure that the frequency and mode selected are within your license class privileges.

    B. Follow generally accepted band plans agreed to by the Amateur Radio community.

    C. Monitor the frequency before transmitting.

    D. All of these choices are correct.

Before you transmit with your new General Class privileges, ask yourself the following:

    Am I within my General Class privileges?

    Am I operating in accordance with the band plan?

    Is anyone else using the frequency?

Keep the frequency privileges chart in the back of our book handy, along with other band plan charts that you find easy to use and understand. This way, you will meet the Part 97 Rules and likely meet thousands of friendly hams. [97.101(a)] **ANSWER D.**

G1B05 When may music be transmitted by an amateur station?

    A. At any time, as long as it produces no spurious emissions.

    B. When it is unintentionally transmitted from the background at the transmitter.

    C. When it is transmitted on frequencies above 1215 MHz.

    D. When it is an incidental part of a manned space craft retransmission.

The only *music* you will ever hear on the ham bands is limited to some of the audio feeds *from the international space station retransmissions* where they sometimes wake up the crew with reveille, or sing "Happy Birthday" to them in outer space. No other music is allowed. [97.113(c)] **ANSWER D.**

☞ **www.amsat.org, www.work-stat.com**

The International Space Station has a big ham station on board.
Photo courtesy of N.A.S.A.

G1B06 When is an amateur station permitted to transmit secret codes?
    A. During a declared communications emergency.
    B. To control a space station.
    C. Only when the information is of a routine, personal nature.
    D. Only with Special Temporary Authorization from the FCC.
Ham stations are allowed to transmit secure *secret codes to control* ham radio equipment located on *satellites in space.* We encourage you to join AMSAT – Radio Amateur Satellite Corporation, a nonprofit scientific organization that supports ham satellite programs. [97.113(a)(4) and 97.207(f)] **ANSWER B.**

G1B07 What are the restrictions on the use of abbreviations or procedural signals in the Amateur Service?
    A. Only "Q" signals are permitted.
    B. They may be used if they do not obscure the meaning of a message.
    C. They are not permitted.
    D. Only "10 codes" are permitted.
Common abbreviations, "Q" codes, and other phrases such as "73," "QRZ?," or "Please QSL," that *do not obscure the meaning of our communications* are perfectly acceptable on the ham bands. Popular "Q" codes are given on page 56. The following is a list of common prowords. [97.113(a)(4)] **ANSWER B.**

Proword	Meaning	Proword	Meaning
Affirmative	Yes	Number	Message number (in numerals) follows
All after	Say again all after _____	Out	End of transmission, no answer required or expected
All before	Say again all before _____		
Break	Used to separate message heading, text and ending	Over	End of transmission, answer is expected. Go ahead. Transmit.
Break	Stop transmitting		
Correct	That is correct	Roger	I have received your transmission satisfactorily
Figures	Numerals follow	Say again	Repeat
From	Originator follows	Slant	Slant bar
Groups	Numeral(s) indicating number of text words follows	This is	This transmission is from the station whose call sign follows
Incorrect	That is incorrect		
Initial	Single letter follows	Time	File time or date-time group of the message follows
I say again	I repeat		
I spell	Phonetic spelling follows	To	Addressee follows
Message follows	A message which requires recording follows	Wait	Short pause
		Wait out	Long pause
More to follow	I have more traffic for you	Word after	Say again word after _____
Negative	No, not received	Word before	Say again word before _____

MARS – Army Radiotelephone Prowords

G1B09 When may an amateur station transmit communications in which the licensee or control operator has a pecuniary (monetary) interest?
- A. When other amateurs are being notified of the sale of apparatus normally used in an amateur station and such activity is not done on a regular basis.
- B. Only when there is no other means of communications readily available.
- C. When other amateurs are being notified of the sale of any item with a monetary value less than $200 and such activity is not done on a regular basis.
- D. Never.

Ham radio "swap nets" are a great way to look for, or to *sell, used amateur radio equipment* over the ham airwaves. All equipment must be ham radio related – no selling your Granddad's Model T. [97.113(a)(3)] **ANSWER A.**

ELMER HINT Recently, the Federal Communications Commission clarified its rules regarding ham stations at your place of employment. Rules do not permit us to use ham radio in place of commercial two way radios for daily business activities, but ham radio disaster preparation nets are an exception. If the purpose of the short weekly net is to support the community in a time of disaster, and as long as the ham radio system is not directly supporting your company's business venture, your company's ham radio emergency operation center may be good to go on the air for weekly community disaster preparedness training.

School teachers, on the clock, are also permitted to use ham radio in the classroom, even though they are getting paid for their instruction.

Here's the bottom line – don't use ham radio to further your business, or add to your company's bottom line. There are plenty of other radio services for commercial comms, and even non-licensed radio services such as Multi Use Radio Service, Part 15 spread spectrum radios, and Family Radio Service are a perfect way to support your operation outside of the ham bands. Ham radio is NOT a replacement for a company radio system.

G2D05 When is it permissible to communicate with amateur stations in countries outside the areas administered by the Federal Communications Commission?
- A. Only when the foreign country has a formal third party agreement filed with the FCC.
- B. When the contact is with amateurs in any country except those whose administrations have notified the ITU that they object to such communications.
- C. When the contact is with amateurs in any country as long as the communication is conducted in English.
- D. Only when the foreign country is a member of the International Amateur Radio Union.

As a new General Class operator, you can work hundreds of countries and become an expert in DX, plus learn a little bit of a foreign language! *As long as neither their nor our administration has notified the International Telecommunications Union(ITU) that ham communications are forbidden*, you are okay to work any ham in that foreign country. [97.111(a)(1)] **ANSWER B.**

G1E01 Which of the following would disqualify a third party from participating in stating a message over an amateur station?

A. The third party's amateur license has been revoked and not reinstated.
B. The third party is not a U.S. citizen.
C. The third party is a licensed amateur.
D. The third party is speaking in a language other than English.

You are not allowed to let a "third party" talk over your equipment if they were previously licensed as a ham and their *license has been revoked*. Don't let them "con" you into letting them speak through your station! [97.115(b)(2)] **ANSWER A.**

Elmer Point: Before you allow third party traffic at your station, make sure your guest operator understands the rules: no business; no profanity; no secret codes; no music, and only a language that you can understand. It's also a good idea to keep a logbook with details of the third party conversation.

G1E05 What types of messages for a third party in another country may be transmitted by an amateur station?

A. Any message, as long as the amateur operator is not paid.
B. Only messages for other licensed amateurs.
C. Only messages relating to Amateur Radio or remarks of a personal character, or messages relating to emergencies or disaster relief.
D. Any messages, as long as the text of the message is recorded in the station log.

During a third party traffic exchange only transmissions of *personal messages are allowed*. In an emergency, messages relating to *disaster relief are also allowed*. [97.115(a)(2), 97.117] **ANSWER C.**

Elmer Point: Going to Europe? U.S. Amateurs with a General Class license will be granted CEPT Novice Radio Amateur License privileges in accordance with ECC Recommendation (05)06 (as amended), which can be found on the internet at www.erodocdb.dk/doks/implement_doc_adm.aspx?docid=2136. Be sure to carry a copy of your FCC license along with a copy of FCC Public Notice DA99-1098 with you in case someone asks if you have approval to operate in their country.

Austria	Finland	Liechtenstein	Slovak Republic
Belgium	France & its	Lithuania	Slovenia
Bosnia & Herzegovina	possessions	Luxembourg	Spain
Bulgaria	Germany	Monaco	Sweden
Croatia	Greenland	Montenegro	Switzerland
Cyprus	Hungary	Netherlands	Turkey
Czech Republic	Iceland	Netherlands Antilles	United Kingdom & its
Denmark	Ireland	Norway	possessions
Estonia	Italy	Portugal	
Faroe Islands	Latvia	Romania	

G1E09 What language must be used when identifying your station if you are using a language other than English in making a contact using phone emission?

A. The language being used for the contact.
B. Any language recognized by the United Nations.
C. English only.
D. English, Spanish, French, or German.

Great band conditions these days – early tomorrow morning, expect Europe to come blasting in on the 20 and 15 meter bands. You hook-up with a chap in Italy, and you're fluent in Italian. Go for it! It's perfectly acceptable to speak the language of the amateur operator you meet on the air. Just be sure to *identify with your call sign in English* every 10 minutes, and when you sign off. Identify in English! [97.119(b)(2)] **ANSWER C.**

G1E07 With which foreign countries is third party traffic prohibited, except for messages directly involving emergencies or disaster relief communications?
   A. Countries in ITU Region 2.
   B. Countries in ITU Region 1.
   C. Every foreign country, unless there is a third party agreement in effect with that country.
   D. Any country which is not a member of the International Amateur Radio Union (IARU).

This question asks where third party traffic is prohibited. Except in an emergency, we are *prohibited from passing international third party traffic unless the United States has a third party agreement in effect with that country*. [97.115(a)(2)] **ANSWER C.**

G1E08 Which of the following is a requirement for a non-licensed person to communicate with a foreign Amateur Radio station from a station with an FCC-granted license at which an FCC licensed control operator is present?
   A. Information must be exchanged in English.
   B. The foreign amateur station must be in a country with which the United States has a third party agreement.
   C. The control operator must have at least a General Class license.
   D. All of these choices are correct.

To pass *third party traffic* to a station in another country, the U.S. must have a *third party agreement* with that country. [97.115(a)(b)] **ANSWER B.**

List of Countries Permitting Third-Party Traffic

Antigua and Barbuda..........V2	El Salvador........................YS	Paraguay............................ZP
Argentina.............................LU	The Gambia C5	Peru.....................................OA
Australia ....VK	Ghana.................................9G	Philippines..........................DU
Austria, Vienna...........4U1VIC	Grenada J3	Pitcairn Island VR6
Belize...................................V3	Guatemala...........................TG	St. Christopher & Nevis V4
Bolivia..................................CP	Guyana 8R	St. Lucia...............................J6
Bosnia-Herzegovina T9	Haiti ....HH	St. Vincent & Grenadines .. J8
Brazil ....PY	Honduras ....HR	Sierra Leone........................9L
Canada.................VE, VO, VY	Israel....................................4X	South Africa ....ZS
Chile.....................................CE	Jamaica.............................. 6Y	Swaziland.........................3D6
Colombia..............................HK	Jordan.................................JY	Trinidad and Tobago 9Y
Comoros D6	Liberia.................................EL	Turkey ....TA
Costa Rica ....TI	Marshall Is..........................V6	United Kingdom..............GB
Cuba....................................CO	Mexico.................................XE	Uruguay...............................CX
Dominica...............................J7	Micronesia...........................V6	Venezuela............................YV
Dominican Republic .... HI	Nicaragua...........................YN	ITU-Geneva...............4U1ITU
Ecuador...............................HC	Panama...............................HP	VIC-Vienna.................4U1VIC

Be a VE

G1D02 What license examinations may you administer when you are an accredited VE holding a General Class operator license?

    A. General and Technician.
    B. General only.
    C. Technician only.
    D. Extra, General and Technician.

As a new General Class operator, we hope you will apply for Volunteer Examiner accreditation. As a VE accredited General Class operator, you and 2 other certified VE General Class (or higher) operators could administer an Element 2 *Technician Class* examination. [97.509(b)(3)(i)] **ANSWER C.**

G1D05 Which of the following must a person have before they can be an administering VE for a Technician Class license examination?

    A. Notification to the FCC that you want to give an examination.
    B. Receipt of a CSCE for General Class.
    C. Possession of a properly obtained telegraphy license.
    D. An FCC General Class or higher license and VEC accreditation.

To take part in an examination session, you need to hold a minimum of an *FCC General Class amateur license*, and you must be *accredited by a volunteer examiner coordinator (VEC)*. Remember, it takes a minimum of 3 accredited examiners to conduct the exam session. We hope you will soon become an accredited examiner. [97.509(b)(3)(i)] **ANSWER D.**

G1D07 Volunteer Examiners are accredited by what organization?

    A. The Federal Communications Commission.
    B. The Universal Licensing System.
    C. A Volunteer Examiner Coordinator.
    D. The Wireless Telecommunications Bureau.

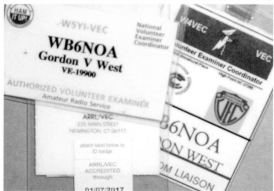

Individual *Volunteer Examiners* are *accredited by a Volunteer Examiner Coordinator*. The largest VECs are the American Radio Relay League (ARRL) and the W5YI-VEC organizations. [97.509(b)(1)] **ANSWER C.**

Look for the official "VEC Seal of Approval" when you go to your exam session. VEC examiners work hard to maintain the integrity and quality of the amateur radio exams.

G1D04 Which of the following is a requirement for administering a Technician Class license examination?
- A. At least three General Class or higher VEs must observe the examination.
- B. At least two General Class or higher VEs must be present.
- C. At least two General Class or higher VEs must be present, but only one need be Extra Class.
- D. At least three VEs of Technician Class or higher must observe the examination.

As a VE accredited General Class operator, *you and 2 other accredited General Class (or higher) volunteer examiners* may administer Technician Class Element 2 FCC examinations. [97.509(3)(i)(c)] **ANSWER A.**

G1D08 Which of the following criteria must be met for a non-U.S. citizen to be an accredited Volunteer Examiner?
- A. The person must be a resident of the U.S. for a minimum of 5 years.
- B. The person must hold an FCC granted Amateur Radio license of General Class or above.
- C. The person's home citizenship must be in ITU region 2.
- D. None of these choices is correct; a non-U.S. citizen cannot be a Volunteer Examiner.

Non U.S. citizens may become volunteer examiners if they *hold an FCC-granted General Class license* or higher. [97.509(b)(3)] **ANSWER B.**

G1D10 What is the minimum age that one must be to qualify as an accredited Volunteer Examiner?

A. 12 years.	C. 21 years.
B. 18 years.	D. There is no age limit.

There is no age limit to obtain a ham license; however, *Volunteer Examiners must be at least 18 years old*. [97.509(b)(2)] **ANSWER B.**

Elmer Point: Our listing of Volunteer Exam Coordinators will lead you to a phone number of your local area testing team. Look for it in the Appendix on page 224. Testing teams are always looking for examinees, so they'll be delighted to hear that you want to take an exam. And once you're a General, you may want to join them as an examiner! ☞ **Visit: www.w5yi-vec.org**

Elmer Point: "Roger on your QTH, and fine business on your new rig. Hope you can QSL our QSO, and I wish you very seven three." Say what? Huh? Here's a glossary with a sampling of ham radio lingo that you'll hear when you're on the air!

CQ CQ CQ this is a station on HF looking for anyone to have a nice friendly contact
CQDX CQDX CQDX this is a station calling ONLY for a contact to a foreign station, not looking for a USA contact
Old Man this really doesn't mean you are old, but rather a term for a fellow ham radio operator
YL usually an unmarried lady
XYL usually a married lady
Harmonics your children
73 best regards to you
88 an affectionate hug to a YL or XYL
Ham a licensed amateur radio operator (with every ham having his or her own idea of this term's origin)
ARRL American Radio Relay League, our number one, non-profit organization that you should join.
APRS Automatic Position Reporting System - automatic GPS radio tracking, usually on 10 MHz HF
DX a station a LONG way away
Break only use this word to break into a conversation with emergency or priority traffic. To enter a conversation politely, use only your callsign, never "Break".
CQ contest you can answer this call if you are familiar with the precise "exchange" the other operator is looking for.
QRZed who is the station calling me?
Down 10 move down in frequency 10 kHz
5 9 9 your signal report is strong, loud, and clear!
In the Mud your signal is extremely weak
QRM interference from another station on a close frequency
QTH your station location
QSL please send me a QSL card (also...I agree)
QRN power line or automobile static
QRU does anyone have traffic for me?
QRP low power station
QRT going off the air
QRX stand by - I need to do something
QSB your signal is fading in and out
QSO a communications contact
QST calling all ham radio operators
QSY we need to move off this frequency
TVI interfering with a television set
Heil a premier after-market microphone system
HF worldwide high frequency bands
MARS Military Affiliate Radio Service
Nets regular frequency meeting spot at a certain time for all interested hams
OO an official observer monitoring for rule violations
My Shack your home radio location
Mobile in motion driving down the road with a big HF rig
Ragchew having a long winded conversation
RFI every time I transmit, my windshield wipers self-activate!
Handi-ham an active radio ham who has overcome physical challenges
Splatter maybe turn down your microphone gain
Traffic an incoming message for you
HI HI radio laughter on CW

Voice Operation

G2B06 What is a practical way to avoid harmful interference on an apparently clear frequency before calling CQ on CW or phone?

    A. Send "QRL?" on CW, followed by your call sign; or, if using phone, ask if the frequency is in use, followed by your call sign.

    B. Listen for 2 minutes before calling CQ.

    C. Send the letter "V" in Morse code several times and listen for a response or say "test" several times and listen for a response.

    D. Send "QSY" on CW or if using phone, announce "the frequency is in use," then give your call and listen for a response.

Soon you will be a General Class operator on the high frequency airwaves. Sometimes, propagation allows you to hear only half of a conversation. So a good way to double check that a frequency is clear for your use is to *send "QRL?" on CW*, followed by your call sign, or *on phone simply ask, "Is the frequency in use?"* followed by your call sign. This will make you one great operator! **ANSWER A.**

G2B07 Which of the following complies with good amateur practice when choosing a frequency on which to initiate a call?

    A. Check to see if the channel is assigned to another station.

    B. Identify your station by transmitting your call sign at least 3 times.

    C. Follow the voluntary band plan for the operating mode you intend to use.

    D. All of these choices are correct.

First, double *check that you are following the band plan* and will be transmitting within your privileges. Then, before placing a call on a frequency listen for about one minute to make sure that specific frequency is open. Finally, ask if the frequency is in use and give your call sign. Repeat the question and your call sign about 3 times and listen between the calls. Now you can be relatively sure that the frequency is open for you to call CQ. **ANSWER C.**

G2B01 Which of the following is true concerning access to frequencies in non-emergency situations?

A. Nets always have priority.
B. QSOs in progress always have priority.
C. Except during FCC declared emergencies, no one has priority access to frequencies.
D. Contest operations must always yield to non-contest use of frequencies.

High frequency nets most always take place at a scheduled time on a published frequency. But what happens if that frequency is already in use by hams who don't realize that the net takes place on that frequency every day? The courteous net controller would politely interrupt and encourage the two operators to join in on the net that "is soon to begin on this frequency." If the other two stations are unable to hear the request or don't wish to move, considering *no one has priority access to frequencies* the only option is to conduct the net on a nearby clear frequency. As a new General Class operator, be a courteous ham and always relinquish your frequency for a published and popular net. **ANSWER C.**

G2A08 Which of the following is a recommended way to break into a contact when using phone?

A. Say "QRZ" several times followed by your call sign.
B. Say your call sign during a break between transmissions by the other stations.
C. Say "Break Break Break" and wait for a response.
D. Say "CQ" followed by the call sign of either station.

When you hear a conversation between two hams, a polite way to join this QSO (communication) is to simply *say your call sign in between transmissions as one station turns it over to the other station*. Say your call sign in a cheerful way, making it sound like you wish to enter the conversation in a friendly way. Don't just blurt out your call sign – sound pleasant, as if asking permission to join in. **ANSWER B.**

G2A11 What does the expression "CQ DX" usually indicate?

A. A general call for any station.
B. The caller is listening for a station in Germany.
C. The caller is looking for any station outside their own country.
D. A distress call.

The term "CQ" is used by hams to "fish" for a new station to answer their call. Say your "CQ" with a smile and sound excited about making the call to anyone hearing you. A drab, lifeless "CQ" is like fishing with old bait. If you hear someone calling *"CQ DX,"* this means they are not looking for just any stateside contact; but rather, they are *seeking calls only from very distant or foreign stations.* These usually are very experienced operators, so stay tuned and learn from the "pros" how to call out and get rare "DX" responses. **ANSWER C.**

This DX station, on the top of a hill, will enjoy some great contacts.

G4A03 What is normally meant by operating a transceiver in "split" mode?

    A. The radio is operating at half power.

    B. The transceiver is operating from an external power source.

    C. The transceiver is set to different transmit and receive frequencies.

    D. The transmitter is emitting an SSB signal, as opposed to DSB operation.

Almost all HF transceivers have a *"split" mode* that allows you to *listen on one frequency* and *transmit on another*. On older equipment, this is done using VFO-A and VFO-B. On newer equipment, some split-mode features may actually let you listen to your own split transmit frequency, while at the same time receiving the incoming signal. Foreign DX operators like to work split because it allows them to create a "window" where they listen several kHz above the frequency they are transmitting on. The receive frequency they are using is within the authorized ham band for U.S. stations. An example might be a foreign station transmitting on 14.145, while listening for U.S. General Class voice calls on 14.227. We listen on 14.145, but transmit on the frequency that they are listening to, 14.227! Operating split requires some learning, so be patient. Most important, only transmit in our band where you have voice privileges. Do not transmit on the foreign station's frequency if they are operating outside your privileges. **ANSWER C.**

Most modern HF rigs have two VFOs to make it easy to work SPLIT mode.

G4A12 Which of the following is a common use for the dual VFO feature on a transceiver?

    A. To allow transmitting on two frequencies at once.

    B. To permit full duplex operation, that is transmitting and receiving at the same time.

    C. To permit monitoring of two different frequencies.

    D. To facilitate computer interface.

The dual VFO feature on the modern transceiver with same-band receive allows you to *listen to two different frequencies simultaneously* when working "split." With the right radio, you can even add a professional headset from Heil Sound that will put one frequency in your left ear and another in your right ear. That's how the pro DXers work split! **ANSWER C.**

G2B03 If propagation changes during your contact and you notice increasing interference from other activity on the same frequency, what should you do?
A. Tell the interfering stations to change frequency.
B. Report the interference to your local Amateur Auxiliary Coordinator.
C. As a common courtesy, move your contact to another frequency.
D. Increase power to overcome interference.

On the worldwide General Class ham bands, propagation will sometimes cause stations that you did not hear moments ago on the same frequency to all of a sudden come in right on top of your ongoing contact. Be a good ham and *move your contact to another frequency,* if you can, to avoid the interference. **ANSWER C.**

G2B05 What is the customary minimum frequency separation between SSB signals under normal conditions?
A. Between 150 and 500 Hz.
B. Approximately 3 kHz.
C. Approximately 6 kHz.
D. Approximately 10 kHz.

When operating single sideband, your emission will take up approximately 3 kHz of bandwidth. Always *stay at least 3 kHz away from any other station* that is using an adjacent frequency. **ANSWER B.**

G4D10 How close to the lower edge of the 40-meter General Class phone segment should your displayed carrier frequency be when using 3 kHz wide LSB?
A. At least 3 kHz above the edge of the segment.
B. At least 3 kHz below the edge of the segment.
C. Your displayed carrier frequency may be set at the edge of the segment.
D. At least 1 kHz above the edge of the segment.

On the 40 meter band, we would want to operate *lower sideband*, and transmit at least *3 kHz above our band edge* of 7.175 MHz. This keeps all of the signal within the frequency range for General Class privileges. **ANSWER A.**

G4D08 What frequency range is occupied by a 3 kHz LSB signal when the displayed carrier frequency is set to 7.178 MHz?
A. 7.178 to 7.181 MHz.
B. 7.178 to 7.184 MHz.
C. 7.175 to 7.178 MHz.
D. 7.1765 to 7.1795 MHz.

7.178 MHz is in the 40 meter band where we usually operate lower sideband, which means our signal will extend DOWN 3 kHz from 7.178 MHz. We would then occupy *7.175 to 7.178 MHz.* **ANSWER C.**

G4D11 How close to the upper edge of the 20-meter General Class band should your displayed carrier frequency be when using 3 kHz wide USB?
A. At least 3 kHz above the edge of the band.
B. At least 3 kHz below the edge of the band.
C. Your displayed carrier frequency may be set at the edge of the band.
D. At least 1 kHz below the edge of the segment.

On the 20 meter band, *USB, stay at least 3 kHz below the top edge of the band*. Don't transmit voice any higher than 14.347 MHz. **ANSWER B.**

G4D09 What frequency range is occupied by a 3 kHz USB signal with the displayed carrier frequency set to 14.347 MHz?

   A. 14.347 to 14.647 MHz.   C. 14.344 to 14.347 MHz.

   B. 14.347 to 14.350 MHz.   D. 14.3455 to 14.3485 MHz.

On the 20 meter band (14.347 MHz) a USB (upper sideband) signal will extend UP 3 kHz. It will occupy *14.347 up to 14.350 MHz*. **ANSWER B.**

G4A11 Which of the following is a use for the IF shift control on a receiver?

   A. To avoid interference from stations very close to the receive frequency.

   B. To change frequency rapidly.

   C. To permit listening on a different frequency from that on which you are transmitting.

   D. To tune in stations that are slightly off frequency without changing your transmit frequency.

You are tuned into "Gordo's net" on 7250 kHz. About 3 kHz away is another conversation, slightly "bleeding over" on your receiver. When the Gordo net begins, simply adjust the IF shift control on your radio and magically the *repositioning of the IF pass band filter will help minimize the sounds of the other station* just a few kilohertz away. Some transceivers may also offer an additional pass band control to further home-in on the signals you want to hear. **ANSWER A.**

G2D10 What is QRP operation?

   A. Remote piloted model control.

   B. Low power transmit operation.

   C. Transmission using Quick Response Protocol.

   D. Traffic relay procedure net operation.

Many ham operators on worldwide frequencies enjoy operating *QRP* – the Q code for *low power operation*. Hams get a big kick out of working all the way around the world with less power than that used by a tiny night-light 4 watt bulb. You can look for QRP operations at specific spots on the band plan. **ANSWER B.**

G2A10 Which of the following statements is true of voice VOX operation versus PTT operation?

   A. The received signal is more natural sounding.

   B. It allows "hands free" operation.

   C. It occupies less bandwidth.

   D. It provides more power output.

Most worldwide radios have a voice-operated relay circuit, abbreviated *"VOX."* If you have a big base station microphone, this is a neat *"hands-free"* circuit to minimize you having to reach over to depress the push-to-talk switch. Just be sure you never leave the VOX circuit on when you are not right at your turned-on equipment! **ANSWER B.**

☞ **www.heilsound.com**

Using a headset with an attached mike on VOX will keep both hands free when you're taking on the worldwide bands.

G1E04 Which of the following conditions require a licensed Amateur Radio operator to take specific steps to avoid harmful interference to other users or facilities?
 A. When operating within one mile of an FCC Monitoring Station.
 B. When using a band where the Amateur Service is secondary.
 C. When a station is transmitting spread spectrum emissions.
 D. All of these choices are correct.
It is always the amateur radio operator's responsibility to prevent harmful interference to others. So, if you are within a mile of an FCC monitoring station, operating on a band where the amateur service is secondary, or experimenting with spread spectrum emissions, you want to be sure that you are not causing harmful interference. You do not want the FCC knocking on your door. *All of these choices are correct*. [97.13(b), 97.303, 97.311(b)] **ANSWER D.**

G1E06 Which of the following applies in the event of interference between a coordinated repeater and an uncoordinated repeater?
 A. The licensee of the uncoordinated repeater has primary responsibility to resolve the interference.
 B. The licensee of the coordinated repeater has primary responsibility to resolve the interference.
 C. Both repeater licensees share equal responsibility to resolve the interference.
 D. The frequency coordinator bears primary responsibility to resolve the interference.

If you decide to put up your own repeater, seek coordination because a *non-coordinated repeater has primary responsibility to resolve interference* to another repeater on the same frequency. [97.205(c)] **ANSWER A.**

Many repeater sites have the best view in town! Some repeater locations fairly bristle with both commercial and amateur antennas. Repeaters not only need to be coordinated, but also need user support to keep them on the air. Mountain top sites like this one usually charge rent for the right to place an antenna on the tower and house the repeater equipment. Join your local repeater club and help support these installations with a monetary donation to the fund!

Repeater information changes on a daily basis. While conventional repeater directories are great, you need to get one every year. This repeater directory app's database is continually being updated, so you know where to find an active repeater no matter where you are, at any time. http://www.rfinder.net/blog/

G2A05 Which mode of voice communication is most commonly used on the HF amateur bands?

A. Frequency modulation.   C. Single sideband.
B. Double sideband.   D. Phase modulation.

When you gain your new privileges on High Frequency, the majority of voice communications are done as *single sideband, SSB*. **ANSWER C.**

G2A06 Which of the following is an advantage when using single sideband as compared to other analog voice modes on the HF amateur bands?

A. Very high fidelity voice modulation.
B. Less bandwidth used and greater power efficiency.
C. Ease of tuning on receive and immunity to impulse noise.
D. Less subject to interference from atmospheric static crashes.

The advantages of *single sideband* are that it *occupies less spectrum* than other transmission modes making it possible for more people to operate on frequencies that are closer together and *is power efficient, which can make your signal travel a long way on skywaves.* **ANSWER B.**

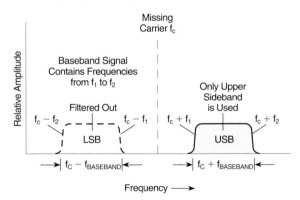

SSB signals are Amplitude Modulated (AM)
with the carrier and one sideband suppressed.

G2A07 Which of the following statements is true of the single sideband voice mode?

A. Only one sideband and the carrier are transmitted; the other sideband is suppressed.
B. Only one sideband is transmitted; the other sideband and carrier are suppressed.
C. SSB is the only voice mode that is authorized on the 20-meter, 15-meter, and 10-meter amateur bands.
D. SSB is the only voice mode that is authorized on the 160-meter, 75-meter and 40-meter amateur bands.

When we transmit using *SSB*, only a single sideband signal, approximately 2.8 kHz wide, is sent out over the air. The *opposite sideband is suppressed*. There is *no carrier* in a properly-adjusted SSB signal. This means your radio gets a complete rest during each break in your syllables, which saves power and is great for battery operation in the field. **ANSWER B.**

G2A04 Which mode is most commonly used for voice communications on the 17-meter and 12-meter bands?

A. Upper sideband.

B. Lower sideband.

C. Vestigial sideband.

D. Double sideband.

Since *17 and 12 meters* are higher in frequency than 20 meters, we always use *upper sideband*. Equipment limitations from long ago established the tradition of using USB for frequencies above 20 meters and LSB for frequencies below the 20 meter band. Although equipment today has changed, the tradition remains. **ANSWER A.**

G2A01 Which sideband is most commonly used for voice communications on frequencies of 14 MHz or higher?

A. Upper sideband.

B. Lower sideband.

C. Vestigial sideband.

D. Double sideband.

14 MHz is in the 20 meter band. On 20, 17, 15, 12, and 10 meters, plus the 5 channels on the new 60 meter band, plus VHF and UHF weak signal operations, we use *upper sideband*. By tradition, and to easily make contacts, use upper sideband on frequencies from 14 MHz and higher, including 60 meters. **ANSWER A.**
☞ **www.ac6v.com/nets.htmnd**

 Slow Scan TV is capable of delivering surprisingly high resolution images over HF, if you have lots of time! If you haven't played with amateur SSTV, you've missed out on a lot of unusual fun. SSTV is quirky with a relatively small but dedicated "club" within ham radio. Some of amateur radio's greatest ingenuity was dedicated to the challenge of sending images over very limited bandwidth. Fortunately, unlike half a century ago, you don't need a shack full of bulky, temperamental hardware! SSTV Pad makes experimenting with this unique mode a snap. SSTV is allowed anywhere HF phone is allowed, but should be restricted to the suggested band plan frequencies. 14.230 KHz is one common SSTV "watering hole." http://www.blackcatsystems.com/ipad/iPad_SSTV_Pad.html

---

G2A03 Which of the following is most commonly used for SSB voice communications in the VHF and UHF bands?

A. Upper sideband.

B. Lower sideband.

C. Vestigial sideband.

D. Double sideband.

When you upgrade to General Class, we hope you will continue to stay active on the VHF and UHF bands, too. If you operate weak signal on *VHF and UHF, use upper sideband for voice.*

Traditionally, on any frequency above 20 meters (14 MHz) voice operations are on upper sideband while on any frequency below 20 meters voice operations are on lower sideband. **ANSWER A.**

When Field Day hits in June, have fun operating portable. Bring sun screen and your log book, too!

G2A02 Which of the following modes is most commonly used for voice communications on the 160-meter, 75-meter, and 40-meter bands?

    A. Upper sideband.   C. Vestigial sideband.

    B. Lower sideband.   D. Double sideband.

We use *lower sideband (LSB) on 160, 75, and 40 meters*. While it is not absolutely illegal to use lower sideband on 20 meters and above, good operating procedure would always indicate that you should "go with the flow" and use the proper sideband. **ANSWER B.**

G2A09 Why do most amateur stations use lower sideband on the 160-meter, 75-meter and 40-meter bands?

    A. Lower sideband is more efficient than upper sideband at these frequencies.

    B. Lower sideband is the only sideband legal on these frequency bands.

    C. Because it is fully compatible with an AM detector.

    D. Current amateur practice is to use lower sideband on these frequency bands.

Remember that the choice of upper and lower sideband is by gentleman's agreement, and you won't find much about it in the FCC rule book, except on 60 meters. On the *160, 75, and 40 meter bands, amateur "practice" is to use lower sideband*. Most modern amateur worldwide high-frequency equipment automatically selects upper sideband for the bands 20 meters and up, and lower sideband for the bands 40 meters and down. **ANSWER D.**

SIDEBAND			FREQUENCY BAND IN METERS							
USB			60		20	17	15	12	10	
LSB	160	75/80		40						

Sideband Usage on Amateur Radio Bands

Elmer Point: Want to learn more about how radios work? We suggest you read and study **Basic Communications Electronics** by Jack Hudson, W9MU, and Jerry Luecke, KB5TZY. It explains how transmitters and receivers work, the science behind antennas, integrated circuits, and more. You can pick up a copy at your ham radio store, online at www.w5yi.org, or by calling W5YI Group at 800-669-9594. Understanding how radios work will add to your enjoyment of your General Class privileges!

☞ **www.W5YI.org**

CW Lives

G2B04 When selecting a CW transmitting frequency, what minimum separation should be used to minimize interference to stations on adjacent frequencies?

A. 5 to 50 Hz

B. 150 to 500 Hz

C. 1 to 3 kHz

D. 3 to 6 kHz

When *operating CW*, try to separate yourself from other CW transmissions by at least *150 to 500 Hz*. This will give your CW signal a distinct tonal difference from the other station and hopefully not cause interference. However, on 60 meter channels, all CW signals should be set so that the carrier frequency is the same as the center frequency, and no CW signal is allowed to move up or down off of the center frequency. **ANSWER B.**

G2C06 What does the term "zero beat" mean in CW operation?

A. Matching the speed of the transmitting station.

B. Operating split to avoid interference on frequency.

C. Sending without error.

D. Matching your transmit frequency to the frequency of a received signal.

When a net control station asks everyone to *"zero beat"* their CW operation, it is asking you to *match their frequency* so that everyone's CW tone will sound about the same. **ANSWER D.**

G2C05 What is the best speed to use when answering a CQ in Morse code?

A. The fastest speed at which you are comfortable copying.

B. The speed at which the CQ was sent.

C. A slow speed until contact is established.

D. At the standard calling speed of 5 wpm.

Ready to try your first CW CQ? Send at a relatively slow rate, and expect that any other station will send at this slow rate in their response to your CQ. Same thing applies in reverse. If you hear a station sending CQ at a very slow speed, chances are they are brand new on Morse code, so *send back* to them *at the same slower speed*. **ANSWER B.**

G2C07 When sending CW, what does a "C" mean when added to the RST report?
A. Chirpy or unstable signal.
B. Report was read from an S meter rather than estimated.
C. 100 percent copy.
D. Key clicks.

If someone sends you an RST report of 5-9-9 *C, it means your signal is unstable or chirping*, probably due to an inadequate power supply or operating from a low battery. **ANSWER A.**

Elmer Point: The S meter on the front of your radio indicates signal strength. S-9 is much stronger than S-5, and S-1 is relatively weak, but it will be up to your own ears and brain to judge readability. R-2 means you can make out the signal with difficulty. R-5 is a loud and clear signal report. A great report would be 5 by 9. A bad one might be 3 by 3. Sometimes hams will generalize for strength, readability and CW tone as Q-5. Let's hope you always get a 5 by 9! Here's the how the RST Signal Reporting System works:

The RST system is a way of reporting on the quality of a received signal by using a three digit number. The first digit indicates Readability (R), the second digit indicates received Signal Strength (S), and the third digit indicates Tone (T).

READABILITY (R) for Voice + CW
1 – Unreadable
2 – Barely readable, occasional words distinguishable
3 – Readable with considerable difficulty
4 – Readable with practically no difficulty
5 – Perfectly readable

SIGNAL STRENGTH (S) for Voice + CW
1 – Faint, barely perceptible signals
2 – Very weak signals
3 – Weak signals
4 – Fair signals
5 – Fairly good signals
6 – Good signals
7 – Moderately strong signals
8 – Strong signals
9 – Extremely strong signals

TONE* (T) Use on CW only
1 – Very rough, broad signals, 60 cycle AC may be present
2 – Very rough AC tone, harsh, broad
3 – Rough, low-pitched AC tone, some trace of filtering
5 – Filtered, rectified AC note, musical, ripple modulated
6 – Slight trace of filtered tone but with ripple modulation
7 – Near DC tone but trace of ripple modulation
8 – Good DC tone, may have slight trace of modulation
9 – Purest, perfect DC tone with no trace of ripple or modulation

*The TONE report refers only to the purity of the signal, and has no connection with its stability or freedom from clicks or chirps. If the signal has the characteristic steadiness of crystal control, add X to the report (e.g., RST 469X). If it has a chirp or "tail" (either on "make" or "break") add C (e.g., RST 469C). If it has clicks or other noticeable keying transients, add K (e.g., 469K). If a signal has both chirps and clicks, add both C and K (e.g., 469CK).

POPULAR Q SIGNALS

Given below are a number of Q signals whose meanings most often need to be expressed with brevity and clarity in amateur work. (Q abbreviations take the form of questions only when each is sent followed by a question mark.)

QRG Will you tell me my exact frequency (or that of _____)? Your exact frequency (or that of _____) is _____ kHz.

QRH Does my frequency vary? Your frequency varies.

QRI How is the tone of my transmission? The tone of your transmission is _____ (1. Good; 2. Variable; 3. Bad).

QRJ Are you receiving me badly? I cannot receive you. Your signals are too weak.

QRK What is the intelligibility of my signals (or those of _____)? The intelligibility of your signals (or those of _____) is _____ (1. Bad; 2. Poor; 3. Fair; 4. Good; 5. Excellent).

QRL Are you busy? I am busy (or I am busy with _____). Please do not interfere.

QRM Is my transmission being interfered with? Your transmission is being interfered with _____ (1. Nil; 2. Slightly; 3. Moderately; 4. Severely; 5. Extremely).

QRN Are you troubled by static? I am troubled by static _____ (1-5 as under QRM).

QRO Shall I increase power? Increase power.

QRP Shall I decrease power? Decrease power.

QRQ Shall I send faster? Send faster (_____ WPM).

QRS Shall I send more slowly? Send more slowly (_____ WPM).

QRT Shall I stop sending? Stop sending.

QRU Have you anything for me? I have nothing for you.

QRV Are you ready? I am ready.

QRW Shall I inform _____ that you are calling on _____ kHz? Please inform _____ that I am calling on _____ kHz.

QRX When will you call me again? I will call you again at _____ hours (on _____ kHz).

QRY What is my turn? Your turn is numbered _____ .

QRZ Who is calling me? You are being called by _____ (on _____ kHz).

QSA What is the strength of my signals (or those of _____)? The strength of your signals (or those of _____) is _____ (1. Scarcely perceptible; 2. Weak; 3. Fairly good; 4. Good; 5. Very good).

QSB Are my signals fading? Your signals are fading.

QSD Is my keying defective? Your keying is defective.

QSG Shall I send _____ messages at a time? Send _____ messages at a time.

QSK Can you hear me between your signals and if so can I break in on your transmission? I can hear you between my signals; break in on my transmission.

QSL Can you acknowledge receipt? I am acknowledging receipt.

QSM Shall I repeat the last message which I sent you, or some previous message? Repeat the last message which you sent me [or message(s) number(s) _____].

QSN Did you hear me (or _____) on _____ kHz? I heard you (or _____) on _____ kHz.

QSO Can you communicate with _____ direct or by relay? I can communicate with _____ direct (or by relay through _____).

QSP Will you relay to _____ ? I will relay to _____ .

QST General call preceding a message addressed to all amateurs and ARRL members. This is in effect "CQ ARRL."

QSU Shall I send or reply on this frequency (or on _____ kHz)?

QSW Will you send on this frequency (or on _____ kHz)? I am going to send on this frequency (or on _____ kHz).

QSX Will you listen to _____ on _____ kHz? I am listening to _____ on _____ kHz.

QSY Shall I change to transmission on another frequency? Change to transmission on another frequency (or on _____ kHz).

QSZ Shall I send each word or group more than once? Send each word or group twice (or _____ times).

QTA Shall I cancel message number _____ ? Cancel message number _____ .

QTB Do you agree with my counting of words? I do not agree with your counting of words. I will repeat the first letter or digit of each word or group.

QTC How many messages have you to send? I have messages for you (or for _____).

QTH What is your location? My location is _____ .

QTR What is the correct time? The time is _____ .

Source: ARRL

G2C02 What should you do if a CW station sends "QRS"?
A. Send slower.
B. Change frequency.
C. Increase your power.
D. Repeat everything twice.

If you are sending code to another station and they respond *"QRS,"* this means for you to please *send* at a *slower* rate. **ANSWER A.**

G2C04 What does the Q signal "QRL?" mean?
A. "Will you keep the frequency clear?"
B. "Are you operating full break-in" or "Can you operate full break-in?"
C. "Are you listening only for a specific station?"
D. "Are you busy?", or "Is this frequency in use?"

Q signals are radio "shorthand" for common requests and questions encountered in radio communications. They were developed when CW was the most common mode of amateur radio communication and are still standard practice for CW operation. QRL is among the most common Q signals. Without a question mark it means, "This frequency is in use." With a question mark, it asks, *"Is this frequency in use?"* That's a good question to ask before transmitting in any mode! **ANSWER D.**

G2C10 What does the Q signal "QRN" mean?
A. Send more slowly.
B. I am troubled by static.
C. Zero beat my signal.
D. Stop sending.

QRN is another very common Q signal and it means, *"I am troubled by static."* With a question mark it asks, "Are you troubled by static?" There are several dozen Q signals. A complete list of Q Signals can be found on page 56. Some of these are used quite often and will become very familiar to you when you work CW. Others are used very little. **ANSWER B.**

G2C11 What does the Q signal "QRV" mean?
A. You are sending too fast.
B. There is interference on the frequency.
C. I am quitting for the day.
D. I am ready to receive messages.

The Q code *"QRV" means* that you are *ready*, with pen or computer at hand, *to receive* the incoming message. If you send "QRV?" you are asking "are there any messages holding for my station?" **ANSWER D.**

G2C09 What does the Q signal "QSL" mean?
A. Send slower.
B. We have already confirmed by card.
C. I acknowledge receipt.
D. We have worked before.

The term *"QSL"* has several meanings in ham radio. On CW and sometimes voice, it means that the *other station has acknowledged your message*. And if the other station asks for a QSL, they are asking for you to send a QSL card with your call sign on the front and QSO details on the back. QSL cards are fun to collect. All General Class hams should have their own QSL card. If you ever receive a QSL card, you should always send one back! **ANSWER C.**

G2C03 What does it mean when a CW operator sends "KN" at the end of a transmission?

A. Listening for novice stations.
B. Operating full break-in.
C. Listening only for a specific station or stations.
D. Closing station now.

When a station turns the communication back to you and sends *"KN"* at the end of their transmission, it *means that they want only you to respond* and all other stations to stand by. **ANSWER C.**

G2C08 What prosign is sent to indicate the end of a formal message when using CW?

A. SK.   C. AR.
B. BK.   D.KN.

The *end of a CW formal message* usually includes *"AR."* This lets all operators know that the formal message has been sent completely. See the list of common CW abbreviations on page 233 of the Appendix. **ANSWER C.**

G4A10 What is the purpose of an electronic keyer?

A. Automatic transmit/receive switching.
B. Automatic generation of strings of dots and dashes for CW operation.
C. VOX operation.
D. Computer interface for PSK and RTTY operation.

That brand new radio you rewarded yourself with in preparation for successfully passing your General exam will likely have a built-in *electronic keyer*. Sure, you could set the keyer to accept your granddad's old J-38 straight key, but why not try your CW skills with paddles, where your thumb and finger create *strings of dits and dahs* with a single touch? **ANSWER B.**

Newer HF rigs have the electronic keyer built in. Older radios can take an external CW keyer box.

G2C01 Which of the following describes full break-in telegraphy (QSK)?

A. Breaking stations send the Morse code prosign BK.
B. Automatic keyers are used to send Morse code instead of hand keys.
C. An operator must activate a manual send/receive switch before and after every transmission.
D. Transmitting stations can receive between code characters and elements.

You will begin your adventures with CW transmissions using VOX mode to turn on the transmitter when you start keying and turn it off a few seconds after you stop keying. This is called semi-break-in. When you really get good at CW, you can set your transceiver to operate CW in the *QSK full break-in mode*. In this mode, the receiver will instantly tune in on what's happening even as you are sending CW on the air. If another station wishes to interrupt, you will *hear its signal between your dots and dashes*. **ANSWER D.**

G1B03 Which of the following is a purpose of a beacon station as identified in the FCC rules?
    A. Observation of propagation and reception.
    B. Automatic identification of repeaters.
    C. Transmission of bulletins of general interest to Amateur Radio licensees.
    D. Identifying net frequencies.
Beacon stations are important for the study of *propagation and reception* from the ionosphere. Always try to stay clear of beacon stations when selecting a frequency on which to transmit. Beacon stations are found at 14.100 MHz, 28.200 - 28.300 MHz, and on the 2 meter band below 144.300 MHz. These are one-way transmissions. Six meter beacons are great for determining a band opening!
[97.3(a)(9)] **ANSWER A.**

Radio Beacon Stations

Slot	Country	Call	14.100	18.110	21.150	24.930	28.200	Operator
1	United Nations	4U1UN	00:00	00:10	00:20	00:30	00:40	UNRC
2	Canada	VE8AT	00:10	00:20	00:30	00:40	00:50	RAC
3	USA	W6WX	00:20	00:30	00:40	00:50	01:00	NCDXF
4	Hawaii	KH6WO	00:30	00:40	00:50	01:00	01:10	UHRO
5	New Zealand	ZL	00:40	00:50	01:00	01:10	01:20	NZART
6	Australia	VK8	00:50	01:00	01:10	01:20	01:30	W1A
7	Japan	JA21CY	01:00	01:10	01:20	01:30	01:40	JARL
8	China	BY	01:10	01:20	01:30	01:40	01:50	CRSA
9	Russia	UA	01:20	01:30	01:40	01:50	02:00	TBO
10	Sri Lanka	4S7B	01:30	01:40	01:50	02:00	02:10	RSSL
11	South Africa	ZS6DN	01:40	01:50	02:00	02:10	02:20	ZS6DN
12	Kenya	5Z4B	01:50	02:00	02:10	02:20	02:30	RSK
13	Israel	4X6TU	02:00	02:10	02:20	02:30	02:40	U of Tel Aviv
14	Finland	OH2B	02:10	02:20	02:30	02:40	02:50	U oh Helsinki
15	Madeira	CS3B	02:20	02:30	02:40	02:50	00:00	ARRM
16	Argentina	LU4AA	02:30	02:40	02:50	00:00	00:10	RCA
17	Peru	OA4B	02:40	02:50	00:00	00:10	00:20	RCP
18	Venezuela	YV5B	02:50	00:00	00:10	00:20	00:30	RCV

The 10-second, phase-3, message format is: "W6WX dah-dah-dah-dah" — each "dah" lasts a little more than one second. W6WX is transmitted at 100 watts, then each "dah" is attenuated in order, beginning at 100 watts, then 10 watts, then 1 watt, and finally 0.1 watt.
Courtesy CQ Magazine

G1B10 What is the power limit for beacon stations?
    A. 10 watts PEP output.   C. 100 watts PEP output.
    B. 20 watts PEP output.   D. 200 watts PEP output.
Beacon stations used for propagation surveys must never transmit more than *100 watts* peak envelope power *(PEP) output*. [97.203(c)] **ANSWER C.**

G1B02 With which of the following conditions must beacon stations comply?
   A. A beacon station may not use automatic control.
   B. The frequency must be coordinated with the National Beacon Organization.
   C. The frequency must be posted on the Internet or published in a national periodical.
   D. There must be no more than one beacon signal transmitting in the same band from the same station location.

Beacon stations are important for the study of propagation. Do not transmit on beacon band plan frequencies. Ham operators are permitted to put up only a *single beacon signal in the same band from a single location*. [97.203(b)]
ANSWER D.

G4A02 What is one advantage of selecting the opposite or "reverse" sideband when receiving CW signals on a typical HF transceiver?
   A. Interference from impulse noise will be eliminated.
   B. More stations can be accommodated within a given signal passband.
   C. It may be possible to reduce or eliminate interference from other signals.
   D. Accidental out of band operation can be prevented.

We encourage you to learn Morse code. In the back of this book is a complete chapter on learning the code. On-air code practice is a great way to boost your copying speed. Sometimes when receiving a weak CW signal you hear interference, too. Try this trick. *Switch* between upper and lower *sideband* to see if one of the sideband filters pulls in the CW signal better and *reduces the interference* from other signals. That's right – you can still hear CW in the SSB mode. Just be sure to go back to CW mode when you are ready to transmit.
ANSWER C.

G8B09 Why is it good to match receiver bandwidth to the bandwidth of the operating mode?
   A. It is required by FCC rules.
   B. It minimizes power consumption in the receiver.
   C. It improves impedance matching of the antenna.
   D. It results in the best signal to noise ratio.

When you switch modes on your new radio, appropriate filters fall into place giving you the *best signal-to-noise ratio*. You might be able to select tighter CW bandwidths to further improve signal-to-noise ratios. **ANSWER D.**

Elmer Point: Which is faster – new-fangled text messaging or old-reliable Morse code? Jay Leno wanted the answer to that question, so on May 13, 2006, Leno invited world text-messaging speed champ Ben Cook of Utah and his friend Jason to appear on The Tonight Show with Jay Leno to test their ability against Chip Margelli, K7JA and Ken Miller, K6CTW. Cook told Leno that he'd managed to send a 160-letter message to his friend in 57 seconds. Who won? Chip and Ken, hands down! Margelli sent his message at 29-wpm, but he was once timed sending code at 61.5 words per minute!

Increasing your CW Proficiency

Many new radio amateurs are surprised when they hear so much CW activity on the amateur bands. It's almost as if a lot of hams actually *like* to use CW, even though they don't have to know CW anymore! Can this possibly be true?

Absolutely! CW is a lot of fun and shows no signs of going away any time soon. It's a lot *more* fun, however, when you're good at it! How do you get good at it? Practice, and lots of it. But it helps to have a good start. Get some good CW practice CDs with *random groups*. The advantage of random groups is that it forces you to copy code *perfectly*, not just "sort of." It's also helpful to use the Farnsworth method in which individual characters are sent at a very high speed, while words are sent at a much lower rate. This helps you avoid "plateaus" and forces you to listen to the sound of complete characters, rather than "counting" dots and dashes. The Farnsworth method works!

Nothing builds up CW proficiency like formal traffic handling. See if you can check into one of the regional NTS CW traffic nets. Contests can help; but contest operation is rather "bursty" and will not guarantee that you will be able to consistently operate for a long time with high accuracy and speed. Also, in a contest, you already have a pretty good idea what's coming next, whereas traffic handling is more like the random groups you practiced!

Get the best key or keyer you can afford. You can operate up to about 30 words per minute with a first rate straight key. A bad straight key will make 20 wpm a real challenge! But if you decide a straight key isn't your cup of tea, be assured that code sent with an electronic keyer is "real CW" too!

In Chapter 5 of this book, Gordo gives you a fun way to learn CW, beginning with the most common letters. He also has recorded an 8-CD audio course for learning Morse code. Call 800-669-9594 to learn more and order a set for yourself.

You can also learn CW on-line! You can even track your progress on your computer. Visit these websites:

☞ http://aa9pw.com/morsecode

☞ www.dxzone.com/catalog/Operating Modes/Morse code/ Learning Morse Code

---

ham apps

Morse Decoder

While no Morse code decoder is as good as a well-trained ear, under good conditions with "machine sent" code, such as code practice sessions from W1AW, some of these decoders work pretty well. https://itunes.apple.com/us/app/morsedecoder/id313071325?mt=8

Digital Operating

HHIHH ⊂ 10001010011001001110010o0101

G2E04 What segment of the 20-meter band is most often used for digital transmissions?
    A. 14.000 - 14.050 MHz.   C. 14.150 - 14.225 MHz.
    B. 14.070 - 14.100 MHz.   D. 14.275 - 14.350 MHz.
Digital modes are found grouped together on each of the ham bands, skillfully placed so they do not cause interference to nearby CW operators. Most digital mode transmissions on the *20 meter band* are found between *14.070 to 14.100 MHz*, a 30-kHz digital "window." Use LSB and a digital decoder to tune into 20 meter digital mode stations. **ANSWER B.**

G2E07 What segment of the 80-meter band is most commonly used for digital transmissions?
    A. 3570 – 3600 kHz.   C. 3700 – 3750 kHz
    B. 3500 – 3525 kHz.   D. 3775 – 3825 kHz
On the *80 meter band*, tune from *3570 to 3600 kHz* for some fascinating data signals that your computer equipped with a specialized program can transform to a screen full of text. **ANSWER A.**

G8C04 Which of the following describes Baudot code?
    A. A 7-bit code with start, stop and parity bits.
    B. A code using error detection and correction.
    C. A 5-bit code with additional start and stop bits.
    D. A code using SELCAL and LISTEN.
Give me FIVE! This is a good way to remember *Baudot is a 5 bit code* with an additional start and stop bit. Give me FIVE! **ANSWER C.**

G2E06 What is the most common frequency shift for RTTY emissions in the amateur HF bands?
    A. 85 Hz.   C. 425 Hz.
    B. 170 Hz.   D. 850 Hz.
Almost all *ham radio RTTY* transmissions use a *170-Hz shift*. Commercial broadcast stations on shortwave use larger frequency shifts. **ANSWER B.**

G8C11 How are the two separate frequencies of a Frequency Shift Keyed (FSK) signal identified?

A. Dot and Dash.	C. High and Low
B. On and Off.	D. Mark and Space

While FSK signals could reasonably be called "High and Low" because of their relative frequencies, there is a specific LOGICAL significance to MARK and SPACE. This is true whether you're operating on a closed loop land line (as many RTTY circuits once were) or over the air. So, *Mark and Space* define the actual "1" and "0" logic states of a two-state digital system. **ANSWER D.**

G2E01 Which mode is normally used when sending an RTTY signal via AFSK with an SSB transmitter?

A. USB.	C. CW.
B. DSB.	D. LSB.

If you plan to operate radioteletype (*RTTY*) using audio-frequency-shift-keying (*AFSK*), your single sideband transmitter must be switched to *LSB, lower sideband*. **ANSWER D.**

☞ www.aorusa.com

You can connect a PSK-31 and RTTY data reader to your radio to decode messages.

G2E14 What could be wrong if you cannot decode an RTTY or other FSK signal even though it is apparently tuned in properly?

A. The mark and space frequencies may be reversed.

B. You may have selected the wrong baud rate.

C. You may be listening on the wrong sideband.

D. All of these choices are correct.

Frequency Shift Keying (FSK) is used by a number of digital modes, the oldest of which is RTTY (RadioTeleTYpe). The computer sound card is the most convenient way to try out a number of different FSK modes, as this allows you to apply the audio directly into the microphone input of a single sideband transmitter with little or no modification. The audio sound card actually creates Audio Frequency Shift Keying (AFSK) which is converted to "true" FSK in a properly-aligned SSB transmitter. *Reversing the MARK and SPACE* audio tones has exactly the same effect as having the SSB *transmitter on the wrong sideband.* Although some software is capable of detecting "reversed" tones, not all sound card programs are that "smart." So if you encounter difficulty decoding an FSK signal of any kind, try reversing the sideband or the audio tones. Also, be sure you're set for the *right baud rate*. While RTTY is standard at 45 baud, other digital modes have multiple available transmission (baud) rates. **ANSWER D.**

G8C01 Which of the following digital modes is designed to operate at extremely low signal strength on the HF bands?

A. FSK441 and Hellschreiber.   C. Clover.
B. JT9 and JT65.   D. RTTY.

A number of extremely weak signal modes were developed by Nobel Laureate and radio amateur Joe Taylor, K1JT. These are known by various "JT" protocols and have some very unique operating methods. These are not fast communications modes but they work when nothing else will. The *JT65* format was developed especially for Moonbounce, and radically reduced the equipment requirements for radio amateurs interested in working this exotic mode. *JT9* was specifically adapted to "low band" HF operation. **ANSWER B.**

Speaking of quirky, nothing takes the cake like Hellschreiber. Hellschreiber is neither FAX, nor RTTY, nor SSTV, though it has elements of all three. It's neither truly analog nor truly digital, but has characteristics of both. It's a very old mode, but one that's been rediscovered by a small dedicated amateur radio community. The best way to describe Hellschreiber is to try it, and this app is the easiest way available to do just that. http://www.blackcatsystems.com/ipad/iPad_iPhone_Hellschreiber. html

---

G2E05 What is the standard sideband used to generate a JT65 or JT9 digital signal when using AFSK in any amateur band?

A. LSB.   C. DSB.
B. USB.   D. SSB.

A number of conventions dictate amateur radio standard usage when there are no specific FCC rules that apply. Such conventions generally come about for a good reason, and unless there's a compelling reason to depart from them, it's best to follow the convention. Since the advent of sound card digital modes, it is conventional to *use upper sideband (USB) for HF digital operation, regardless of the band*. **ANSWER B.**

G2E08 In what segment of the 20-meter band are most PSK31 operations commonly found?

A. At the bottom of the slow-scan TV segment, near 14.230 MHz.
B. At the top of the SSB phone segment, near 14.325 MHz.
C. In the middle of the CW segment, near 14.100 MHz.
D. Below the RTTY segment, near 14.070 MHz.

PSK31 was the first popular sound card digital mode, followed quickly by countless other sound card digital modes. No elaborate setup or interface connections are necessary for sound card modes, which is why they are so popular. If you haven't played around with *PSK31*, the best place to find a lot of activity is on *14.070 Hz*. Be sure your receiver is set to upper sideband. **ANSWER D.**

Here are a couple of apps for decoding PSK31 that require no physical connection to your receiver:
http://www.blackcatsystems.com/ipad/iPad_PSK31_Pad.html
https://play.google.com/store/apps/details?id=com.wolphi.
psk31&hl=en

G8C02 How many data bits are sent in a single PSK31 character?

A. The number varies.
B. 5.
C. 7.
D. 8.

The sounds of *PSK31* take on the characteristics of a steady whistle with just a little warble on the airwaves. It's that variable warble that is part of VARICODE characters represented by a variable-length combination of bits. Just like the name VARICODE implies, *the number of data bits varies.* More information on digital activities can be found in the ARRL's *HF Digital Handbook*, edited by Steve Ford, WB8IMY. **ANSWER A..**

G8C08 Which of the following statements is true about PSK31?

A. Upper case letters make the signal stronger.
B. Upper case letters use longer Varicode signals and thus slow down transmission.
C. Varicode Error Correction is used to ensure accurate message reception.
D. Higher power is needed as compared to RTTY for similar error rates.

When RTTY was king of the digital modes, only CAPITAL letters were available. To the uninitiated, "plain" RTTY looks like you're always yelling! PSK31 has the entire character set available, but with a price. If you try "yelling" in PSK31, you slow down considerably, *because capital letters have longer codes!* So, use caps when you need to, but not all the time. **ANSWER B.**

G2E11 What is indicated on a waterfall display by one or more vertical lines adjacent to a PSK31 signal?

A. Long Path propagation.
B. Backscatter propagation.
C. Insufficient modulation.
D. Overmodulation.

PSK31 is noted for being a very narrowband mode. On a waterfall display, a proper PSK31 signal will appear as a single thin line. The appearance of *multiple lines* is a good indication of intermodulation distortion, generally *resulting from overmodulation* of the transmitter. To avoid overmodulation, you should always use just enough audio to achieve between 25% and 50% of the available peak envelope power (PEP) that your SSB transmitter can provide. PSK31 is a weak signal mode. You will be surprised just how little power is needed for effective communications. It's always safer to use too little power than too much! **ANSWER D.**

HF offers more interesting modes than you can shake a keyboard at! A waterfall display, like that shown to the right of the main transceiver, is the most common way of sorting out competing signals when tuning in digital signals.

G2E12 Which of the following describes a waterfall display?
A. Frequency is horizontal, signal strength is vertical, time is intensity.
B. Frequency is vertical, signal strength is intensity, time is horizontal.
C. Frequency is horizontal, signal strength is intensity, time is vertical.
D. Frequency is vertical, signal strength is horizontal, time is intensity.

A waterfall display is a special type of spectral display. It shows the demodulated audio frequency of a radio signal using one of the many sound card digital modes. Unlike a standard display of a spectrum analyzer or panadapter, the waterfall display has memory; it will show a record of radio events over a significant period of time. The standard waterfall display shows *frequency along the horizontal axis, intensity by means of color, and time by vertical "scrolling."* The waterfall display can show you a lot of information about what's happening near your receive frequency. **ANSWER C.**

G8C09 What does the number 31 represent in "PSK31"?
A. The approximate transmitted symbol rate.
B. The version of the PSK protocol.
C. The year in which PSK31 was invented.
D. The number of characters that can be represented by PSK31.

Phase shift keying (PSK) sounds like a steady carrier with a little superimposed warble on 14.070 MHz. *PSK31* occupies only about 31 Hertz of bandwidth, with an *approximate transmitted symbol rate of 31*. Baud is the symbol or (bit) rate. In RTTY, each character takes five bits so the character rate is 1/5 of the baud rate. In PSK31, the symbols are different lengths, so the baud rate is an average. Capital letters have more symbols per character and so are slower to transmit. There are some excellent software programs to decode PSK31, many that you can download for free. **ANSWER A.**

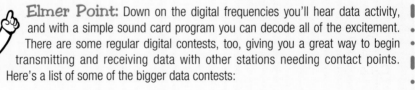

Elmer Point: Down on the digital frequencies you'll hear data activity, and with a simple sound card program you can decode all of the excitement. There are some regular digital contests, too, giving you a great way to begin transmitting and receiving data with other stations needing contact points. Here's a list of some of the bigger data contests:

- New Years' Day RTTY Contest
- First weekend in January ARRL RTTY Roundup
- First weekend in February Low Power Digital Contest
- Second weekend in February Worldwide RTTY Call Letter Prefix Contest
- Second weekend in March RTTY Sprint
- Third weekend in April PSK-31 Activity weekend
- Third weekend in July North American RTTY Activity weekend
- First weekend in September PSK-31 Contest
- First weekend in October Hellschreiber Contest

G8C12 Which type of code is used for sending characters in a PSK31 signal?
    A. Varicode.   C. Volumetric
    B. Viterbi.   D. Binary

PSK31 is actually a rather unusual code. It is optimized for very narrow bandwidths. *PSK31 uses* a code known as *Varicode* for its different symbol lengths. **ANSWER A.**

G8A01 How is an FSK signal generated?
    A. By keying an FM transmitter with a sub-audible tone.
    B. By changing an oscillator's frequency directly with a digital control signal.
    C. By using a transceiver's computer data interface protocol to change frequencies.
    D. By reconfiguring the CW keying input to act as a tone generator.

While the method of using an SSB transmitter to convert an AFSK signal to an FSK signal is pretty much universal these days, there's still something to be said for generating FSK the old, direct way. One advantage of "old school" FSK is that it allows you to use very powerful and efficient Class C RF amplifiers. This method is still in common use by serious RTTY contesters and DXers. The most direct way of *creating FSK is to shift the frequency of an oscillator* by "keying in" a small amount of capacitance across its resonant tuned circuit. If the oscillator is a low powered solid state circuit, it can be keyed directly with a digital gate chip. **ANSWER B.**

The SignalLink box plugs in between your transceiver and computer, allowing you to use your keyboard to key your transmitter with a minimum of muss and fuss.

G8B10 What is the relationship between transmitted symbol rate and bandwidth?
    A. Symbol rate and bandwidth are not related.
    B. Higher symbol rates require wider bandwidth.
    C. Lower symbol rates require wider bandwidth.
    D. Bandwidth is always half the symbol rate.

You know why big boats go so slow out of the harbor, right? If they went any faster they would create big wakes that would upset every other boat on either side of them. Same thing for ham *radio digital modes* – if you're going to *send fast*, you'll need to go to higher bands that will permit the *faster sending speed and wider bandwidth*. **ANSWER B.**

G1C08 What is the maximum symbol rate permitted for RTTY or data emission transmitted at frequencies below 28 MHz?
    A. 56 kilobaud.   C. 1200 baud.
    B. 19.6 kilobaud.   D. 300 baud.

RTTY and data emissions below *28 MHz* (below the 10 meter band) must creep along no faster than *300 baud*. This slow symbol rate is required to minimize bandwidth allocation on the very crowded high-frequency bands. [97.307(f)(3)] **ANSWER D.**

G1C07 **What is the maximum symbol rate permitted for RTTY or data emission transmission on the 20-meter band?**
A. 56 kilobaud.   C. 1200 baud.
B. 19.6 kilobaud.   D. 300 baud.

Data emissions on the *20 meter band* must creep along no faster than *300 baud*. This slow symbol rate is required to minimize bandwidth usage on the very crowded HF frequency bands. [97.305(c), 97.307(f)(3)] **ANSWER D.**

G1C10 **What is the maximum symbol rate permitted for RTTY or data emission transmissions on the 10-meter band?**
A. 56 kilobaud.   C. 1200 baud.
B. 19.6 kilobaud.   D. 300 baud.

On *10 meters* we are permitted to increase RTTY and data emission transmission speeds to *1200 baud*. This is 4 times faster than the slower speed required on frequencies below the 10 meter band. [97.305(c) and 97.307(f)(4)] **ANSWER C.**

G1C11 **What is the maximum symbol rate permitted for RTTY or data emission transmissions on the 2-meter band?**
A. 56 kilobaud.   C. 1200 baud.
B. 19.6 kilobaud.   D. 300 baud.

The next possible answer up from 1200 bauds is 19.6 kilobauds (kilo means 1000). *19,600 baud* is real quick for *2 meters.* Remember, the faster rates are permitted on higher frequencies where more bandwidth is available for the signal. [97.305(c), 97.307(f)(5)] **ANSWER B.**

G1C09 **What is the maximum symbol rate permitted for RTTY or data emission transmitted on the 1.25-meter and 70-centimeter bands?**
A. 56 kilobaud.   C. 1200 baud.
B. 19.6 kilobaud.   D. 300 baud.

We can open the speed throttle up to *56 kilobaud* when we transmit on *1.25 meters* (222 MHz band) and *70 cm* (440 MHz band). You will find some exciting data links on these bands. [97.305(c), 97.307(f)(5)] **ANSWER A.**

Maximum Symbol (Baud) Rate for Amateur Bands

Amateur Band (meters)	Maximum Symbol Rate (bauds)
160 to 12 m	300 bauds
10 m	1200 bauds
6 and 2 m	19,600 bauds
1.25 and 0.70 m	56,000 bauds
33 cm and higher	Not Specified

G8C03 **What part of a data packet contains the routing and handling information?**
A. Directory.   C. Header.
B. Preamble.   D. Footer.

Within the *header* are *routing addresses and handling information* for digipeaters that direct your packet over a specific route – even coast-to-coast and worldwide! If you are into APRS (Automatic Position/Packet Reporting System), you can set up your packet header for local or wide-area relay of your position report. **ANSWER C.**

G1E11 Which of the following is the FCC term for an unattended digital station that transfers messages to and from the Internet?
A. Locally controlled station.
B. Robotically controlled station.
C. Automatically controlled digital station.
D. Fail-safe digital station.

Echolink and IRLP are two very popular Internet-to-Amateur Radio technologies. The radio transmitter/receiver or repeater involved in the system is known as an *automatically controlled digital station*. In this case, there are actually two control operators responsible for legal operation: the distant Internet computer operator, as well as the amateur who communicates to the "RF" side of the link. While you may not think of yourself as a radio operator as you sit at a computer thousands of miles away from the actual transmitter, you are ultimately responsible for the transmissions of that remote station. [97.221] **ANSWER C.**

G1E13 On what bands may automatically controlled stations transmitting RTTY or data emissions communicate with other automatically controlled digital stations?
A. On any band segment where digital operation is permitted.
B. Anywhere in the non-phone segments of the 10-meter or shorter wavelength bands.
C. Only in the non-phone Extra Class segments of the bands.
D. Anywhere in the 1.25-meter or shorter wavelength bands, and in specified segments of the 80-meter through 2-meter bands.

In recent years there have been major changes in the rules pertaining to automatically controlled HF stations. Because the potential exists for severe interference from automatically controlled HF stations, you must be extremely careful to follow the rules, which include performing this function only in the specified HF band segments (*the 1.25 meter or shorter wavelength bands, and in specified segments of the 80-meter through 2-meter bands*). In addition, an automatically controlled, remote HF relay station absolutely must have an effective "listen before talking" protocol implemented to avoid transmitting "on top of" an existing station. [97.221, 97.305] **ANSWER D.**

G1E03 What is required to conduct communications with a digital station operating under automatic control outside the automatic control band segments?
A. The station initiating the contact must be under local or remote control.
B. The interrogating transmission must be made by another automatically controlled station.
C. No third party traffic may be transmitted.
D. The control operator of the interrogating station must hold an Extra Class license.

All amateur radio communications must be made by a *control operator*. Sometimes it can be a bit tricky determining the identity of the control operator. In the case of Echolink or IRLP, the control operator may be located clear across the country from the actual transmitter. If you "bring up" a distant repeater from your Echolink computer, you are the control operator responsible for what goes out over the air. Now, while there are amateur sub-bands allocated specifically to automatic control, Echolink or IRLP transmission do not fall under this exception; they occur in "normal" ham bands. [97.221] **ANSWER A.**

EchoLink

As hard as it may be to believe, there are some places where there's no direct access to any repeater. Echolink lets you work thousands of remote repeaters around the world through the Internet. You do need a valid ham license to register through EchoLink, as you are the control operator, even if you're a continent away https://itunes.apple.com/us/app/echolink/id350688562?mt=8

IRLP

Similar but different from Echolink, IRLP also lets you connect to repeaters via the Internet, but with a somewhat different protocol. Recent developments allow the Echolink and IRLP networks to "play together." https://itunes.apple.com/us/app/irlp*me/id453904909?mt=8

G1E12 Under what circumstances are messages that are sent via digital modes exempt from Part 97 third party rules that apply to other modes of communication?

A. Under no circumstances.
B. When messages are encrypted.
C. When messages are not encrypted.
D. When under automatic control.

Third party traffic rules have remained essentially unchanged throughout the history of Amateur Radio, and are unlikely to be changed significantly in the foreseeable future. You must not perform any third party traffic handling with any entity that does not have a third party agreement. *No exceptions!* [97.115] **ANSWER A.**

G6B10 What two devices in an Amateur Radio station might be connected using a USB interface?

A. Computer and transceiver.
B. Microphone and transceiver.
C. Amplifier and antenna.
D. Power supply and amplifier.

The two devices in your new General Class station that could be *connected using a USB* interface are your *computer* and that brand new high frequency *transceiver*. **ANSWER A.**

The universal serial bus (USB) has made it simple to connect your ham radio to your computer.

G6B12 Which of the following connectors would be a good choice for a serial data port?

A. PL-259.
B. Type N.
C. Type SMA
D. DE-9

Yup, answer D is spelled correctly, "DE-9." I know, I know, we usually call it a "DB-9," but for this examination go with the technically correct term "DE-9." If you have an older laptop that you want to tie to your new ham radio to decode data, the computer may only offer a *DE-9 serial data port connector*. So just remember, for this test the DE-9 connector is the correct answer. **ANSWER D.**

DE-9 Connector

G6B14 Which of these connector types is commonly used for audio signals in Amateur Radio stations?

A. PL-259.
B. BNC.
C. RCA Phono.
D. Type N.

Let's look for the correct answer by identifying the use of each possible answer. A PL-259, Type N or BNC connector is used to join the antenna to your radio. The *RCA phono jack* is the *common connector for an audio* connection, just as it always was for connections on your stereo system. **ANSWER C.**

RCA Connectors

G6B17 What is the general description of a DIN type connector?

A. A special connector for microwave interfacing.
B. A DC power connector rated for currents between 30 and 50 amperes.
C. A family of multiple circuit connectors suitable for audio and control signals.
D. A special watertight connector for use in marine applications.

DIN type connectors are found on cables having up to 8 or more pins with receptacles located on the back of your HF transceiver. Each manufacturer has a unique arrangement of what is fed to each pin for audio, power, and control signals. Be careful when you start wiring in that new terminal node controller or linear amplifier since sometimes there is voltage on one of those pins. You want to make absolutely sure you never short these voltage lines to ground because there may not be fused protection inside the radio for this connection. **ANSWER C.**

DIN Connectors

G8B08 Why is it important to know the duty cycle of the mode you are using when transmitting?
  A. To aid in tuning your transmitter.
  B. Some modes have high duty cycles which could exceed the transmitter's average power rating.
  C. To allow time for the other station to break in during a transmission.
  D. All of these choices are correct.

Hooking-up your high-frequency ham transceiver to your computer opens up a whole new world for receiving and sending data signals. Receiving is almost a direct connection to your computer through the sound card, but sending data may require an external modem. Sending data using on-and-off handshake modes like PACTOR II or G-TOR cycles your transceiver to transmit and receive for a duty cycle (on transmit) of perhaps 50%. But other modes like PSK31 and MFSK16 are transmitting a constant key-down data stream without interruption. Now your *duty cycle is 100%* and the heat sinks on the back of your transceiver are going to get roasty-toasty. To keep your equipment from going into meltdown, consider adding an external fan and reducing power output to the point the rear heat sinks won't fry eggs. If you get the heat sinks so warm that you can't touch them, you *could damage the transmitter* leading to a mighty expensive repair. **ANSWER B.**

G2E13 Which communication system sometimes uses the Internet to transfer messages?
  A. Winlink.
  B. RTTY.
  C. ARES.
  D. Skywarn.

Winlink is a popular gateway technology, linking Amateur Radio and the Internet. Direct radio frequency communications between *Winlink* stations are also possible, but most of the traffic is between a remote HF station and the *Internet* via an "RMS" (Remote Messaging Station). **ANSWER A.**

G2E10 Which of the following is a way to establish contact with a digital messaging system gateway station?
  A. Send an email to the system control operator.
  B. Send QRL in Morse code.
  C. Respond when the station broadcasts its SSID.
  D. Transmit a connect message on the station's published frequency.

A gateway is an interface between different communications systems, such as between the Internet and Amateur Radio. Winlink is one of the most popular gateway technologies, combining email and (normally) HF radio. Gateway HF stations operate on specific published frequencies. To access one of these gateways from a remote HF station, *transmit a connect command* via your Winlink client software. Once connected, the HF link is "transparent;" from your terminal it looks just like you're on an Internet email client. **ANSWER D.**

Elmer Point: Want to learn more about how digital electronics work – from DSP systems to your computer, and all those gizmos inside your new HF radio? Get a copy of **Basic Digital Electronics** by Al Evans. You can pick-up a copy at your local ham radio dealer, on-line at www.w5yi.org, or by calling The W5YI Group at 800-669-9594.

G2E09 How do you join a contact between two stations using the PACTOR protocol?

    A. Send broadcast packets containing your call sign while in MONITOR mode.

    B. Transmit a steady carrier until the PACTOR protocol times out and disconnects.

    C. Joining an existing contact is not possible; PACTOR connections are limited to two stations.

    D. Send a NAK response continuously so that the sending station has to pause.

PACTOR and a number of other digital modes operate in a connected mode. In this mode, "handshaking" or "acknowledgements" perform error correction in an extremely reliable manner. The downside to this is that *the connected mode only works between two stations*. This is why PACTOR is very effective for automatic relaying, but is not suitable for real time "ragchewing." There are a number of other digital modes, however, that are suitable to roundtables and general conversation. **ANSWER C.**

G2E02 How can a PACTOR modem or controller be used to determine if the channel is in use by other PACTOR stations?

    A. Unplug the data connector temporarily and see if the channel-busy indication is turned off.

    B. Put the modem or controller in a mode which allows monitoring communications without a connection.

    C. Transmit UI packets several times and wait to see if there is a response from another PACTOR station.

    D. Send the message: "Is this frequency in use?"

A "rogue" PACTOR station can create untold havoc on the HF bands, not to mention a great deal of ill will among other users. Means must be implemented, either automatically or manually, to determine if a frequency is in use before transmitting. The "unconnected" or *monitor mode* of a PACTOR controller allows the control operator to do this. Always determine that the frequency is clear before transmitting. **ANSWER B.**

G2E03 What symptoms may result from other signals interfering with a PACTOR or WINMOR transmission?

    A. Frequent retries or timeouts.

    B. Long pauses in message transmission.

    C. Failure to establish a connection between stations.

    D. All of these choices are correct.

While most HF digital modes are fairly robust and generally include some kind of error correction, no system is perfect. Just the quirks of HF propagation itself present a challenge to most HF digital modes. When interference from other transmissions are in the mix, it's sometimes amazing HF "digi" works at all! An HF communications link undergoing interference can suffer symptoms ranging from *long pauses* in message transmissions, frequent message *retries and timeouts* to complete *connection failures*. Digital technology is pretty amazing, but it's still subject to the laws of physics, some of which you have no control over! **ANSWER D.**

G8B05 **What is the approximate bandwidth of a PACTOR3 signal at maximum data rate?**

A. 31.5 Hz.
B. 500 Hz.
C. 1800 Hz.
D. 2300 Hz.

Pactor3 is a relatively "fast" transmission mode as far as HF digital modes go. It occupies approximately *2300 Hz*, about the same bandwidth as a typical SSB "phone" signal, and can be effectively transmitted through standard amateur HF SSB equipment, even at its fastest rate. PACTOR3 doesn't always transmit at maximum speed, however. A sophisticated adaptive protocol adjusts the speed depending on propagation conditions. **ANSWER D.**

G8C06 **What action results from a failure to exchange information due to excessive transmission attempts when using PACTOR or WINMOR?**

A. The checksum overflows.
B. The connection is dropped.
C. Packets will be routed incorrectly.
D. Encoding reverts to the default character set.

Sometimes it's good to know when to quit, even if you're an automatic relay station! PACTOR and WINMOR, both common protocols for the Winlink service, will make numerous attempts to establish or maintain an HF link, and can usually do so under the most horrendous conditions. When it is clearly fruitless to attempt continuing on, PACTOR and WINMOR know when to quit. Both modes will deliberately *drop the connection* after a predetermined number of tries. **ANSWER B.**

G8C05 **In the PACTOR protocol, what is meant by an NAK response to a transmitted packet?**

A. The receiver is requesting the packet be retransmitted.
B. The receiver is reporting the packet was received without error.
C. The receiver is busy decoding the packet.
D. The entire file has been received correctly.

PACTOR is an exciting data mode that leads to near-perfect reception of a message. The transmitted message is sent in short bursts, allowing the receiving station to quickly transmit ACK for perfect copy, or *NAK*, meaning *"send it again, Sam, I missed a few characters."* This back-and-forth between two PACTOR stations leads to error free copy. **ANSWER A.**

G8C10 **How does forward error correction (FEC) allow the receiver to correct errors in received data packets?**

A. By controlling transmitter output power for optimum signal strength.
B. By using the varicode character set.
C. By transmitting redundant information with the data.
D. By using a parity bit with each character.

Forward error correction, abbreviated FEC, is achieved by *sending each character twice*. This allows the receiver to correct errors by double-checking the received data. The data mode AMTOR B (amateur teleprinting over radio) uses FEC. **ANSWER C.**

G8C07 **How does the receiving station respond to an ARQ data mode packet containing errors?**

A. It terminates the contact.
B. It requests the packet be retransmitted.

C. It sends the packet back to the transmitting station.

D. It requests a change in transmitting protocol.

ARQ stands for *Automatic Repeat Request*. Your Packet TNC will automatically request that the sending station *re-transmit the packet* if it detects errors in the reception of that data. **ANSWER B.**

G7C05 Which of the following is an advantage of a transceiver controlled by a direct digital synthesizer (DDS)?

A. Wide tuning range and no need for band switching.

B. Relatively high power output.

C. Relatively low power consumption.

D. Variable frequency with the stability of a crystal oscillator.

An HF transceiver with a *direct digital synthesizer* may allow you to dial in a frequency all the way down to 1 Hz! If you plan to do digital work on the air, that 1 Hz tuning and the *frequency stability* delivered by the DDS will be appreciated by other operators. The DDS circuitry keeps your signal stable on a frequency making reception of the digital signal more reliable. **ANSWER D.**

G7C11 What is meant by the term "software defined radio" (SDR)?

A. A radio in which most major signal processing functions are performed by software.

B. A radio that provides computer interface for automatic logging of band and frequency.

C. A radio that uses crystal filters designed using software.

D. A computer model that can simulate performance of a radio to aid in the design process.

You go over to your buddy's ham shack and you see his big computer connected to a tiny, book-sized box that contains the innards of the actual ham radio. Where's the rest of the rig? The *computer handles almost all of the major signal processing* using software. That little box contains the final output transistors and a cooling fan. Together you get that great *software-defined radio (SDR)* output on your favorite band. This is a super way to keep your rig up to date – just download any modifications, and presto, your rig is like brand new! **ANSWER A.**

The Software Defined Radio (SDR) has taken amateur radio by storm! This hybrid Ten Tec Jupiter (bottom left) can be operated the "vintage" way using its front panel knobs, or the totally modern "virtual" way by means of SDR software, shown on the laptop computer to the right.

DIGITAL ACCESSORIES

The following websites are excellent places for you to look for digital accessories for you ham radio and computer. Thanks to Don Wilson, N9ZGE, for sharing this with us.

AH-4	www.icomamerica.com/en/downloads/Default.aspx?Category=136
Airmail	www.siriuscyber.net/ham/
APRSPoint	www.aprspoint.com/
Digipan	www.digipan.net/
Donner	donnerstorenet.ipage.com/DCC/
Farallon Elecronics	www.farallon.us/webstore/
Ferrite Beads	www.dxengineering.com/Parts.asp?ID=1128&PLID=182&SecID=152&DeptID=42&PartNo=DXE-CSB-COMBO
Ferrite Beads	www.audiosystemsgroup.com/publish.htm
FTDI Drivers	www.ftdichip.com/FTDrivers.htm
GPS 18x OEM	buy.garmin.com/shop/shop.do?cID=158&pID=27594&ra=true
Ham Radio Deluxe	www.ham-radio-deluxe.com/
IC-718	www.icomamerica.com/en/products/amateur/hf/718/default.aspx
KPC3Plus	www.kantronics.com/products/kpc3.html
MFJ-1270C	www.mfjenterprises.com/man/pdf/MFJ-1270C.pdf
MicroHam	www.microham-usa.com/Products/USB3.html
MixW	http://mysite.verizon.net/jaffejim/
MMSSTV	http://mmhamsoft.amateur-radio.ca/pages/mmsstv.php
N4PY	www.n4py.com/
Packet Engine Pro	www.sv2agw.com/ham/pepro.htm
Palomar-Ferrite Cores	www.palomar-engineers.com/index.html
PrintScreen	www.gadwin.com/download/
PTC-IIusb	www.scs-ptc.com/shop/categories/modems-en
QuickMix	www.brothersoft.com/quickmix-10463.html
RIGblaster P&P	www.westmountainradio.com/product_info.php?products_id=pnp
RigExpert	www.rigexpert.com/index?s=standard
RMS Express & Paclink	www.winlink.org/ClientSoftware
SignaLink USB	www.tigertronics.com/
Sound Card Packet	www.kc2rlm.info/soundcardpacket/
TM-271	www.kenwoodusa.com/Communications/Amateur_Radio/Mobiles/TM-271A
TM-271 Data Mod	www.kb2ljj.com/data/kenwood/TM-271A-E.htm
TM-271 Data Mod	www.mods.dk/view.php?ArticleId=3739
TNC-X	www.tnc-x.com/
Two Meter Antenna	www.mfjenterprises.com/Product.php?productid=MFJ-1750
USB to Serial Converter	www.ftdichip.com/Products/Cables/USBRS232.htm
Winlink Update	ftp://autoupdate.winlink.org/User%20Programs/

In an Emergency

G2B12 When is an amateur station allowed to use any means at its disposal to assist another station in distress?
- A. Only when transmitting in RACES.
- B. At any time when transmitting in an organized net.
- C. At any time during an actual emergency.
- D. Only on authorized HF frequencies.

One night you're tuning around the 20 meter band and you hear a maritime mobile ham calling for help on 14.150. Even though this is a frequency outside of your General Class limits, you are allowed to handle the distress call and possibly save some lives at sea! As long as the distress is a matter of life safety or the immediate protection of property, you are good to go with almost *any power level and any frequency*. But to do so, keep an accurate log, and *make certain that the communications qualify as an actual emergency.* [97.405(b)]
ANSWER C.

G2B11 What frequency should be used to send a distress call?
- A. Whichever frequency has the best chance of communicating the distress message.
- B. Only frequencies authorized for RACES or ARES stations.
- C. Only frequencies that are within your operating privileges.
- D. Only frequencies used by police, fire or emergency medical services.

Before you head out on your adventure, pre-plan and pre-program the frequencies in use in your expected travel area that could hear your call for help. *Any active frequency would be a good spot to place a distress call*. Do not rely on police, medical, or fire frequencies because most are protected with digital coded inputs that would not be able to decode your signal. Rather, rely on normal, active Amateur Radio communication frequencies. [97.405] **ANSWER A.**

G2B02 What is the first thing you should do if you are communicating with another amateur station and hear a station in distress break in?
- A. Continue your communication because you were on the frequency first.
- B. Acknowledge the station in distress and determine what assistance may be needed.
- C. Change to a different frequency.
- D. Immediately cease all transmissions.

Act immediately to handle a station in distress. Find out WHO is in distress, WHERE they are located, and WHAT assistance may be needed. If it's a boat, find out how many persons are on board and instruct everyone to put on their personal flotation device. **ANSWER B.**

G1B04 Which of the following must be true before amateur stations may provide communications to broadcasters for dissemination to the public?

A. The communications must directly relate to the immediate safety of human life or protection of property and there must be no other means of communication reasonably available before or at the time of the event.

B. The communications must be approved by a local emergency preparedness official and conducted on officially designated frequencies.

C. The FCC must have declared a state of emergency.

D. All of these choices are correct.

Your new General Class ham station is not to be used for routine news gathering for your local television station. However, *in a disaster*, where a ham on scene tells you the center span of a bridge has just collapsed, it *would be permissible for you to contact your local news agency and make this safety of human life transmission* so motorists don't accidentally fly off the span. [97.113(b)]

ANSWER A.

G2B09 Who may be the control operator of an amateur station transmitting in RACES to assist relief operations during a disaster?

A. Only a person holding an FCC issued amateur operator license.

B. Only a RACES net control operator.

C. A person holding an FCC issued amateur operator license or an appropriate government official.

D. Any control operator when normal communication systems are operational.

Radio Amateur Civil Emergency Service (*RACES*) is a public service by *licensed amateur radio operators* to provide volunteer communications to government agencies in time of extraordinary need. The Federal Emergency Management Agency (FEMA) provides planning guidance and technical assistance for establishing a RACES unit of licensed amateur radio operators at the state and local government levels. Only licensed amateur radio operators with a current RACES authorization may be the control operator at a RACES station. [97.407(a)]

ANSWER A.

Amateur Radio has a long, friendly history with all our military and civilian services through MARS, RACES, and other similar auxiliary services. Here, ham operator and pilot Jeff, N6JSV, is ready for a helicopter disaster drill for city RACES training using an APRS handheld radio.

G2B10 When may the FCC restrict normal frequency operations of amateur stations participating in RACES?
A. When they declare a temporary state of communication emergency.
B. When they seize your equipment for use in disaster communications.
C. Only when all amateur stations are instructed to stop transmitting.
D. When the President's War Emergency Powers have been invoked.

During a time of war when the President exercises his *War Emergency Powers*, *RACES* may become the only communications allowed via amateur radio. All other non-RACES ham operators would be ordered to stop transmitting – only RACES operators could remain on the air. [97.407(b)] **ANSWER D.**

RACES Logo.

▼ IF YOU'RE LOOKING FOR	▼ THEN VISIT
All About RACES	www.USRACES.org
News on Emergency Groups	www.N4KSS.net/Reflectors.html
All about ARES	www.QSL.net/ARES
Military Radio Groups	www.NAVYMARS.org
More About Joining ARES	www.ARRL.org/ARES
ARRL Emergency Volunteers	www.ARRL.org/Volunteer

The Effect of the Ionosphere on Radio Waves

To help you with the questions on radio wave propagation, here is a brief explanation of the effect the ionosphere has on radio waves.

The ionosphere is the electrified atmosphere from 40 miles to 400 miles above the Earth. You can sometimes see it as "northern lights." It is charged-up daily by the Sun, and does some miraculous things to radio waves that strike it. Some radio waves are absorbed during daylight hours by the ionosphere's D layer. Others are bounced back to Earth. Yet others penetrate the ionosphere and never come back again. The wavelength of the radio waves determines whether the waves will be absorbed, refracted, or will penetrate. Here's a quick way to memorize what the different layers do during day and nighttime hours:

The D layer is about 40 miles up. The D layer is a Daylight layer; it almost disappears at night. D for Daylight. The D layer absorbs radio waves between 1 MHz to 7 MHz. These are long wavelengths. All others pass through.

The E layer is also a daylight layer, and it is very Eccentric. E for Eccentric. Patches of E layer ionization may cause some surprising reflections of signals on both high frequency as well as very-high frequency. The E layer height is usually 70 miles.

The F1 layer is one of the layers farthest away. The F layer gives us those Far away signals. F for Far away. The F1 layer is present during daylight hours, and is up around 150 miles. The F2 layer is also present during daylight hours, and it gives us the Furthest range. The F2 layer is 250 miles high, and it's the best for the Farthest range on medium and short waves. The F2 layer is strongest in the summer months. During winter months, both the F1 and F2 layers may become unpredictable, but always strong enough to support exciting skywaves! At nighttime, the F1 and F2 layers combine to become just the F layer at 180 miles. This F layer at nighttime will usually bend radio waves between 1 MHz and 15 MHz back to earth. At night, the D and E layers disappear.

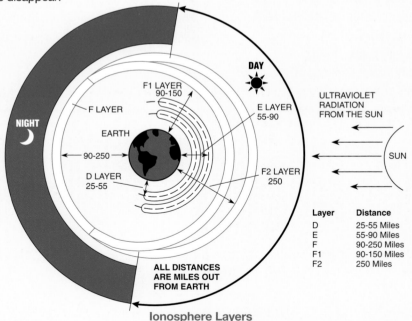

Ionosphere Layers

Source: *Antennas — Selection and Installation*, © 1986, Master Publishing, Inc., Niles, Illinois

Skywave Excitement

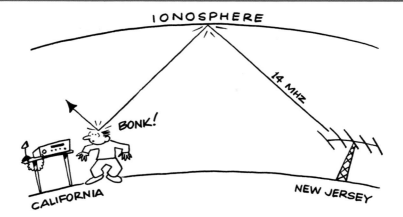

G3C03 Why is the F2 region mainly responsible for the longest distance radio wave propagation?
  A. Because it is the densest ionospheric layer.
  B. Because it does not absorb radio waves as much as other ionospheric regions.
  C. Because it is the highest ionospheric region.
  D. All of these choices are correct.
The higher the altitude of the ionospheric region refracting the high frequency radio waves the greater the radio range. The *F2* region is the *highest layer* and gives the *longest propagation*. **ANSWER C.**

G3B09 What is the approximate maximum distance along the Earth's surface that is normally covered in one hop using the F2 region?
  A. 180 miles.   C. 2,500 miles.
  B. 1,200 miles.   D. 12,000 miles.
The *F2 region* is our highest reflective ionospheric region, approximately 250 miles up. This gives worldwide signals their longest bounce, generally about *2500 miles*. **ANSWER C.**

G3C02 Where on the Earth do ionospheric layers reach their maximum height?
A. Where the Sun is overhead.
B. Where the Sun is on the opposite side of the Earth.
C. Where the Sun is rising.
D. Where the Sun has just set.

The ionosphere is influenced by ultraviolet radiation from the Sun. Maximum ultraviolet radiation occurs *when the Sun is at its highest* elevation overhead. *Ionospheric layers reach their maximum height at the same time*. **ANSWER A.**

G3C04 What does the term "critical angle" mean as used in radio wave propagation?
A. The long path azimuth of a distant station.
B. The short path azimuth of a distant station.
C. The lowest takeoff angle that will return a radio wave to the Earth under specific ionospheric conditions.
D. The highest takeoff angle that will return a radio wave to the Earth under specific ionospheric conditions.

Have you ever skipped stones on a lake? If thrown at too great an angle to the surface of the water, the stone will not skip but rather penetrate into the water. Radio waves in the ionosphere act similarly; there is a point – the highest take-off angle – that cannot be exceeded or a radio wave will not reflect back to Earth. Just remember *"highest take-off angle."* It is the makeup of the ionosphere that determines the highest takeoff angle that will refract a high frequency signal back to Earth. You can play with different antennas all day long, but that magic refractive ionosphere is the number one key to a signal that can be heard around the world! **ANSWER D.**

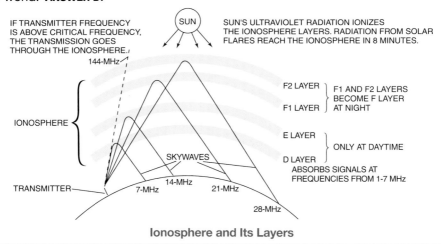

Ionosphere and Its Layers

G3B08 What does MUF stand for?
A. The Minimum Usable Frequency for communications between two points.
B. The Maximum Usable Frequency for communications between two points.
C. The Minimum Usable Frequency during a 24 hour period.
D. The Maximum Usable Frequency during a 24 hour period.

The *maximum usable frequency (MUF)* peaks during the day in the morning hours to the east, for working Europe, and in the afternoon and evening hours, to the west, for working Asia. This is the fun of *working ham radio skywaves* –

the ionosphere and the maximum usable frequency will constantly give us some excitement if we just keep tuned in. **ANSWER B.**

G3B05 What usually happens to radio waves with frequencies below the MUF and above the LUF when they are sent into the ionosphere?
  A. They are bent back to the Earth.
  B. They pass through the ionosphere.
  C. They are amplified by interaction with the ionosphere.
  D. They are bent and trapped in the ionosphere to circle the Earth.
Frequencies below the Maximum Usable Frequency (MUF) and above the Lowest Usable Frequency (LUF) are *bent back to Earth* by the ionosphere. For maximum range, operate as close to MUF as possible. **ANSWER A.**

G3B04 What is a reliable way to determine if the MUF is high enough to support skip propagation between your station and a distant location on frequencies between 14 and 30 MHz?
  A. Listen for signals from an international beacon in the frequency range you plan to use.
  B. Send a series of dots on the band and listen for echoes from your signal.
  C. Check the strength of TV signals from Western Europe.
  D. Check the strength of signals in the MF AM broadcast band.
Is a particular band open to the rest of the world? A simple way to find out is spin the big VFO knob and listen to what you hear. If it is full of signals, the band is open to somewhere in the world. If you spin the knob and all you hear is a couple of local hams yakking back and forth, the absence of activity indicates the band is not propagating very far! Listen to the Northern California DX Foundation *beacons*, at 14.100 MHz. If you know a little bit of CW, and keep track of precise time, you'll know which part of the world is coming in on 20 meters and higher by listening to the beacons on the following frequencies.

        14.100 MHz
        18.110 MHz
        21.150 MHz
        24.930 MHz
        28.200 MHz

Each beacon transmits its CW call sign on a rotational basis, followed by four 1-second dashes. The call sign and first dash are sent at 100 watts, the second dash at 10 watts, and the third dash at 1 watt. You're doing great if you can hear the last dash at 100 milliwatts! **ANSWER A.**

☞ **www.NCDXF.org/beacon**

Your home computer can play an important part in chasing rare DX stations!

G3B03 Which of the following applies when selecting a frequency for lowest attenuation when transmitting on HF?
  A. Select a frequency just below the MUF.
  B. Select a frequency just above the LUF.
  C. Select a frequency just below the critical frequency.
  D. Select a frequency just above the critical frequency.

The term *"lowest attenuation"* means least amount of signal fading. The trick is to try to operate on the highest high frequency ham band that gives you skywave propagation to somewhere else in the country or the world. Operating *just below the maximum usable frequency (MUF)* will lead to some extraordinary crystal-clear communications. **ANSWER A.**

G3B12 What factor or factors affect the MUF?
  A. Path distance and location.
  B. Time of day and season.
  C. Solar radiation and ionospheric disturbances.
  D. All of these choices are correct.

Getting a signal halfway around the Earth is a ham radio tradition. But there are plenty of things to consider when attempting to make a contact – solar activity, day or night, fall or summer, and how far away the other station is located. *All of the choices are correct.* **ANSWER D.**

Solar flares and sunspots affect radiowave propagation
Photo courtesy of N.A.S.A.

G3B10 What is the approximate maximum distance along the Earth's surface that is normally covered in one hop using the E region?
  A. 180 miles.
  B. 1,200 miles.
  C. 2,500 miles.
  D. 12,000 miles.

The *E layer* is between 50 and 90 miles up. Because it's closer to Earth, high-frequency waves don't bounce as far as they do off of the F layer. E skip is usually about *1200 miles*. During the summertime, "sporadic E" may sometimes "short skip" as little as 600 miles. **ANSWER B.**

G3B02 Which of the following is a good indicator of the possibility of sky-wave propagation on the 6-meter band?
A. Short skip sky-wave propagation on the 10-meter band.
B. Long skip sky-wave propagation on the 10-meter band.
C. Severe attenuation of signals on the 10-meter band.
D. Long delayed echoes on the 10-meter band.

Now that you are upgrading from Technician to General, don't abandon all the excitement on 6 meters. In fact, your new General Class privileges on 10 meters will help you forecast an upcoming 6-meter band opening. Making contacts via *skywaves on 10 meters with stations less than 300 miles away* indicates an extremely strong Sporadic E-skip "cloud" out there in the ionosphere. *E-skip on 6 meters* and maybe even 2 meters will more than likely be possible within the next half hour! **ANSWER A.**

G3C01 Which ionospheric layer is closest to the surface of the Earth?
A. The D layer.
B. The E layer.
C. The F1 layer.
D. The F2 layer.

The *D layer* (D, then E then F then F1 then F2... there is an order there) is the layer *closest to* the surface of the *Earth*. During daylight hours the Darn D layer is usually responsible for absorbing ham radio medium-frequency skywave signals. **ANSWER A.**

Altitudes in Miles of Ionospheric Layers

Layers	Day Summer	Winter	Night
F2	>250		
F1	90-150		
F		90-150	90-250
E	55-90	55-90	
D	40	40	

G3C12 Which ionospheric layer is the most absorbent of long skip signals during daylight hours on frequencies below 10 MHz?
A. The F2 layer.   C. The E layer.
B. The F1 layer.   D. The D layer.

During the day, the Darn D Layer hinders distant signals. Here's an example of what it can do to your signal. The 40-meter band is a great one for 500-mile, daylight, skywave contacts. Even though they may fade in and out a little bit, they are almost always there from Sun-up to around 4:00 p.m. local time. After 4:00 p.m., the D-layer associated with absorption begins to disappear, and the 40 meter band begins to "go long." Your 500-mile buddies will disappear, and next thing you hear are stations a couple thousand miles away pouring in. Then, as the 40 meter band continues on well into the night, in come the dreaded megawatt, foreign, double-sideband, shortwave broadcast stations that share our frequencies, too. What you will hear at night and in the early morning hours on 40 meters are extremely loud whistles from foreign broadcast, double-sideband, full-carrier stations, and the key to operating 40 meters in the early morning hours is finding a spot to dodge the foreign broadcast signals. **ANSWER D.**

G3C05 Why is long distance communication on the 40-meter, 60-meter, 80-meter and 160-meter bands more difficult during the day?
　　A. The F layer absorbs signals at these frequencies during daylight hours.
　　B. The F layer is unstable during daylight hours.
　　C. The D layer absorbs signals at these frequencies during daylight hours.
　　D. The E layer is unstable during daylight hours.
The Darn D layer does more harm than good to medium- and high-frequency signals during daylight hours. During the day, SSB and CW operations on 160 and 80 meters are confined to ground wave coverage. On 40 meters, daytime skip distances are generally no greater than 600 miles when the *D layer* is *absorbing MF and HF signals*. **ANSWER C.**

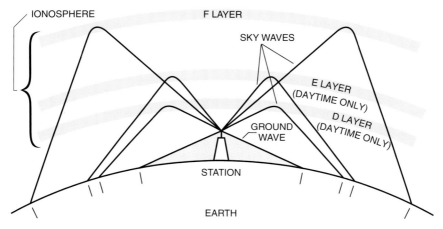

Radio Wave Propagation
Source: *Mobile 2-Way Radio Communications,* **G. West,** © 1993, Master Publishing, Inc.

G3B07 What does LUF stand for?
　　A. The Lowest Usable Frequency for communications between two points.
　　B. The Longest Universal Function for communications between two points.
　　C. The Lowest Usable Frequency during a 24 hour period.
　　D. The Longest Universal Function during a 24 hour period.
The term *"lowest usable frequency"* refers specifically to *stations attempting skywave contact*. If you and a buddy are separated by 500 miles and want to stay in touch on the 75/80 meter ham band using a specific frequency, you may find early morning and evening contacts loud and clear, while attempts at noon result in no contact on that frequency. This is because at noon the LUF has become many megahertz higher due to changes in the ionosphere from the effects of the Sun. Your chosen frequency is now lower than the LUF. But hang around – the LUF will begin to drop quickly around sundown and your contact will be restored! **ANSWER A.**

G3B06 What usually happens to radio waves with frequencies below the LUF?
　　A. They are bent back to the Earth.
　　B. They pass through the ionosphere.
　　C. They are completely absorbed by the ionosphere.
　　D. They are bent and trapped in the ionosphere to circle the Earth.

During daylight hours, the lowest usable frequency for a skywave contact may be around 3 MHz. This means the 160 meter band, just under 2 MHz, will not be usable for daylight *skywave* contacts because they are *completely absorbed by the ionosphere*. But as soon as the Sun goes down, hang on for some great DX contacts! **ANSWER C.**

G3B11 What happens to HF propagation when the LUF exceeds the MUF?
    A. No HF radio frequency will support ordinary skywave communications over the path.
    B. HF communications over the path are enhanced.
    C. Double hop propagation along the path is more common.
    D. Propagation over the path on all HF frequencies is enhanced.
When the lowest usable frequency (LUF) exceeds the maximum usable frequency (MUF), high frequency *radio communications along a specific ionospheric signal path disappears*. This sometimes occurs with increased geomagnetic activity from sunspots. **ANSWER A.**

Don't Forget Medium Wave

Amateur Radio started in the frequency range now known as Medium Wave (MW). Highly recommended reading is *"200 Meters and Down"* by Clinton Desoto, which explores this history. We have one full-fledged MW band, 160 meters, often called the Gentleman's Band. We also have an experimental band near 500 kHz, which may soon become an official Amateur Radio band.

There's a world of interesting radio in the MW region. Long distance communications can be a challenge because of the antenna requirements, but reliable local operation can be had with reasonable antennas. Simple wire antennas are pretty much the norm for MW communications, or if you have a tower, you can usually "load it up" on MW. We are no longer limited by the regional power restrictions that once hampered effective 160 meters communications. 160 meters is a great deal of fun and we have plenty of elbow room down there. Modern digital methods make effective 160 meter communications far more effective than in the not-too-distant past. Give it a try!

G3C09 What type of radio wave propagation allows a signal to be detected at a distance too far for ground wave propagation but too near for normal skywave propagation?
    A. Faraday rotation.   C. Sporadic-E skip.
    B. Scatter.   D. Short-path skip.
Scatter communications (sometimes called backscatter) is one way to reach a station that is in that zone of no-reception – the skip zone. When Gordo communicates from southern California to Seattle, San Francisco is in his skip zone and will not receive his signals. But if he aims his beam antenna west toward Hawaii, some of his signal is backscattered into the Bay Area, giving him communications to a station that is too far for ground wave, and too close for normal skywaves. **ANSWER B.**

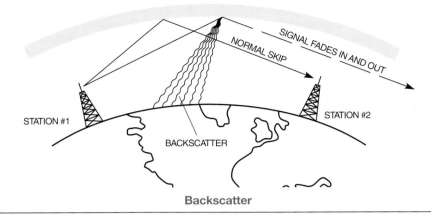

Backscatter

G3C08 Why are HF scatter signals in the skip zone usually weak?

A. Only a small part of the signal energy is scattered into the skip zone.

B. Signals are scattered from the magnetosphere which is not a good reflector.

C. Propagation is through ground waves which absorb most of the signal energy.

D. Propagation is through ducts in F region which absorb most of the energy.

During periods of scatter communications, *only a fraction of the original signal is scattered* back to those stations that are too far for ground wave reception, yet too close for the main part of your signal that is being reflected by the ionosphere. The station in your skip zone gets only a very weak incoming skywave signal. **ANSWER A.**

G3C07 What makes HF scatter signals often sound distorted?

A. The ionospheric layer involved is unstable.

B. Ground waves are absorbing much of the signal.

C. The E-region is not present.

D. Energy is scattered into the skip zone through several different radio wave paths.

The wavy sound of HF scatter signals, especially backscatter, is caused by the *signal* being *reflected* back *through several radio wave paths*, creating multi-path distortion. **ANSWER D.**

Your modern HF transceiver may also include the 6 meter, 2 meter, and 440 bands. Six meters is the "Magic Band" and can offer unusual and surprising propagation. And don't forget the DX portion of 2 meters, far away from the "madding crowd," where the still small voice of weak signal operation prevails.

G3C10 Which of the following might be an indication that signals heard on the HF bands are being received via scatter propagation?

A. The communication is during a sunspot maximum.
B. The communication is during a sudden ionospheric disturbance.
C. The signal is heard on a frequency below the Maximum Usable Frequency.
D. The signal is heard on a frequency above the Maximum Usable Frequency.

If you chose a *frequency slightly greater than the maximum usable frequency*, you can sometimes take advantage of the ionosphere to scatter your communications to an area that normally would not hear radio wave reflection from the ionosphere. **ANSWER D.**

G3C06 What is a characteristic of HF scatter signals?

A. They have high intelligibility.
B. They have a wavering sound.
C. They have very large swings in signal strength.
D. All of these choices are correct.

High frequency *scatter communications* bounce a portion of your signal off of densely ionized patches in the ionosphere. Since the ionosphere is constantly in motion, the signals will fade in and out, much like ocean waves, resulting in a *wavering sound*. **ANSWER B.**

G2D04 Which of the following describes an azimuthal projection map?

A. A map that shows accurate land masses.
B. A map that shows true bearings and distances from a particular location.
C. A map that shows the angle at which an amateur satellite crosses the equator.
D. A map that shows the number of degrees longitude that an amateur satellite appears to move westward at the equator with each orbit.

Long-range communications do not necessarily go in straight lines. When we navigate our signals around the world, we need a *chart* that takes into account the curvature of the Earth and *where we are located*. An azimuthal map shows your ham shack at the center of the Earth and will help you determine the shortest path between your station and that rare DX station. **ANSWER B.**

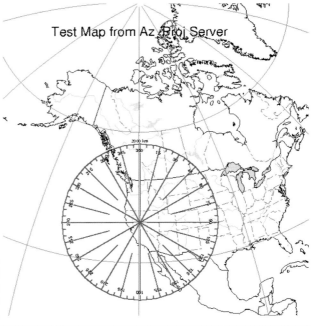

Test Map from Az Proj Server

Ham operators with a beam antenna will use an azimuthal map like this one to determine short path and long path headings to reach DX stations.

G3B01 How might a sky-wave signal sound if it arrives at your receiver by both short path and long path propagation?
A. Periodic fading approximately every 10 seconds.
B. Signal strength increased by 3 dB.
C. The signal might be cancelled causing severe attenuation.
D. A well-defined echo might be heard.

Do you have Gordo's audio course? If so, you can hear the distinctive sound of simultaneous short path and long path reception. Incoming *signals will have a well-defined echo* because the short path signal is coming to you from a much closer distance than the long path signal coming all the way around the globe. The echo you hear is caused by the difference in the time it takes the signal to reach you via long path and short path. **ANSWER D.**

G2D06 How is a directional antenna pointed when making a "long-path" contact with another station?
A. Toward the rising Sun.
B. Along the gray line.
C. 180 degrees from its short-path heading.
D. Toward the north.

Some ionospheric conditions may let you to establish better communications with a distant station on General Class worldwide frequencies over a long path around the world rather than over the direct short path. If you hear the station with an echo, try turning your beam *antenna 180 degrees* in the opposite direction *from the short path* direction to see whether or not the station will come in better on the long path. **ANSWER C.**

G3A11 Approximately how long is the typical sunspot cycle?
A. 8 minutes.
B. 40 hours.
C. 28 days.
D. 11 years.

The *sunspot cycle* peaks every *11 years*. Currently, we are on solar cycle 24, and just beginning to slide down the back side of the peak that took place in 2014-2015. For the next 5 years, expect long range F2 skip on 6 meters and 10 meters to subside, but every summer we will continue to get good 6 meter and 10 meter short skip E layer excitement. On the lower bands, like 40, 60, and 75/80 meters, nighttime band openings will continue to improve. And no matter where we are in the solar cycle, 20 meters will always provide long range band openings all over the country and regularly all around the world! **ANSWER D.**

G3A01 What is the significance of the sunspot number with regard to HF propagation?

A. Higher sunspot numbers generally indicate a greater probability of good propagation at higher frequencies.
B. Lower sunspot numbers generally indicate greater probability of sporadic E propagation.
C. A zero sunspot number indicates radio propagation is not possible on any band.
D. All of these choices are correct..

Sunspots are temporary "cold" regions on the surface of the Sun, somewhat like bubbles on the surface of a vat of boiling spaghetti sauce. They emit lots of ultraviolet radiation, which is primarily responsible for creating an active ionosphere. Generally speaking, hams are happy when there are a lot of sunspots! The frequency of sunspots varies with the solar cycle. When there are *a lot of sunspots, the "high bands" (20, 17, 15, 12, 10, and 6 meters) come alive*, while during the down times, the low bands (160, 80, 60, 40, and 30 meters) are the only bands suitable for long distance communications. But there are always exceptions, so don't put too much stock in sunspot numbers alone. Get on the air and see what's there! If you don't hear anything, always call CQ! **ANSWER A.**

G3A10 What causes HF propagation conditions to vary periodically in a 28 day cycle?

A. Long term oscillations in the upper atmosphere.
B. Cyclic variation in the Earth's radiation belts.
C. The Sun's rotation on its axis.
D. The position of the Moon in its orbit.

We find recurring skywave conditions about every 28 days as the *Sun makes a complete rotation*. Ham operators carefully monitor solar activity and find that stronger sunspots may reappear 28 days later for more excitement on the air waves. **ANSWER C.**

☞ **www.spaceweather.com**

G3A09 What effect does a high sunspot number have on radio communications?

A. High-frequency radio signals become weak and distorted.
B. Frequencies above 300 MHz become usable for long-distance communication.
C. Long-distance communication in the upper HF and lower VHF range is enhanced.
D. Microwave communications become unstable.

As we begin our downward slide on the 11 year solar cycle 24, we will see less skywave activities on VHF 6 meters, and HF 10 meters and 12 meters. Fifteen will be a good daytime skywave band, and 20 meters will stay "open" around the country and world until darkness begins. But get up early, and enjoy 20 meters to Europe on special mornings! High sunspot activity *enhances long-distance communication in the upper HF and lower VHF range*. **ANSWER C.**

G3A04 Which of the following are least reliable for long distance communications during periods of low solar activity?

A. 80 meters and 160 meters.　　C. 30 meters and 20 meters.
B. 60 meters and 40 meters.　　D. 15 meters, 12 meters and 10 meters.

As we begin to enter those few years of *low solar activity, we won't hear much skywave activity on 6, 10, 12, and 15 meters.* No problem – just switch down to 20 meters during the days, or 40 and 75 meters at night, and enjoy predictable good skywave DX without all the noise that sometimes elevated solar activity brings! This is why you are getting the General license, to enjoy all the ham bands for great worldwide signals, day and night! **ANSWER D.**

G3A05 What is the solar flux index?

A. A measure of the highest frequency that is useful for ionospheric propagation between two points on the Earth.
B. A count of sunspots which is adjusted for solar emissions.
C. Another name for the American sunspot number.
D. A measure of solar radiation at 10.7 centimeters wavelength.

The *solar-flux* index is *measured* daily on *10.7 cm* in Ottawa, Canada. You may tune into the radio propagation solar activity reports transmitted by WWV at 18 minutes past the hour. Frequencies of 10 and 15 MHz will give you best reception during the day, and 5 MHz may give you best reception at night. **ANSWER D.**

G3A12 What does the K-index indicate?

A. The relative position of sunspots on the surface of the Sun.
B. The short term stability of the Earth's magnetic field.
C. The stability of the Sun's magnetic field.
D. The solar radio flux at Boulder, Colorado.

Earth is surrounded by the magnetosphere that acts as a barrier protecting us from some of the charged particles coming from eruptions on the Sun. The magnetosphere occasionally develops holes and cracks that may allow tremendous amounts of solar energy to disturb our natural *geomagnetic stability*. Some of the energy that penetrates the magnetosphere can be seen as auroras. A low *K index* means good, stable high-frequency propagation. **ANSWER B.**

G3A13 What does the A-index indicate?

A. The relative position of sunspots on the surface of the Sun.
B. The amount of polarization of the Sun's electric field.
C. The long term stability of the Earth's geomagnetic field.
D. The solar radio flux at Boulder, Colorado.

The *A-Index* is a 24 hour averaging of the planetary K-Index, and is a great indicator of *long term stability* of the Earth's geomagnetic field. **ANSWER C.**

G3A03 Approximately how long does it take the increased ultraviolet and X-ray radiation from solar flares to affect radio propagation on the Earth?

A. 28 days.
B. 1 to 2 hours.
C. 8 minutes.
D. 20 to 40 hours.

Ultraviolet radiation travels at the speed of light. It takes about *8 minutes* for sunlight and ultraviolet rays to reach the Earth's ionosphere. Heavy sunspot activity may affect worldwide propagation for up to 3 days. **ANSWER C.**

G3A06 What is a geomagnetic storm?
    A. A sudden drop in the solar flux index.
    B. A thunderstorm which affects radio propagation.
    C. Ripples in the ionosphere.
    D. A temporary disturbance in the Earth's magnetosphere.

We're surrounded! Above our weather layer of the atmosphere, called the troposphere, is the ionosphere with its D layer, and above that the E layer, and on top of the E layer are the F-1 and F-2 layers. But did you know there is yet another layer up around 400 miles, called the magnetosphere? When the *Sun sends out a coronal mass ejection*, the charged particles may *interact with our magnetosphere*, and disrupt high frequency communications for several days. **ANSWER D.**

G3A02 What effect does a Sudden Ionospheric Disturbance have on the daytime ionospheric propagation of HF radio waves?
    A. It enhances propagation on all HF frequencies.
    B. It disrupts signals on lower frequencies more than those on higher frequencies.
    C. It disrupts communications via satellite more than direct communications.
    D. None, because only areas on the night side of the Earth are affected.

The *lower bands*, such as 160, 80, 40, and even 20 meters, *become so noisy* that it is impossible to hear any distant signals coming in from skywaves during a sudden ionospheric disturbance. **ANSWER B.**

Elmer Point: Your new HF General Class radio also offers full shortwave reception. Try 10- or 15-MHz to hear the WWV time ticks. At 18 minutes past the hour, listen to your latest ionospheric and solar weather reports! A K index between 1 to 4, and an A index of 0 to 7 means the ionosphere is quiet and very predictable for long-range skywaves. But a K index of 5 or 6 with an A index of 30 to 49 indicates that HF band conditions will become unpredictable and unstable. And hang on to your receivers – a K index of 7 to 9 or an A index of 50 and higher means the HF bands will likely be unusable for regular skywave contacts due to a major solar storm with strong geomagnetic activity disrupting HF signals. With high K and A indexes, time to go outside after dark and look for an aurora! Here's a summary of K and A Index readings:

K Index	A Index	HF Skip Conditions
K1 – K4	A0 – A7	Bands are normal
K4	A8 – A15	Bands are unsettled
K4	A16 – A30	Bands are unpredictable
K5	A30 – A50	Lower bands are unstable
K6	A50 – A99	Few skywaves below 15 MHz
K7 – K9	A100 – A400	Radio blackout is likely. Go fishing or watch for an aurora.

G3A08 Which of the following effects can a geomagnetic storm have on radio propagation?
A. Improved high-latitude HF propagation.
B. Degraded high-latitude HF propagation.
C. Improved ground-wave propagation.
D. Improved chances of UHF ducting.

During periods of major geomagnetic disturbances, high-frequency propagation over *high-latitude paths will be degraded*. At the same time, activity on 6 meters VHF might be hopping! **ANSWER B.**

G3A16 What is a possible benefit to radio communications resulting from periods of high geomagnetic activity?
A. Auroras that can reflect VHF signals.
B. Higher signal strength for HF signals passing through the polar regions.
C. Improved HF long path propagation.
D. Reduced long delayed echoes.

During periods of high geomagnetic activity beautiful auroras may be viewed at night, away from city lights, as far south as latitude 37° north. The aurora itself is created when gases in our upper atmosphere are bombarded by coronal mass ejections, kind of like a neon light. Depending on which gas gets stirred up determines what color Northern Lights you may see. A trip to Alaska during equinox will usually lead to some awe-inspiring Northern Lights viewing. You will definitely be impressed by an aurora. *The aurora can also reflect VHF signals*, adding to the excitement. **ANSWER A.**

Geomagnetic disturbances caused by the Sun create the Northern Lights.

G3A15 How long does it take charged particles from coronal mass ejections to affect radio propagation on the Earth?

A. 28 days.	C. 4 to 8 minutes
B. 14 days.	D. 20 to 40 hours

We can see a sunspot in the amount of time it takes light to travel from the Sun to the Earth – 8 minutes. But this question asks about the slower moving *sunspot charged particles* that lumber toward Earth as part of the solar wind. This wind can take as long as *20 to 40 hours* to begin to disturb radio wave propagation on the ham bands. This means we have almost 2 days advanced alert that band conditions may be changing. Tune into WWV at 18 minutes past the hour and listen to the 30-second solar report.

WWV 5 MHz	Best at night	WWV 15 MHz	Best days
WWV 10 MHz	Day and night	WWV & WWVH 20 MHz	Some days

You can usually tune in WWV 10 MHz during the days, but only before a big sunspot event finally hits Earth. When disruption occurs, WWV sometimes fades out completely! **ANSWER D.**

G3A14 How are radio communications usually affected by the charged particles that reach the Earth from solar coronal holes?

A. HF communications are improved.
B. HF communications are disturbed.
C. VHF/UHF ducting is improved.
D. VHF/UHF ducting is disturbed.

A solar coronal hole can be seen as a dark spot on the face of the Sun emitting charged particles into the solar wind. If you took your thermometer up there, there would be an extreme temperature drop within the eruption. You can actually track sunspots as they rotate around the Sun on a 27.5-day cycle. There are usually a pair of sunspots – one with a positive magnetic north field, and the other with a negative south field. Just ask Galileo – he was the first to observe these sunspots in 1610. Sunspots with a solar coronal hole will normally *disrupt high-frequency communications*, but for the joy of 6 and 2 meter operators, they can create aberrations in the magnetosphere that will cause VHF long-range band openings.
ANSWER B.

G3A07 At what point in the solar cycle does the 20-meter band usually support worldwide propagation during daylight hours?

A. At the summer solstice.
B. Only at the maximum point of the solar cycle.
C. Only at the minimum point of the solar cycle.
D. At any point in the solar cycle.

We told you so – *20 meters* will *always* be the fun band *for daytime skywave activity*, no matter where we are on our slide down solar cycle 24! And at night, when 20 meters fades out, turn the band switch to 40 meters, dodge the foreign broadcast carriers, and work the world into daybreak the next morning! With a General Class ham ticket, the world of skywave DX is yours to enjoy, on all ham bands! **ANSWER D.**

Shortwave Listening: Gateway to Understanding HF

For many decades, most radio amateurs got their first exposure to long distance radio communications by listening to shortwave radio. By the time we old timers got our "tickets" we had a pretty good idea of what to expect when it came to HF communications because we had spent time listening.

SWL (shortwave listening) is still alive and well throughout the world. Every radio amateur should have a shortwave radio in the shack. Excellent receivers are available for less than one hundred dollar and provide a nice break from normal ham activity, even for experienced radio amateurs. Remember, one of our reasons for existing as radio amateurs is to "promote international good will." In order to promote international good will, you have to know about the world beyond your back yard, and shortwave radio is a great way to expand your world view. By learning what's going on in other countries, when you get on the air with a ham from one of those faraway places you'll have something to talk about!

One excellent resource for you shack is *The Worldwide Listening Guide* by John Figliozzi. It lists English language shortwave broadcasts from around the world, and tells you how to tune into programming over the Internet and other listening options. You can obtain a copy from The W5YI Group by calling 800-669-9594 or visit www.w5yi.org.

There's a lot of interesting stuff outside of the amateur bands; take time to explore the *whole* radio spectrum!

Website Resources

▼ IF YOU'RE LOOKING FOR	▼ THEN VISIT
antennas, DSP, and more	www.amcominc.com
THE place for QSO cards	www.w4mpy.com
DX reference guide	www.ac6v.com
amateur radio satellite operations	www.amsat.org
the latest news about ham radio	www.arnewsline.org
microphones, headsets, and more	www.heilsound.com
digital ham radio accessories and more	www.packetradio.com
Disaster preparedness & emergency comms info	www.fema.gov
NASA research site with cool articles	www.grc.nasa.gov
DSP, antenna analyzers, and more	www.timewave.com
HF modems for digital modes	www.halcomm.com
HF modems and gear for digital modes	www.kantronics.com
digital amateur radio organization	www.tapr.org
azimuthal maps, solar information, and more	www.wm7d.net
software defined radios	www.flexradio.com

Your HF Transmitter

Elmer Point: Ham radio single sideband transceivers in the $800 range will likely offer adjustable digital signal processing filters to perfectly set transmit audio characteristics and bandwidth as well as receive bandwidth selections. This is why Gordo recommends buying new HF transceivers that now include new digital network filters if it fits your budget.

G8A05 What type of modulation varies the instantaneous power level of the RF signal?
A. Frequency shift keying.
B. Phase modulation.
C. Frequency modulation.
D. Amplitude modulation.

The instantaneous power level of the signal varies with *amplitude modulation*.
ANSWER D.

G7C02 Which circuit is used to combine signals from the carrier oscillator and speech amplifier then send the result to the filter in some single sideband phone transmitters?
A. Discriminator.
B. Detector.
C. IF amplifier
D. Balanced modulator

In an SSB transceiver, the *balanced modulator* processes the signal from the carrier oscillator and the speech amplifier and sends it on to the filter. **ANSWER D.**

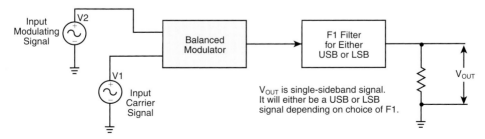

Filtering an SSB Signal

G7C01 Which of the following is used to process signals from the balanced modulator then send them to the mixer in some single sideband phone transmitters?
 A. Carrier oscillator.
 B. Filter.
 C. IF amplifier.
 D. RF amplifier.

The *balanced modulator* produces an upper and lower sideband signal, with the carrier reduced to near zero.   The upper and lower sideband signals are then fed *into* a narrow *filter* network which cancels out either the upper or the lower sideband signal based on other settings of the radio. **ANSWER B.**

G8A07 Which of the following phone emissions uses the narrowest bandwidth?
 A. Single sideband.
 B. Double sideband.
 C. Phase modulation.
 D. Frequency modulation.

The phone emission that uses the *least bandwidth is single sideband (SSB)*, usually about 2.8 kHz. The modern high frequency ham radio may include adjustable transmit SSB filter networks that can decrease the amount of occupied bandwidth on transmit from the normal 2.8 kHz down to 2.6 kHz. While the resulting signal sounds void of bass response, its narrow 2.6 kHz of bandwidth really helps get the signal through to a distant station when noise levels are high. **ANSWER A.**

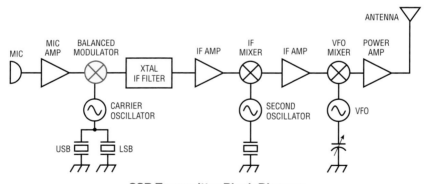

SSB Transmitter Block Diagram

G8A06 What is one advantage of carrier suppression in a single sideband phone transmission versus full carrier amplitude modulation?
 A. Audio fidelity is improved.
 B. Greater modulation percentage is obtainable with lower distortion.
 C. Available transmitter power can be used more effectively.
 D. Simpler receiving equipment can be used.

Radios use their 100 watts of power to generate signals and carrier. AM, FM and other modes of transmission send a signal on a carrier. The signal and the carrier use some of the power. Carrier suppression in SSB allows the circuitry of the radio to put *additional power* into each sideband signal. Your signal travels farther with this additional power for exciting DX skywave activities. **ANSWER C.**

G4D01 What is the purpose of a speech processor as used in a modern transceiver?

A. Increase the intelligibility of transmitted phone signals during poor conditions.
B. Increase transmitter bass response for more natural sounding SSB signals.
C. Prevent distortion of voice signals.
D. Decrease high-frequency voice output to prevent out of band operation.

The *speech processor* on modern transceivers should be used with caution. Too much processing may distort your signal. But just a little bit of speech processing could *increase the intelligibility* of your transmitted voice signal and your average power. When conditions are good, turn the processor off! Speech processing is like sending an e-mail in all upper case letters! Turn it off!

ANSWER A.

You can add a speech processor to an older ham set. The accessory unit plugs in between your mic and the transceiver microphone input.

G4D02 Which of the following describes how a speech processor affects a transmitted single sideband phone signal?

A. It increases peak power.
B. It increases average power.
C. It reduces harmonic distortion.
D. It reduces intermodulation distortion.

Turning on your transceiver's *speech processor* will not increase PEP output power if you are 100 percent modulated. It will *increase the average power,* which many times makes your signal sound "too hot" for comfort. Stay off that speech processor button unless it's absolutely necessary. **ANSWER B.**

G8A09 What control is typically adjusted for proper ALC setting on an amateur single sideband transceiver?

A. The RF clipping level.
B. Transmit audio or microphone gain.
C. Antenna inductance or capacitance.
D. Attenuator level.

That new high frequency transceiver that you are going to reward yourself with when you pass your exam has a built in transmit safeguard called *Automatic Level Control (ALC).* The ALC acts as an electronic governor to throttle back *transmit power* in case you overdrive the input circuits with too much *mic gain* or too much computer drive for data. You can monitor ALC action on the rig's multi-meter. Look for a small, now-and-then jiggle of the ALC indicator, which will indicate proper drive levels. If you overdrive the ALC section of your transmitter, you'll see the ALC meter going up into the red danger area. If this happens, immediately back off mic gain or computer drive power to your transmitter.
ANSWER B.

G4A14 What is likely to happen if a transceiver's ALC system is not set properly when transmitting AFSK signals with the radio using single sideband mode?

A. ALC will invert the modulation of the AFSK mode.
B. Improper action of ALC distorts the signal and can cause spurious emissions.
C. When using digital modes, too much ALC activity can cause the transmitter to overheat.
D. All of these choices are correct.

Sound card digital modes work by applying AFSK signals to the input of a properly aligned single sideband transmitter, which then become FSK signals. An FSK signal should consist of two and only two frequencies. Intermodulation distortion, usually resulting from *overdriving an SSB transmitter will create additional frequencies* near the desired ones. These additional products can make the signal difficult or impossible to decode, and can also cause interference to nearby stations if "intermod" is severe enough. When using sound card modes, the ALC should be disabled, or the audio level reduced to the point where no ALC action occurs. The proper drive level for a sound card mode is when the PEP output power of the transmitter is between 25% and 50% of its maximum capable PEP. When in doubt, keep the drive on the low side. **ANSWER B.**

G4A05 What is a reason to use Automatic Level Control (ALC) with an RF power amplifier?

A. To balance the transmitter audio frequency response.
B. To reduce harmonic radiation.
C. To reduce distortion due to excessive drive.
D. To increase overall efficiency.

The ALC output jack on your new transceiver needs to be tied into the ALC input jack on that linear amplifier. This gives your equipment a "handshake" when the drive level is correctly set. Without this simple plug-in connection between amplifier and radio, the amp could be overdriven and the *signal distorted due to excess drive*. Further, the amplifier could go into thermal melt down from being overdriven. Be sure to hook up that needed ALC "handshake" cable between rig and amp. **ANSWER C.**

G4A07 What condition can lead to permanent damage to a solid-state RF power amplifier?

A. Insufficient drive power.   C. Shorting the input signal to ground.
B. Low input SWR.   D. Excessive drive power.

Don't run excessive drive power when operating in the digital modes! Sending ultra-long messages with excessive drive power can cause the radio to get red hot and ultimately damage a power amplifier output device. Give your HF radio plenty of ventilation. It has its own built-in fan. Make sure you don't obstruct airflow. Protect your gear with ventilation and by limiting drive power to prevent excessive heating. Keep your cool! **ANSWER D.**

G8A08 Which of the following is an effect of overmodulation?

A. Insufficient audio.   C. Frequency drift.
B. Insufficient bandwidth.   D. Excessive bandwidth.

If you *over-modulate* on high frequency, you're going to spread your signal over a *wider bandwidth* than that of a properly modulated HF signal. If someone says

you are "splattering," turn down the mic gain and turn off the speech processor.
ANSWER D.

 Every radio amateur needs a good audio signal generator, either for aligning equipment or merely driving the shack dog crazy. This is a great tool for tuning up a linear amplifier as well. Just place in front of your microphone and follow the detailed tune-up procedure we describe on page 110. https://itunes.apple.com/us/app/audiosiggen/id347248794?mt=8

G4D03 Which of the following can be the result of an incorrectly adjusted speech processor?
A. Distorted speech.
B. Splatter.
C. Excessive background pickup.
D. All of these choices are correct.

Most newer high frequency transceivers have a speech processor button that will turn processing on or off. Turn the speech processor off! *Speech processing* brings in *excessive background pickup*, may cause your *signal to sound distorted*, and can also cause the signal to *splatter to adjacent frequencies*. Leave your speech processor turned off as a new General Class ham! You'll learn how to use it correctly later. **ANSWER D.**

G8A10 What is meant by the term flat-topping when referring to a single sideband phone transmission?
A. Signal distortion caused by insufficient collector current.
B. The transmitter's automatic level control (ALC) is properly adjusted.
C. Signal distortion caused by excessive drive.
D. The transmitter's carrier is properly suppressed.

If you turn the microphone gain too high on SSB, the signal will *sound distorted*. The signal waveform shown on an oscilloscope has the top clipped off so it has a flat top. **ANSWER C.**

Elmer's Oscilloscope Waveform
Showing "Flattopping"

G4B15 What type of transmitter performance does a two-tone test analyze?
A. Linearity.
B. Percentage of suppression of carrier and undesired sideband for SSB.
C. Percentage of frequency modulation.
D. Percentage of carrier phase shift.

The faithful reproduction of your voice over single-sideband depends on equipment with excellent linearity. With new digital signal processing techniques on modulation, plus a new family of after-market, high-performance microphones, the *2-tone test* that enables you to view the wave forms on an oscilloscope is a great way to test for *transmitter linearity*. But you know, even though the 2-tone test is your best answer for transmitter linearity I always like to ask fellow hams simply how I sound to them coming over their radio. No oscilloscope needed! **ANSWER A.**

G4B07 What signals are used to conduct a two-tone test?
    A. Two audio signals of the same frequency shifted 90 degrees.
    B. Two non-harmonically related audio signals.
    C. Two swept frequency tones.
    D. Two audio frequency range square wave signals of equal amplitude.

If you plan to regularly service your own equipment, you can find a little "warbler" box that generates two non-harmonically related audio tones for testing. The device may either be plugged into the transmitter mike input, or the mike held up to the speaker on the device. *The 2 tones must not be harmonically related* in order to provide the best test. Listen to this sound on Gordo's audio CD course. **ANSWER B.**

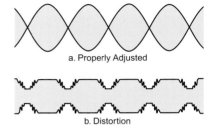
a. Properly Adjusted

b. Distortion

Two-Tone Test

Similar to the signal generator described above, this app can supply two tones simultaneously. While primarily designed for generating standard DTMF tone pairs, this can also generate the two tones you need for checking the alignment of SSB transmitters. https://play.google.com/store/apps/details?id=net.simplyadvanced.simplytonegenerator

G8A11 What is the modulation envelope of an AM signal?
    A. The waveform created by connecting the peak values of the modulated signal.
    B. The carrier frequency that contains the signal.
    C. Spurious signals that envelop nearby frequencies.
    D. The bandwidth of the modulated signal.

While Single Sideband (SSB) is the predominant "phone" mode on the HF bands, there is still a significant amount of activity on full-carrier double sideband Amplitude Modulation. Information is impressed on an AM carrier by altering the amplitude of the RF wave in accordance with the applied audio signal. *The envelope of an AM signal is the "outline" or extreme outer limit of the radio frequency signal.* 100% modulation is defined as when the envelope goes to zero (pinches off) during negative modulation peaks, or increases to twice the amplitude of the unmodulated RF carrier during positive modulation peaks. Because the human voice is quite asymmetrical, the positive and negative modulation peaks can be very different. Clever circuitry can take advantage of this asymmetry by assuring that the larger peaks are always the positive ones. This is standard practice in the AM broadcast industry, and has been adopted by many dedicated amateur AM operators. **ANSWER A.**

G4B01 What item of test equipment contains horizontal and vertical channel amplifiers?
    A. An ohmmeter.   C. An ammeter.
    B. A signal generator.   D. An oscilloscope.

An oscilloscope is your best piece of test equipment if you are a technical amateur operator. But it takes skill to work a "scope," so don't buy one unless you plan to do a lot in circuit design or signal calibration. The *oscilloscope has horizontal- and vertical-channel amplifiers*. **ANSWER D.**

G4B03 Which of the following is the best instrument to use when checking the keying waveform of a CW transmitter?
A. An oscilloscope.
C. A sidetone monitor.
B. A field strength meter.
D. A wavemeter.

The oscilloscope is your best instrument to check for transmit signal quality. When magazine editors review the *waveform of a CW signal* or a two-tone test, they usually show photographs of the *oscilloscope* display. **ANSWER A.**

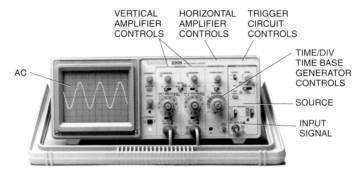

A Typical Large Workbench Oscilloscope Showing an AC Waveform
Source: *Basic Electronics* © 1994, Master Publishing, Inc., Niles, Illinois

G4B04 What signal source is connected to the vertical input of an oscilloscope when checking the RF envelope pattern of a transmitted signal?
A. The local oscillator of the transmitter.
B. An external RF oscillator.
C. The transmitter balanced mixer output.
D. The attenuated RF output of the transmitter.

We take the *attenuated RF output* of the transmitter and couple it to the vertical input of an oscilloscope to check the quality of the transmitted signal. **ANSWER D.**

G4B02 Which of the following is an advantage of an oscilloscope versus a digital voltmeter?
A. An oscilloscope uses less power.
B. Complex impedances can be easily measured.
C. Input impedance is much lower.
D. Complex waveforms can be measured.

When you whistle into your SSB microphone and look at the resulting wave forms on an oscilloscope, you will see that only an *oscilloscope can truly represent complex voice wave forms* so that they can be precisely measured. **ANSWER D.**

SmartScope:
Most of us old timers remember when an oscilloscope was about the size of a shopping cart like the one pictured above. SmartScope is a high performance oscilloscope that you can put in your pocket. This clever little box plugs into your smartphone and gives you a real test instrument that would have cost thousands of dollars a couple of decades ago. www.lab-nation.com/store

G4A09 Why is a time delay sometimes included in a transmitter keying circuit?

    A. To prevent stations from interfering with one another.
    B. To allow the transmitter power regulators to charge properly.
    C. To allow time for transmit-receive changeover operations to complete
        properly before RF output is allowed.
    D. To allow time for a warning signal to be sent to other stations.

Older tube-type high frequency equipment incorporated a transmit/receive relay to toggle output and input antenna connections. Newer HF transceivers have gone solid state with almost instantaneous *switching between receiving and transmitting*. In order to accommodate an external linear amplifier, you may need to review the *time delay transmitter keying circuit* to allow the amplifier to switch on just before it begins to receive transmit power from the transceiver.
ANSWER C.

G7B13 What is the reason for neutralizing the final amplifier stage of a transmitter?

    A. To limit the modulation index.
    B. To eliminate self-oscillations.
    C. To cut off the final amplifier during standby periods.
    D. To keep the carrier on frequency.

After new tubes have been installed in a powerful amplifier, follow the steps in the instruction manual for *neutralization*, which *will eliminate* the possibility of *self-oscillation*. **ANSWER B.**

G8A03 What is the name of the process that changes the instantaneous frequency of an RF wave to convey information?

    A. Frequency convolution.   C. Frequency conversion.
    B. Frequency transformation.   D. Frequency modulation.

A type of modulation that changes the frequency of an RF wave is called *frequency modulation (FM)*. **ANSWER D.**

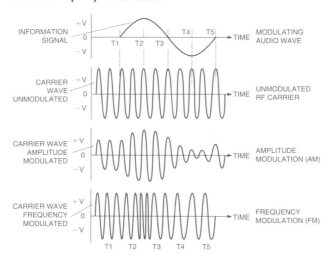

Modulation of RF Carrier

G8B04 What is the stage in a VHF FM transmitter that generates a harmonic of a lower frequency signal to reach the desired operating frequency?
  A. Mixer.
  B. Reactance modulator.
  C. Pre-emphasis network.
  D. Multiplier.
Inside a VHF FM transmitter is a low-power oscillator that operates at HF levels. It's the job of the *multiplier* to select a harmonic of this signal to produce the desired operating frequency. Hint: Remember that harmonics are like chords on a piano. Each note is 1/3rd or so higher than the last. They are mathematically related. So, it is logical that the stage of the transmitter is called a "multiplier." It's the answer choice that is mathematical! **ANSWER D.**

G8B06 What is the total bandwidth of an FM phone transmission having 5 kHz deviation and 3 kHz modulating frequency?
  A. 3 kHz.
  B. 5 kHz.
  C. 8 kHz.
  D. 16 kHz.
You can calculate this answer by multiplying 2 times the sum of the deviation and the modulating frequency. The deviation is 5 kHz plus 3 kHz of audio modulating frequency, which gives a sum of 8 kHz. Two times 8 kHz equals *16 kHz*. This would be the *total bandwidth* of the FM phone transmission. **ANSWER D.**

Your VHF/UHF FM handheld should be properly set up right out of the box, and may include selectable deviation bandwidth settings. It's a good idea to check the deviation occasionally. Many local amateur radio clubs hold "clinics" where you can have your radio checked out with proper test equipment.

G8B07 What is the frequency deviation for a 12.21 MHz reactance modulated oscillator in a 5 kHz deviation, 146.52 MHz FM phone transmitter?
  A. 101.75 Hz.
  B. 416.7 Hz.
  C. 5 kHz.
  D. 60 kHz.
The deviation of any Frequency Modulated transmitter is increased when you follow the oscillator with a frequency multiplier. In fact, the deviation is multiplied by exactly the same factor as the radio frequency. If we multiply the oscillator frequency by 12 to get to the final output frequency, the deviation is multiplied by the same amount. This means that if the final deviation is 5 kHz, we can divide that by 12 to come up with the required oscillator deviation.
5,000 ÷ 12 = 416.66 Hz, rounded to *416.7 Hz*. **ANSWER B.**

G8A04 What emission is produced by a reactance modulator connected to a transmitter RF amplifier stage?
    A. Multiplex modulation.
    B. Phase modulation.
    C. Amplitude modulation.
    D. Pulse modulation.

A *reactance modulator* produces Frequency Modulation when applied to an oscillator, and *Phase Modulation when applied to a subsequent amplifier stage*. **ANSWER B.**

G8A02 What is the name of the process that changes the phase angle of an RF wave to convey information?
    A. Phase convolution.
    B. Phase modulation
    C. Angle convolution.
    D. Radian inversion.

A type of modulation that changes the phase of an RF wave is called *phase modulation (PM)*. **ANSWER B.**

G7B08 How is the efficiency of an RF power amplifier determined?
    A. Divide the DC input power by the DC output power.
    B. Divide the RF output power by the DC input power.
    C. Multiply the RF input power by the reciprocal of the RF output power.
    D. Add the RF input power to the DC output power.

The efficiency of an RF power amplifier is calculated by *dividing the radio frequency output power by the DC input power to that stage*. If you get 100 Watts of CW output power with 250 watts of DC input power, your efficiency is 40%, about typical. Since the RF output stage is by far the primary consumer of power in any modern HF rig, you can closely estimate the RF "final" input power by looking at the total DC current drawn by the rig, and multiplying that by the DC voltage, typically around 13.8 Volts. CAUTION! Unless you have a rather uncommon peak envelope power (PEP) meter, you cannot determine RF power output using speech, or whistling, or any such method. You must use a CW carrier (SSB transceivers have a TUNE function specifically for this). The peak power of the human voice can be over 6 times the average power. Typical peak RF output power (as well as DC input power) can be many times what your slow-moving meters can indicate. **ANSWER B.**

G5B06 What is the output PEP from a transmitter if an oscilloscope measures 200 volts peak-to-peak across a 50 ohm dummy load connected to the transmitter output?

A. 1.4 watts.	C. 353.5 watts.
B. 100 watts.	D. 400 watts.

This particular question has you looking at an oscilloscope that indicates 200 volts peak-to-peak across a 50-ohm dummy load. We are looking for Power (P). We have Resistance (R) in ohms and Voltage (E) in volts. Consulting the magic circle on page 132 we find the relationship for power when we have resistance and voltage to be:

$$Power = Voltage^2 \div Resistance - P = E^2 \div R$$

But we don't have the pieces we need quite yet for this formula. We have 200 volts peak-to-peak (V_{pp}). We need peak voltage for the calculations. 200 volts peak to peak $\div$ 2 = 100 volts peak. The question is asking for PEP (Peak Envelope Power) which is calculated as the root mean square (RMS) of the output power, according to the FCC.

$$V_{rms} = 0.707 \times V_{pk}$$
$$V_{rms} = 0.707 \times 100 = 70.7$$

Now we can find power using the formula:

$$P = 70.7^2 \div 50 = 4998.49 \div 50 = 99.96 \text{ or about 100 watts.}$$

This is an easy one to work out on a calculator – and yes, calculators are allowed in the exam room and we strongly recommend that you have one with you. Here are the keystrokes: Clear, Clear, 200 $\div$ 2 = 100 $\times$ 0.707 = 70.7 $\times$ 70.7 = 4998.49 $\div$ 50 = 99.96 rounded to 100 watts. It was only a little hard because the numbers given were not quite as we needed them. But that was easy enough to fix with just a few other formulas. **ANSWER B.**

G5B14 What is the output PEP from a transmitter if an oscilloscope measures 500 volts peak-to-peak across a 50 ohm resistive load connected to the transmitter output?

A. 8.75 watts.
B. 625 watts.
C. 2500 watts.
D. 5000 watts.

Again, take half of the peak-to-peak voltage to obtain peak voltage. Multiply 250 $\times$ 0.707, square the result (176.75) by multiplying it by itself, and divide by 50. Here are the calculator keystrokes: Clear, Clear 250 $\times$ 0.707 = 176.75 $\times$ 176.75 = 31,240.56 $\div$ 50 = 624.81, which rounds off to *625 watts*. **ANSWER B.**

G5B11 What is the ratio of peak envelope power to average power for an unmodulated carrier?

A. 0.707.
B. 1.00.
C. 1.414.
D. 2.00.

An unmodulated carrier is simultaneously peak and average. So the ratio of peak envelope power to average power on a steady unmodulated carrier is simply *1.00*. **ANSWER B.**

G5B13 What is the output PEP of an unmodulated carrier if an average reading wattmeter connected to the transmitter output indicates 1060 watts?
    A. 530 watts.   C. 1500 watts.
    B. 1060 watts.   D. 2120 watts.

Remember, a steady carrier illustrates both peak power as well as average power. If your watt meter reads *1060 watts* average power, this is the same as peak envelope power. **ANSWER B.**

G5B01 What dB change represents a two-times increase or decrease in power?
    A. Approximately 2 dB.   C. Approximately 6 dB.
    B. Approximately 3 dB.   D. Approximately 12 dB.

The decibel is used to describe a change in power levels. It is a measure of the ratio of power output to power input. A *two-times increase* results in a change of *3 dB*. **ANSWER B.**

G4D07 How much must the power output of a transmitter be raised to change the S meter reading on a distant receiver from S8 to S9?
    A. Approximately 1.5 times.   C. Approximately 4 times.
    B. Approximately 2 times.   D. Approximately 8 times.

Seeing an S meter change from S8 to S9 is an increase of a single S unit. One S unit is 6 dB, and 6 dB is a *4-times change*. **ANSWER C.**
Here is how the dB system for power works:
        0 dB = 0 times change
        1 dB = 1.3 times change
        2 dB = 1.6 times change
        3 dB = 2 times change ◄
        6 dB = 4 times change ◄
        9 dB = 8 times change
      10 dB = 10 times change
      20 dB = 100 times change ◄

G4D05 How does a signal that reads 20 dB over S9 compare to one that reads S9 on a receiver, assuming a properly calibrated S meter?
    A. It is 10 times less powerful.
    B. It is 20 times less powerful.
    C. It is 20 times more powerful.
    D. It is 100 times more powerful.

An S meter reading of *20 dB over S-9*, compared to just an S-9 signal, illustrates the signal is *100 times stronger.* **ANSWER D.**

G7B11 For which of the following modes is a Class C power stage appropriate for amplifying a modulated signal?
    A. SSB.
    B. CW.
    C. AM.
    D. All of these choices are correct.

The Class C amplifier is ideal for high efficiency, non-linear amplification of Morse code (CW) and frequency or phase shifted digital emissions. Varying amplitude emissions like SSB or AM would not sound right if the amplifier is operating in the *Class C* region. But for *CW*, it will work great. **ANSWER B.**

G7B12 Which of these classes of amplifiers has the highest efficiency?

A. Class A.

B. Class B.

C. Class AB.

D. Class C.

Yes, Grandpa, I will learn the code! CW (Morse code) will always continue to be a popular mode for ham operators, even though the code test has been completely eliminated. A small CW-only transceiver operating Class C offers high efficiency with little current being consumed from the battery in between dots and dashes. *Class C, high efficiency*. **ANSWER D.**

G7B10 Which of the following is a characteristic of a Class A amplifier?

A. Low standby power.

B. High Efficiency.

C. No need for bias.

D. Low distortion.

The *Class A amplifier* in a high frequency transceiver is usually found within the microphone input stage, where *low distortion* is an absolute requirement. **ANSWER D.**

G7B14 Which of the following describes a linear amplifier?

A. Any RF power amplifier used in conjunction with an amateur transceiver.

B. An amplifier in which the output preserves the input waveform.

C. A Class C high efficiency amplifier.

D. An amplifier used as a frequency multiplier.

Linear amplifiers will indeed pump up your *output waveform exactly as it appears to the amplifier input*; however, it is unwise to run any linear amplifier on high frequency mobile or on a simple home antenna until you are experienced with your equipment and discover that 100 watts can work all around the world. **ANSWER B.**

Linear RF power amplifier.

Elmer Point: Don't run out and buy a linear amplifier. The 100-watt output from your HF ham transceiver is plenty powerful enough to work the world. If you want to blast your signal out stronger, go for a directional antenna. The directional antenna also will increase incoming received signal strength – something that linear amplifier can't do. Linear amps are for those hams who have been on the air for at least a year, and who put up a 60 foot tower with a big directional beam on top. What the amplifier will do is increase their ability to bust through a pileup. Pileups occur when numerous hams are simultaneously trying to get their call signs through to a rare DX station during a contest. When you're just getting started on the General Class airwaves, steer clear of contest operation where pileups take place.

☞ www.ameritron.com

G4A08 What is the correct adjustment for the load or coupling control of a vacuum tube RF power amplifier?
A. Minimum SWR on the antenna.
B. Minimum plate current without exceeding maximum allowable grid current.
C. Highest plate voltage while minimizing grid current.
D. Maximum power output without exceeding maximum allowable plate current.

On the load control of that old power amp, seasoned hams will tell you to "tune for maximum smoke." Well, not really – but tune for a *maximum power output* reading, making sure you do not exceed 1500 watts output. **ANSWER D.**

G4A04 What reading on the plate current meter of a vacuum tube RF power amplifier indicates correct adjustment of the plate tuning control?

A. A pronounced peak.
B. A pronounced dip.

C. No change will be observed.
D. A slow, rhythmic oscillation.

A vacuum tube amplifier is operating properly when the tuning is adjusted for a "dip" (minimum current), and the loading is such that the plate current at the tuning dip is at its rated value. If possible, RF output power should also be monitored while adjusting the tuning and loading. The loading should never be increased beyond the point where output power no longer increases. Whenever any adjustment is made to the loading, the tuning should once again be checked for a *dip*, and should always be the last adjustment made. It also needs to be adjusted if you change frequency by more than a few kilohertz. **ANSWER B.**

☞ **www.radioblvd.com • www.heathkit-museum.com**

Amplifier Tune-Up

While the FCC rules specify that amateurs should use the minimum power necessary to maintain communications, there are many instances where being able to run the full legal limit of 1500 watts is necessary, especially when conditions are poor. The typical method of achieving high power (QRO) is to use a *linear amplifier* after your transmitter, which raises the output power from 100 watts or so, to 1,000 – 1,500 watts. A linear amplifier will typically gain you about 10 dB or about 1-1/2 S-units at the distant receiver.

While you should always follow the instruction manual for your particular linear amplifier, the following procedure will allow you to operate just about any linear amplifier cleanly and safely. As with doing any on-the-air transmitter adjustments, always do this on a clear frequency, and do it quickly. Any extended tests should be done into a dummy load.

Linear amplifier tuning must be done with a steady unmodulated carrier, which can be generated by placing your transmitter or transceiver in the AM, FM, or CW mode. For initial tune-up, you want to feed your linear amplifier about 50 watts. Key your transmitter and quickly adjust the PLATE TUNING for a dip; that is, a minimum plate current reading. Next, using an RF output indicator, (an SWR meter in the FORWARD position works fine), adjust the LOADING for an increase in power. Readjust the TUNING for a plate current minimum. Continue to increase the loading in small steps while adjusting the TUNING for a dip in plate current after each step until no further increase in output power is seen. Finally, you can increase your transmitter's output power to full output, which will drive your linear amplifier to its full output power as well. If you change your transmitter frequency by more than 10 KHz or so, be sure to recheck your amplifier's TUNING for a plate current dip again.

Again, these are generic rules; be sure to consult your manual!

Your Receiver

G7C07 What is the simplest combination of stages that implement a superheterodyne receiver?

- A. RF amplifier, detector, audio amplifier.
- B. RF amplifier, mixer, IF discriminator.
- C. HF oscillator, mixer, detector.
- D. HF oscillator, prescaler, audio amplifier.

The early (before you were born) ham radio high frequency receiver operated as TRF – tuned radio frequency. The receiver was nice and sensitive, but not all that stable. Today, our modern ham radio receivers use superheterodyne technology with excellent frequency stability. The term "superheterodyne" indicates a receiver with local oscillators and mixers that detect an incoming signal clean of other signals, which may be just above and below the desired signal. The stages that that describe a *superheterodyne receiver* are the *HF oscillator, the mixer, and the detector*. **ANSWER C.**

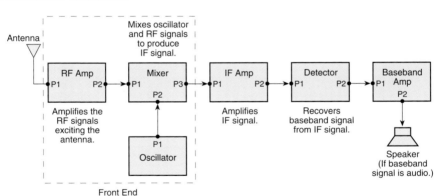

Block Diagrams of Generic and Dual-Conversion AM Receivers
Source: *Basic Communications Electronics*, © 1999 Master Publishing, Inc., Niles, IL

G7C03 **What circuit is used to process signals from the RF amplifier and local oscillator then send the result to the IF filter in a superheterodyne receiver?**
A. Balanced modulator.
B. IF amplifier.
C. Mixer.
D. Detector.

In any superheterodyne receiver, the incoming radio frequency is converted to an intermediate frequency (or IF) by means of a local oscillator and mixer. The combination of a local oscillator and a mixer is sometimes called a converter. An SSB receiver is no different in this regard than any modern receiver. In an SSB receiver section, it is the *mixer* that processes signals from the RF amplifier and the local oscillator. **ANSWER C.**

G7C04 **What circuit is used to combine signals from the IF amplifier and BFO and send the result to the AF amplifier in some single sideband receivers?**
A. RF oscillator.
B. IF filter.
C. Balanced modulator.
D. Product detector.

A product detector is necessary in order to demodulate either a CW or an SSB signal. In an SSB receiver, it is the *product detector* that processes the signal from the IF amplifier and the BFO (beat frequency oscillator). The signal then goes on to the audio frequency amplifier. **ANSWER D.**

G8B03 **What is another term for the mixing of two RF signals?**
A. Heterodyning.
B. Synthesizing.
C. Cancellation.
D. Phase inverting.

The term *heterodyne* comes from the Greek *hetero,* meaning *different,* and dyne, meaning "to act upon" or "to do work." When the instantaneous voltages of two different frequency signals are multiplied, the result is two new frequencies: the sum of, and the difference between, the two original frequencies. Heterodyne circuits are used in most modern transmitters and receivers to convert frequencies, to perform modulation, or to perform demodulation of combinations of RF signals consisting of what is received through your antenna and what is generated inside your radio for this function. **ANSWER A.**

G8B01 **What receiver stage combines a 14.250 MHz input signal with a 13.795 MHz oscillator signal to produce a 455 kHz intermediate frequency (IF) signal?**
A. Mixer.
B. BFO.
C. VFO.
D. Discriminator.

Most modern receivers are of the superheterodyne type, where the incoming radio frequency and the oscillator signal are combined to produce an intermediate frequency (IF). So, when you see that word "combines," think of the *mixer* section of a receiver stage. **ANSWER A.**

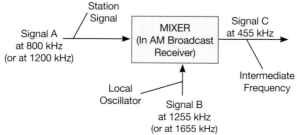

Block diagram of an AM broadcast receiver mixer.
Source: *Basic Communications Electronics,* © 1999 Master Publishing, Inc., Niles, IL

G8B02 If a receiver mixes a 13.800 MHz VFO with a 14.255 MHz received signal to produce a 455 kHz intermediate frequency (IF) signal, what type of interference will a 13.345 MHz signal produce in the receiver?

A. Quadrature noise.
B. Image response.
C. Mixer interference.
D. Intermediate interference.

In strong signal areas where there may be local transmissions coming in from shortwave stations outside of normal ham band limits, interference called *"image response"* may develop *at the sum and difference of your VFO and intermediate frequency (IF) signal*. 13.800 MHz minus 455 kHz is 13.345 MHz, the lower image response frequency. **ANSWER B.**

G4C12 Which of the following is an advantage of a receiver DSP IF filter as compared to an analog filter?

A. A wide range of filter bandwidths and shapes can be created.
B. Fewer digital components are required.
C. Mixing products are greatly reduced.
D. The DSP filter is much more effective at VHF frequencies.

The new, modern high frequency transceiver usually includes digital signal processing (DSP). This allows the user to *create multiple filter bandwidth settings*, along with *bandwidth shape* for "sharp cutoff" or "smooth cutoff" response. This wide range of filter combinations – all digital – really helps reduce interference under difficult conditions. Some other very useful functions of digital signal processing are noise reduction, notch filtering, and audio equalization and expansion. **ANSWER A.**

Being Selective

Understanding receiver selectivity can go a long way toward increasing your amateur radio enjoyment and success.

A typical SSB radio signal, after demodulation, can pass an audio frequency range between 300 and 3000 Hz. This results in a total audio bandwidth of 2700 Hz, which is what most SSB filters are set up for by default. While many competitive hams use SSB filters as narrow as 2.1 kHz, and *voice intelligibility* can be had with even narrower filters than that, super narrow SSB signals can be annoying to listen to for long periods of time. The nice thing about modern digital signal processing (DSP) rigs is that the selectivity is continuously variable over a large range so you can adjust this periodically to greatly reduce "listener fatigue" if band conditions permit.

Somewhat ironically, super modern DSP methods show their greatest advantage on the *oldest* mode of radio communication, CW. With more conventional receivers, it was difficult to have a filter width of less than about 500 Hz without severe "ringing" occurring. Modern DSP filters can give you a bandwidth as narrow as 150 Hz with no detectable ringing. This allows you to easily separate tightly-packed CW stations jammed into a small sliver of radio spectrum. As our exclusive CW bands become gradually smaller over the years, this is a very important factor to consider.

For sound card digital modes, the actual receiver selectivity isn't as much of an issue. If you like, you can use a "wide open" receiver filter and let the decoding software do all the filtering for you. This is a great advantage because you can hear signals well outside the "waterfall" window that you might otherwise miss.

G7C09 Which of the following is needed for a Digital Signal Processor IF filter?

A. An analog to digital converter.   C. A digital processor chip.
B. A digital to analog converter.   D. All of the these choices are correct.

A digital signal processor (whether RF, IF, or audio) performs its magic by first *converting analog signals into digital data*. The *processor performs "number crunching"* on that data to emulate filtering, noise reduction, compression, expansion, or a number of other functions. Then it *reconverts the digital data back to an analog signal* that the human ear can understand. So, *all of these answers are correct* in the modern DSP IF filter. For a number of practical reasons, DSP is usually (but not always) performed in the IF stage (or stages) of a receiver. **ANSWER D.**

G4C11 Which of the following is a function of a Digital Signal Processor?

A. To provide adequate grounding.
B. To remove noise from received signals.
C. To increase antenna gain.
D. To increase antenna bandwidth.

Digital signal processing (DSP) is found in almost all new high frequency amateur transceivers. Among many other functions, *DSP* helps *remove noise from*

received signals. While DSP can do some amazing things, there are still many tasks in the ham shack that can only be done with old fashioned hardware. **ANSWER B.**

☞ **www.bhi-ltd.co.uk**
   www.westmountainradio.com

Older HF transceivers will easily take aftermarket DSP amplified speakers that simply plug in!

Elmer Point: If you start out with a used, older, HF radio, you can buy an audio DSP speaker system for about $225. You'll be amazed at how the DSP noise subtraction circuit improves the sounds coming from the radio. But better yet, buy a new HF transceiver with DSP filtering in the IF and now you'll really hear a big difference of cleaned-up reception. DSP is not magic, however. The best way to improve reception is to search out whatever it is around your house that is generating all the noise and get it shut down when you begin to operate with those distant, rare, weak-signal stations. Fans and florescent lights are huge noise generators.

G7C10 How is Digital Signal Processor filtering accomplished?

A. By using direct signal phasing.
B. By converting the signal from analog to digital and using digital processing.
C. By differential spurious phasing.
D. By converting the signal from digital to analog and taking the difference of mixing products.

If an analog signal is converted into digital data, mathematical operations can be applied in the time domain that ordinarily would be done in the frequency domain. For example, a filter's frequency response has an equivalent time response that can be mathematically "tweaked" using a Fast Fourier Transform (FFT) operation. This results in much more predictable, accurate, and often amazing possibilities. After all the number crunching is done, the results are converted back to analog signals that our ears can understand. The input of a *DSP* circuit *takes an analog signal, converts it to a digital signal* where processing such as noise subtraction takes place, *and restores it to an analog signal* so we can hear it again! **ANSWER B.**

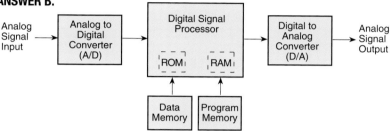

Block Diagram of a Basic Digital Signal Processing (DSP) System
Source: *Basic Communications Electronics*, © 1999 Master Publishing, Inc., Niles, IL

G4A13 What is one reason to use the attenuator function that is present on many HF transceivers?
    A. To reduce signal overload due to strong incoming signals.
    B. To reduce the transmitter power when driving a linear amplifier.
    C. To reduce power consumption when operating from batteries.
    D. To slow down received CW signals for better copy.
On the front of your radio is a button marked ATT – attenuator. When you push it in you'll notice that the strength of the received signal drops. Why would you want to lessen reception? Easy answer – there are times you may not want to hear everything your radio is receiving. At full sensitivity, you receive interference from other stations on frequencies near that of the station you are listening to. Also, an extremely strong signal may swamp your receiver, called overload. *The attenuator will reduce overload on a strong incoming signal.* **ANSWER A.**

G4A01 What is the purpose of the notch filter found on many HF transceivers?
    A. To restrict the transmitter voice bandwidth.
    B. To reduce interference from carriers in the receiver passband.
    C. To eliminate receiver interference from impulse noise sources.
    D. To enhance the reception of a specific frequency on a crowded band.
Your 40 meter privileges are shared with foreign broadcast stations. From early evening to a couple of hours after sun-up, you'll hear some mighty interesting full-carrier, double-sideband AM shortwave stations coming from the Far East. We can sometimes *dodge the interference*, thanks to your HF transceiver's *"notch filter."* The notch filter may be varied to reject a specific frequency "whistle" coming from these shortwave stations. Adjust it carefully and the whistle disappears. Newer transceivers may incorporate automatic notch filters that use digital signal processing capable of notching-out several interfering frequencies. **ANSWER B.**

G4C13 Which of the following can perform automatic notching of interfering carriers?
A. Bandpass tuning.
B. A Digital Signal Processor (DSP) filter.
C. Balanced mixing.
D. A noise limiter.

New ham gear incorporates a circuit called "ANF" on the front panel – automatic notch filter. This is handy on 40 meters where there is a lot of foreign broadcast carrier noise that will drive you crazy without the automatic notch filter. *"ANF"* uses *digital signal processing* technology to magically eliminate the noise. **ANSWER B.**

The automatic notch filter takes out steady tones, like shortwave broadcast carriers on 40 meters!

G7C08 What type of circuit is used in many FM receivers to convert signals coming from the IF amplifier to audio?
A. Product detector.   C. Mixer.
B. Phase inverter.   D. Discriminator.

In a frequency modulation receiver, signals coming from the intermediate frequency amplifier are fed into the *discriminator*, which acts as a frequency to voltage conversion stage, sending the resulting "decoded" signal on to the audio amplifier. **ANSWER D.**

G4D06 Where is an S meter found?
A. In a receiver.   C. In a transmitter.
B. In an SWR bridge.   D. In a conductance bridge.

The *S meter* on your new HF transceiver ties directly in to the *receiver* section of the radio and is tied in to the receiver's automatic gain control (AGC) signal strength circuitry. On most HF transceivers, there is also a front panel setting for receiver AGC. Set it at "automatic" or "slow" when copying single sideband voice emissions. Set it to "fast" when copying CW. In the "slow" or "automatic" settings, the S meter will faithfully read out incoming signal levels. If the AGC is turned "OFF", the S meter won't budge! Leave it on "slow" or "automatic".
ANSWER A.

G4D04 What does an S meter measure?
A. Conductance.   C. Received signal strength.
B. Impedance.   D. Transmitter power output.

High frequency ham transceivers all incorporate an S meter. *S meters measure received signal strength*. The S meter can be used to determine if your antenna system is working properly. Try this: on 40 meters, you should see an approximately S-2 indication of normal background noise. If you see a higher reading of background noise, this is an indication that your antenna is performing properly. However, if your S meter doesn't budge on 40 meter noise, something is probably wrong with your antenna system. **ANSWER C.**

Separation Anxiety

The HF *transceiver*, which combines both transmitting and receiving functions in a single "box," is actually a relatively recent development in the big picture of amateur radio. While the typical transceiver offers simplicity and convenience, especially for single sideband operation, many experienced hams prefer the flexibility and performance offered by separate transmitters and receivers, or "separates." Transmitting and receiving are two very different functions, and there are always performance compromises made when designing one device to do it all. The same principal applies to *antennas*, by the way.

Many of the venerable "classic" radio manufacturers built primarily (or only) transmitters or receivers, and hams came up with some clever arrangements to make them "play nicely" with each other. The most important skill to learn when using separates of any kind is how to properly "spot" or "zero beat" the transmitter; that is

Here we have a vintage Hallicrafters SX-117 receiver sitting atop a Johnson Ranger II Transmitter. The SX-117 is a triple conversion single sideband receiver with a few advanced features for its time in the early 1960s. The Ranger II is a very popular AM transmitter, still in use by many dedicated boat anchor operators. It transmits a nearly broadcast-quality AM signal.

to make sure that the transmitter is on exactly the same frequency as the receiver. The "spot" function transmits a very weak signal that can only be heard (in theory!) on the local receiver. To do this, adjust the transmitter to the receiver as closely as possible using the VFO (main tuning) dial, hit the spot button and carefully tune the transmitter until the carrier "note" on the receiver drops to a very low frequency. Release the spot button and you should be good to go.

Some single-manufacturer separates allow you to control both the transmitter and receiver frequencies by either the receiver or transmitter VFO. (Collins and Drake were two representative manufacturers of "matched separates" allowing this function, and there are still a ton of these on the air.) This is especially convenient when operating split (intentionally transmitting and receiving on different frequencies, an absolute must for working serious DX).

So, if you encounter a shack consisting of "separates" there's no need for anxiety. In fact, once you've used separates, you may find operation with a transceiver dull and restrictive.

Website Resources

▼ IF YOU'RE LOOKING FOR	▼ THEN VISIT
Ham Equipment Reviews	www.eham.net
HRO – Ham Radio Outlet	www.hamradio.com
AES – Amateur Radio Supply	www.aesham.com
Full-Line of Ham Accessories	www.mfjenterprises.com
Advanced Specialties	www.advancedspecialties.net
Alltronics	www.alltronics.com
Amateur Accessories	www.amateuraccessories.com
Amateur Radio Supplies	www.amateurradiosupplies.com
Asscociated Radio	www.associatedradio.com
Austin Amateur Radio	www.aaradio.com
B&H Sales	www.hamradiocenter.com
DBJ Radio & Electronics	www.dbjre.com
DX Engineering	www.dxengineering.com
GigaParts, Inc.	www.gigaparts.com
Hamcity	www.hamcity.com
HamStop.com	www.hamstop.com
Houston Amateur Radio Supply	www.texasparadise.com/hars
KJI Electronics, Inc.	www.kjielectronics.com
Lentini Communications, Inc.	www.lentinicomm.com
Main Trading Company	www.mtcradio.com
R & L Electronics	www.randl.com
Radio City	www.radioinc.com
The Ham Station	www.hamstation.com
Universal Radio Inc	www.universal-radio.com

Note: This list includes many ham radio dealers where you can purchase your HF radio and accessories

Oscillators & Components

G7B07 What are the basic components of virtually all sine wave oscillators?

A. An amplifier and a divider.
B. A frequency multiplier and a mixer.
C. A circulator and a filter operating in a feed-forward loop.
D. A filter and an amplifier operating in a feedback loop.

Oscillators are crucial elements to all radio transmitters and most receivers. They are the primary signal creators in all that we do. An *oscillator is an amplifier with positive feedback*. It usually also has a tuned circuit to set its frequency of oscillation, but may alternately employ a phase shift network or filter. In order for an oscillator to sustain oscillation, the total gain must be greater than unity at the frequency of oscillation. To keep an oscillator "in motion," a tuned circuit at one specific frequency will provide the necessary positive *feedback loop*. Just like keeping Grandpa swinging back and forth on his brand new senior citizen swing set, a small amount of feedback in the right direction at the right time continuously keeps him in motion. **ANSWER D.**

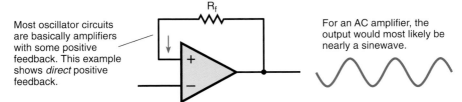

Most oscillator circuits are basically amplifiers with some positive feedback. This example shows *direct* positive feedback.

For an AC amplifier, the output would most likely be nearly a sinewave.

a. Amplifier with Positive Feedback – Oscillator

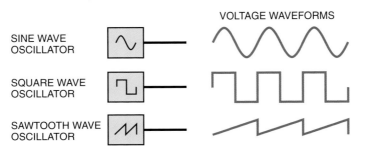

VOLTAGE WAVEFORMS

SINE WAVE OSCILLATOR

SQUARE WAVE OSCILLATOR

SAWTOOTH WAVE OSCILLATOR

b. Oscillator Waveforms

An oscillator is basically an amplifier with positive feedback from output to input.
Source: *Basic Electronics* © 1994, Master Publishing, Inc., Niles, Illinois

G7B09 What determines the frequency of an LC oscillator?
    A. The number of stages in the counter.
    B. The number of stages in the divider.
    C. The inductance and capacitance in the tank circuit.
    D. The time delay of the lag circuit.
The symbol used to denote inductance is L; Capacitance is C. An LC oscillator involves inductance and capacitance. The LC oscillator is found in the radio frequency circuits of your HF transceiver. It consists of a tuned *inductance and capacitance* resonant circuit found in the tank circuit of the radio. **ANSWER C.**

G6A10 Which element of a triode vacuum tube is used to regulate the flow of electrons between cathode and plate?
    A. Control grid.   C. Screen Grid.
    B. Heater.   D. Trigger electrode.
In the triode vacuum tube, the *control grid* acts like a variable valve to regulate the flow of electrons between the cathode and plate. Hint: Regulate = Control. **ANSWER A.**

High-power vacuum tubes require neutralization.

G6A12 What is the primary purpose of a screen grid in a vacuum tube?
    A. To reduce grid-to-plate capacitance.
    B. To increase efficiency.
    C. To increase the control grid resistance.
    D. To decrease plate resistance.
Yes, hams still run rigs with vacuum tubes.   The tetrode tube uses an anode, cathode and a *screen grid* that *reduces grid-to-plate capacitance.* This collects secondary emissions from the plate, which will slightly increase screen grid current. **ANSWER A.**

G6A11 Which of the following solid state devices is most like a vacuum tube in its general operating characteristics?
    A. A bipolar transistor.   C. A tunnel diode.
    B. A field effect transistor.   D. A varistor.
The *field effect transistor (FET)* has high input impedance, and it has a gate, drain, and source. The gate is similar to the control grid of a tube, with the gate generating an electric field that increases or decreases the amount of current flow. **ANSWER B.**

G6A08 Why must the cases of some large power transistors be insulated from ground?
   A. To increase the beta of the transistor.
   B. To improve the power dissipation capability.
   C. To reduce stray capacitance.
   D. To avoid shorting the collector or drain voltage to ground.

Power transistor mounted on a massive heat sink.

Be careful where you place the power supply that changes household power to 12 volts DC. Older transformer-type power supplies mount their power transistors on the large heat sinks that are exposed to the open air. If the supply's power transistor is accidentally pushed up against something else that is *ground*, you *will short out the collector voltage* and likely destroy the power transistor. **ANSWER D.**

G6A07 What are the stable operating points for a bipolar transistor used as a switch in a logic circuit?
   A. Its saturation and cutoff regions.
   B. Its active region (between the cutoff and saturation regions).
   C. Its peak and valley current points.
   D. Its enhancement and depletion modes.

When the bipolar transistor reaches saturation, collector and emitter base junctions are forward-biased. When the bipolar transistor is used as a switch in a logic circuit, an extremely small change in collector-base voltage will cause a large change in collector current, allowing the transistor to switch between cut-off and saturation within the collector current specifications to keep the transistor from self-destructing. It is in this *saturation and cut-off region* that the transistor will act as a switch. **ANSWER A.**

G6A09 Which of the following describes the construction of a MOSFET?
   A. The gate is formed by a back-biased junction.
   B. The gate is separated from the channel with a thin insulating layer.
   C. The source is separated from the drain by a thin insulating layer.
   D. The source is formed by depositing metal on silicon.

Many times, we find the MOSFET transistor in the "front end" of a modern HF transceiver. The MOSFET is a Metal-Oxide Semiconductor Field-Effect Transistor in which the *gate is separated from the channel with an extremely thin insulating layer*. Manufacturers usually install a gate-protective Zener diode, which prevents the gate insulation from being punctured by small static charges or excessive voltages from an event like a nearby lightning strike. **ANSWER B.**

G6A03 What is the approximate junction threshold voltage of a germanium diode?
   A. 0.1 volt.   C. 0.7 volts.
   B. 0.3 volts.   D. 1.0 volts.

The *Germanium diode* is sometimes found in the detector stage of a receiver. Their low forward voltage drop is minimal and the approximate *junction threshold voltage* of this diode is *0.3 volts*. These signal diodes are sensitive and can burn out if you accidentally overheat them while soldering in a replacement. **ANSWER B.**

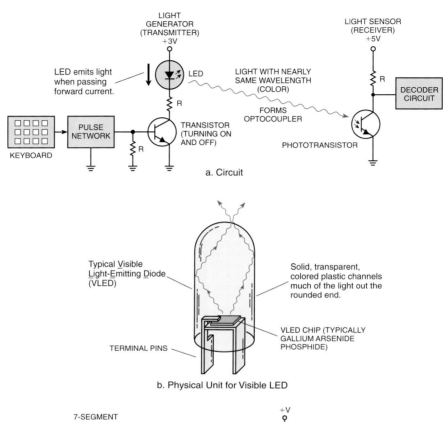

LIGHT
GENERATOR
(TRANSMITTER)
+3V

LIGHT SENSOR
(RECEIVER)
+5V

LED emits light
when passing
forward current.

LED

LIGHT WITH NEARLY
SAME WAVELENGTH
(COLOR)

R

DECODER
CIRCUIT

R

FORMS
OPTOCOUPLER

KEYBOARD

PULSE
NETWORK

R

TRANSISTOR
(TURNING ON
AND OFF)

PHOTOTRANSISTOR

a. Circuit

Typical Visible
Light-Emitting Diode
(VLED)

Solid, transparent,
colored plastic channels
much of the light out the
rounded end.

VLED CHIP (TYPICALLY
GALLIUM ARSENIDE
PHOSPHIDE)

TERMINAL PINS

b. Physical Unit for Visible LED

7-SEGMENT
VLED DISPLAY

EACH
SEGMENT
IS A VLED
CHIP

A
F   G   B
E   C
D

H

DECIMAL
POINT

SEGMENT

+V

A   B   C   D   E   F   G   H

CLOSING
SWITCH
LIGHTS UP
SEGMENT

R   R   R   R   R   R   R   R

c. VLED Array

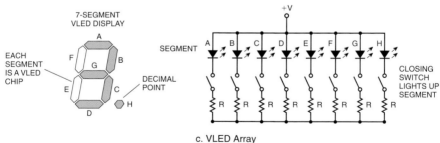

An array of LEDs and resistors mounted on a printed circuit board.

G6A05 What is the approximate junction threshold voltage of a conventional silicon diode?

A. 0.1 volt. C. 0.7 volts.
B. 0.3 volts. D. 1.0 volts.

We find *silicone diodes* in the rectifier section of your transceiver's power supply. The silicone diode offers stable operation at high temperatures, a *junction threshold voltage* of about *0.7 volts*, high reverse resistance, and long-term reliability. **ANSWER C.**

You can bet that when you see a quartet of large silicon diodes in close proximity that they are the main ingredients of a full-wave rectifier.

G6A06 Which of the following is an advantage of using a Schottky diode in an RF switching circuit rather than a standard silicon diode?

A. Lower capacitance. C. Longer switching times.
B. Lower inductance. D. Higher breakdown voltage.

The Schottky diode is a fast-switching, point-contact diode with lower capacitance offering faster switching capability than a standard silicon diode. This is an important consideration in HF transceivers for handling many digital modes where fast switching time between transmit and receive is required. *Lower capacitance* is the advantage of the *Schottky diode* over a common silicone diode. **ANSWER A.**

G6B07 Which of the following is an advantage of an LED indicator compared to an incandescent indicator?

A. Lower power consumption. C. Longer life.
B. Faster response time. D. All of these choices are correct.

It seems there's a worldwide conspiracy to deprive all of us of the warm, inviting glow of the incandescent lamp. However, progress marches on, and most small indicator lamps in the ham shack have been replaced by Light Emitting Diode (LED) devices of one sort or another. LEDs do have the advantages of *nearly infinite life, low power consumption, and nearly instant response time*. This may not seem like much of an issue with something like a dial lamp, but in a device like an optical encoder or optoisolator, the "lag" time of an incandescent lamp could be a real problem. LEDs come in a wide variety of colors and brightness levels, inconceivable just a few short years ago. Larger "natural light" LED bulbs

are now also available and suitable for general shack lighting without that eerie cold blue feel of earlier LED devices. **ANSWER D.**

The LED has all but replaced the small incandescent lamp in most modern ham equipment. Be sure to use a proper current-limiting resistor to protect small indicator LEDs. In the old days, tiny panel bulbs wouldn't last for more than a few years before burning out. LEDs last forever!

G6B08 How is an LED biased when emitting light?

A. Beyond cutoff.   C. Reverse Biased.
B. At the Zener voltage.   D. Forward Biased.

Not all semiconductors are based on silicon, contrary to a common misconception. There are many exotic materials that function as semiconductors, and do more than your garden variety diode or transistor. One of the first light emitting semiconductor materials was Gallium Arsenide Phosphide, GaAsp (GASP!). While an LED has two terminals and conducts better in one direction than the other, its similarity to a "normal" diode ends there. Many more exotic materials have been discovered and exploited for the manufacture of LEDs. The *light emitting diode* is always forward biased when it is emitting light. When current is passed through the PN junction, *forward biased*, the light emitting diode almost instantly turns on. **ANSWER D.**

G6B09 Which of the following is a characteristic of a liquid crystal display?

A. It requires ambient or back lighting.
B. It offers a wide dynamic range.
C. It has a wide viewing angle.
D. All of these choices are correct.

The basic properties of liquid crystal compounds were discovered in the late 1800s, long before anyone had a clue what to do with them (not even hams!) A liquid crystal display employs one or more of hundreds of possible substances that change optical properties when exposed to an electric field. Liquid crystals produce no light of their own, but can alter either the reflection or transmission of light in accordance with their electrical stimulation. A transmissive LCD display needs some source of backlighting, while a reflective LCD does not. Like the LED, LCD technology has evolved tremendously in recent years, making ham radios and other electronic gadgets just a lot more fun to look at. Many of your new high frequency transceivers use a *liquid crystal display (LCD)* which requires *backlighting* at night. The monochrome (black and white) liquid crystal displays achieve their own "brilliance" out in the sunshine. Color LCDs have dramatically improved visibility in direct sunlight, and with backlighting the color LCD looks terrific especially at night! **ANSWER A.**

The black on amber LCD can easily be seen under any lighting condition!.

Elmer Point: If you plan to operate your radio in the field, make sure it offers a liquid crystal display. An amber background with black numbers is best for reading the display in bright sunlight. Color LCD displays are great at night, but they may require some shade during the day. Older HF transceivers may use LED or vacuum florescent display, and these are next to impossible to see when operating Field Day in a tent out in the sunshine. Go for amber LCD with black numbers for best viewing.

G6B11 What is a microprocessor?

A. A low power analog signal processor used as a microwave detector.
B. A computer on a single integrated circuit.
C. A microwave detector, amplifier, and local oscillator on a single integrated circuit.
D. A low voltage amplifier used in a microwave transmitter modulator stage.

Thanks to microprocessors, your new General Class high frequency transceiver works much like a miniature *computer* with everything *on a single integrated circuit chip*. So much capability packed into such a small component! **ANSWER B.**

G6B02 What is meant by the term MMIC?

A. Multi Megabyte Integrated Circuit.
B. Monolithic Microwave Integrated Circuit.
C. Military Manufactured Integrated Circuit.
D. Mode Modulated Integrated Circuit.

The *monolithic microwave integrated circuit (MMIC)* is a favorite among microwave operators, up on 10 GHz. On the "X" band, we use MMICs in the microwave equipment as fixed-gain amplifiers with excellent signal to noise ratios. **ANSWER B.**

RF
GROUND

RF OUTPUT
AND $+V_{cc}$

RF INPUT
(DIAGONAL
CUT)

Monolithic Microwave Integrated Circuit
Photo Courtesy of Hewlett Packard Co.

G6B06 What kind of device is an integrated circuit operational amplifier?

A. Digital.
B. MMIC.
C. Programmable Logic.
D. Analog.

We nickname the operational amplifier an *"op amp"*. It is an *analog integrated circuit device*. The op amp offers high gain over a large range of input frequencies and is a direct-coupled differential amplifier whose characteristics are determined by components external to the amplifier unit. **ANSWER D.**

G6B01 Which of the following is an analog integrated circuit?

A. NAND Gate.
B. Microprocessor.
C. Frequency Counter.
D. Linear voltage regulator.

Analog circuits offer a smooth ride down Grandpa's old house banister. Digital circuits are like bumping down individual steps. We find digital circuits in frequency counters, NAND gates, and microprocessors. Inside your new high frequency transceiver will be an *analog linear voltage regulator* regulating current to keep the desired voltage steady and within specifications. **ANSWER D.**

G7B02 Which of the following is an advantage of using the binary system when processing digital signals?

A. Binary "ones" and "zeros" are easy to represent by an "on" or "off" state.
B. The binary number system is most accurate.
C. Binary numbers are more compatible with analog circuitry.
D. All of these choices are correct.

Now that high frequency transceivers employ numerous digital circuits, we need to review a little Boolean algebra. Oh, you missed that class? A binary number

Elmer Point: Here is a very important point for your understanding of digital electronics: To write and keep track of the many possible combinations of high or low signals in digital information, the combinations are treated as binary numbers. Binary numbers are also called base two numbers. An example is shown below.

These days, most children learn about decimal numbers in elementary school. When written in ordinary decimal form, integers (whole numbers) are expressed as so many ones, so many tens, so many hundreds, and so forth. Each place in the number has a value ten times the place to the right. This requires using ten (for decimal) different symbols called decimal numerals or digits: 0, 1, 2, 3, 4, 5, 6, 7, 8, and 9. But in binary form, whole numbers are expressed as so many ones, so many twos, so many fours, and so forth. Each place in the number has twice the value of the next place to the right. Binary numbers use only two digits instead of ten: just 0 and 1.

So, in binary form, a number is written as a string of ones and zeroes. For instance, the integer one is written as 1. Two would be 10, which we read as "one-zero". It means a two and no one. Three would be 11 ("one-one", not eleven), meaning a two and a one. Four would be 100, called "one-zero-zero", meaning a four, no two, and no one. Five would be 101, meaning a four, no two, and a one. One hundred would be 1100100. That means a sixty-four, a thirty-two, no sixteen, no eight, a four, no two, and no one.

Each zero or one in a binary number is called a *bi*nary digi*t*, or bit for short. Bit also means a little piece of information. In fact, a bit is the smallest possible piece of information in a digital system. It expresses a choice between only two possibilities. In a binary number, for instance, a particular bit can say either, "Yes, there is a 64 in this number," or, "No, there is not a 64 in this number."

In digital systems, binary numbers are used to write and keep track of the many possible combinations of the two electrical states.

Source: *Basic Electronics* © 1994, Master Publishing, Inc., Niles, Illinois

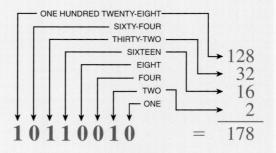

Binary Number:
Each place has a value **twice as great** as the next place to the right. **Two numerals or digits** are used:
0 (Zero = "No")
1 (One = "Yes")
These digits are called bits.

Binary System

0 could result in your little handheld radio's LCD display showing a blank (OFF) segment. The binary number 1 may tell the LCD display to turn a segment ON. The reason your LCD handheld display draws such little current is that once each segment gets its command to be either OFF (0) or ON (1), it remains that way until it receives another binary command. Many digital logic circuits in your new HF transceiver provide command "paths" from one stage to another. Logic symbols give us a clue about what it takes to trigger the next ON or OFF sequence – and sometimes reversing them! Engineers write "Truth Tables" to program multiple inputs and a single output logic path. The most basic form of using the binary system for the processing of digital signals will lead to binary 0s triggering an OFF state and binary 1s triggering an ON state. *Just remember "binary," 1s and 0s, ONs or OFFs*. **ANSWER A.**

G7B06 What is a shift register?
    A. A clocked array of circuits that passes data in steps along the array.
    B. An array of operational amplifiers used for tri-state arithmetic operations.
    C. A digital mixer.
    D. An analog mixer.
A *shift register passes* flip-flop *data up or down* to each other, rather than just an output. Parallel data may be converted to serial data, or the reverse, through a shift register. **ANSWER A.**

G6B03 Which of the following is an advantage of CMOS integrated circuits compared to TTL integrated circuits?
    A. Low power consumption.
    B. High power handling capability.
    C. Better suited for RF amplification.
    D. Better suited for power supply regulation.
Two different kinds of transistors are commonly used in the digital world, the bipolar junction transistor, BJT, and the Field Effect Transistor, FET. Standard TTL logic is based on BJTs, while CMOS logic is based on FETs, specifically MOSFETS. The truth tables for TTL and CMOS are identical. However, there are some practical, physical differences. TTL is very fast, but is subject to noise, which can result in "false triggering." In addition, it can use considerable power in high density circuits. CMOS is more immune to noise, and uses considerably less power, but at the cost of speed. While most commercial amateur equipment uses digital logic in the form of large scale or Very Large Scale integrated circuits, such as microprocessors, many homebrew projects still use individual TTL or CMOS gates. Many inveterate home-brewers have drawers full of these small-scale devices. The big advantage of CMOS Logic over TTL is that *CMOS* offers *low power consumption*. **ANSWER A.**

G6B04 What is meant by the term ROM?
    A. Resistor Operated Memory.
    B. Read Only Memory.
    C. Random Operational Memory.
    D. Resistant to Overload Memory.
Today's transceivers with their many specialized features contain *read only memory (ROM)*. It is programmed at the factory to set band limits, tuning ranges, and many other functions that define your radio. This read only memory is permanent and does not need a battery backup. **ANSWER B.**

Elmer Point: The NAND and NOR gates, (negative AND and negative OR, respectively), have the same characteristics as their positive equivalents, followed by an inverter sometimes called a NOT gate. The truth table for all 5 basic gates is shown below. While gates do exist that have more than two input terminals, these are relatively rare. Any multiple-input gate can be built up from a combination of two-input gates.

AND		
Input A	Input B	Output
0	0	0
1	0	0
0	1	0
1	1	1

OR		
Input A	Input B	Output
0	0	0
1	0	1
0	1	1
1	1	1

NAND		
Input A	Input B	Output
0	0	1
1	0	1
0	1	1
1	1	0

NOR		
Input A	Input B	Output
0	0	1
1	0	0
0	1	0
1	1	0

XOR		
Input A	Input B	Output
0	0	0
1	0	1
0	1	1
1	1	0

When logic gates are *cascaded*, the output state of one gate becomes the input state of the following gate terminal. It is easy to follow complex combinational logic if you simply write down the state of each terminal.as you move from left to right through the schematic. With a little practice, you should be able to follow some pretty complicated logic circuits in your head!

G6B05 What is meant when memory is characterized as non-volatile?

    A. It is resistant to radiation damage.

    B. It is resistant to high temperatures.

    C. The stored information is maintained even if power is removed.

    D. The stored information cannot be changed once written.

Non-volatile memory is what we see in newer transceivers, and *even though you pull the plug information remains in memory* even though there may not be a built-in battery backup. **ANSWER C.**

G7B03 Which of the following describes the function of a two input AND gate?

    A. Output is high when either or both inputs are low.

    B. Output is high only when both inputs are high.

    C. Output is low when either or both inputs are high.

    D. Output is low only when both inputs are high.

Digital logic circuits are, well, logical. Their functions can be explained by some simple grammatical statements. The basic decision-making element of a digital logic circuit is the gate. An AND gate, as the name suggest, gives an answer "C" if "A" and "B" are true. If we use a 1 to represent a TRUE condition, and a 0 to represent a FALSE condition, we can easily describe the behavior of the gate. C will only be TRUE if A and B are TRUE. Or C is a 1 if and only if A and B are 1. The behavior of any type of gate is defined by a Truth Table. There are five basic types of combinational logic gates: AND, OR, NAND, NOR, and exclusive OR, (XOR). If an input or output is "high," we represent it with the binary number 1. If we look at a truth table, an *AND gate* will only give us a *high output when BOTH inputs are high*. **ANSWER B.**

G7B04 Which of the following describes the function of a two input NOR gate?

    A. Output is high when either or both inputs are low

    B. Output is high only when both inputs are high

    C. Output is low when either or both inputs are high

    D. Output is low only when both inputs are high

Now they ask about the NOR gate. The two input *NOR gate* will give us a *LOW output when EITHER or BOTH inputs are high*. **ANSWER C.**

G7B05 How many states does a 3-bit binary counter have?

    A. 3.

    B. 6.

    C. 8.

    D. 16.

Each flip-flop requires two input pulses to generate one output pulse. Each time you add another flip-flop in series, you multiply the number of inputs required to generate one output by a factor of two. $2 \times 2 \times 2 = 8$. In short, being Base 2, 3-bit is $2^3 = 8$. **ANSWER C.**

G7B01 Complex digital circuitry can often be replaced by what type of integrated circuit?

A. Microcontroller.

B. Charge-coupled device.

C. Phase detector.

D. Window comparator.

You likely know that large scale integrated "chips" (LSIs) contain microprocessors. There also are integrated circuits that will handle *complex digital circuitry*, called *microcontrollers*. **ANSWER A.**

An LSI mounted on a printed circuit board

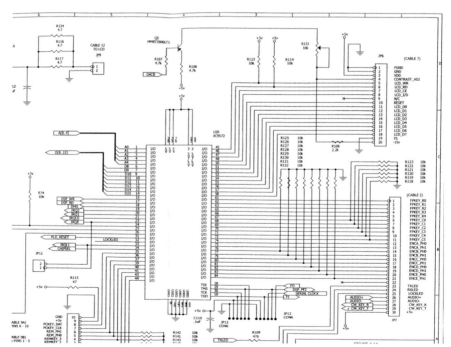

Here is a terminal diagram, or *pinout,* of a large scale integrated circuit (LSI) like the one pictured. This shows the connections between the device and the outside world. The internal *schematic diagrams* of LSIs are seldom seen by mere mortals, as they may have tens or hundreds of millions of transistors inside! Fortunately, you don't need to know the internal wiring, just the *functions* as seen by the external world.

Rolling Your Own Equipment

A great many radio amateurs derive a thrill from designing and building their own equipment from scratch. Remember, Amateur Radio is something you learn, not just the things you buy!

Regardless of your technical aptitude, you can always participate to some degree in "homebrewing" amateur radio gear. You don't have to build an all-mode DC-to-Daylight transceiver from scratch to be considered a homebrewer! There are countless simple accessories you can put together in an evening. Antenna switches, dummy loads, test oscillators and such are useful projects. Building a dipole antenna is a simple homebrew project that nearly every ham has participated in at one time or another. At the very least, every radio amateur should know how to handle a soldering iron.

There was a time in the not-too-distant past when every town had a radio store or TV repair shop. These were treasure troves full of inexpensive electronics components where the eager young ham could find anything he needed to build whatever ham radio widget he could imagine. For the most part, the corner parts stores have gone away. While components are still readily available online and through mail order electronics retail stores, it can be inconvenient to find all the parts necessary to complete a project.

This is where it helps to know who the hams are in your neighborhood. There is an untold wealth of electronic parts languishing in ham shacks all over the country. This collection would put the "big" electronics stores to shame if it were all in one place. The big problem is, this vast storehouse of components is rarely in any kind or order! On-line ham radio forums, local ham flea markets, and military surplus (DRMO/DLA) sales and auctions are also great sources of radio parts.

The best way to learn is by doing. It never hurts to sit at the feet of an experienced Elmer for learning the finer points. The **ARRL Handbook** is full of great projects, as are any of the popular Amateur Radio periodicals.

Where there's a project, there's a way to find the parts! Happy Homebrewing!

---

ham apps Speaking of the more homebrew inclined ham, we have a neat interface between Arduino and your smart phone: This hybrid between Arduino and smart phone technology lets you develop your very own ham radio app. Many modern hams consider software "The New Homebrew." http://www.amarino-toolkit.net/

Elmer Point: Your Granddad ham likely knew that a chap named Georg Simon Ohm (1789-1854) experimented with electricity and discovered that the resistance (R) of a conductor depends on its length in feet, cross-sectional area in circular mils, and the resistivity, which is a parameter that depends on the molecular structure of the conductor and its temperature. Ohm's Law states:

The current in an electrical circuit is directly proportional to the voltage and inversely proportional to the resistance.

The Ohm's Law and Power Circle shown here includes 12 equations that allow us to solve for voltage (E), current (I), resistance (R), and power (P), if we know the other values. There isn't much tough math in this section, but keep this page bookmarked to help you solve common electrical formulas.

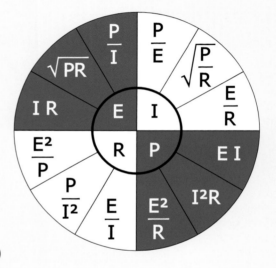

To solve for Voltage (E):

E = I (current) $\times$ R (resistance)

E = $\sqrt{\text{P (power)} \times \text{R (resistance)}}$

E = P (power) $\div$ I (current)

To solve for Current (I):

I = P (power) $\div$ E (voltage)

I = $\sqrt{\text{P (power)} \div \text{R (resistance)}}$

I = E (voltage) $\div$ R (resistance)

To solve for Resistance (R):

R = E^2 (voltage squared) $\div$ P (power)

R = P (power) $\div$ I^2 (current squared)

R = E (voltage) $\div$ I (current)

To solve for Power (P):

P = E (voltage) $\times$ I (current)

P = I^2 (current squared) $\times$ R (resistance)

P = E^2 (voltage squared) $\div$ R (resistance)

Source: The ARRL Handbook, 2207, © 2006, American Radio Relay League

Electrical Principles

G5B12 What would be the RMS voltage across a 50 ohm dummy load dissipating 1200 watts?

A. 173 volts.　　　　　　　　C. 346 volts.
B. 245 volts.　　　　　　　　D. 692 volts.

When you work with high-frequency mobile antennas or, in this question, a high-frequency dummy load, you may wish to calculate the voltage across it to make sure things won't arc over or to determine the maximum voltage that can be applied without exceeding the power rating. In this question we are looking for Voltage (E). We have Resistance (R) in ohms and Power (P) in watts. Hint: resistance is always in ohms and power is always in watts. Consulting the magic circle we find the relationship for voltage when we have resistance and power to be:

$$E = \text{Square root of } P \times R = \sqrt{P \times R}$$
$$E = \text{Square root of } 50 \times 1200 = \sqrt{50 \times 1200}$$
$$E = \text{Square root of } 60,000 = \sqrt{60,000}$$
$$E = 244.948$$

This is an easy one to work out on a calculator – and yes, calculators are allowed in the exam room. We strongly recommend that you have one. Here are the keystrokes: Clear, Clear, 50 × 1200 = 60,000. Now simply tap the square root sign and, voila, the correct answer pops out at (approximately) 245 volts, which shows up as Answer B on your exam. Don't forget, examiners are allowed to scramble the A, B, C, D order, so look for *245 volts* as the correct answer. **ANSWER B.**

G5B03 How many watts of electrical power are used if 400 VDC is supplied to an 800 ohm load?

A. 0.5 watts.
B. 200 watts.

C. 400 watts.
D. 3200 watts.

Look at the magic circle on page 132. The equation for this problem is $P = E^2 \div R$. E^2 (400^2) is 160,000 divided by R (800) is 200, so the answer is *200 watts*. Calculator keystrokes are: Clear, 400 $\times$ 400 $\div$ 800 = 200. **ANSWER B.**

G5B04 How many watts of electrical power are used by a 12 VDC light bulb that draws 0.2 amperes?

A 2.4 watts.
B. 24 watts.

C. 6 watts.
D. 60 watts.

Using the magic circle for power, you see that power (P) is equal to voltage (E) times current (I). Multiply volts times amps and you end up with *2.4 watts*. Calculator keystrokes are: Clear, 12 $\times$ 0.2 = 2.4 (in watts). **ANSWER A.**

G5B05 How many watts are dissipated when a current of 7.0 milliamperes flows through 1.25 kilohms resistance?

A. Approximately 61 milliwatts.
B. Approximately 61 watts.

C. Approximately 11 milliwatts.
D. Approximately 11 watts.

Unless metric prefixes are second nature to you, we always recommend converting everything to the fundamental units before doing any further calculations. It can be very confusing, especially in the heat of an exam, to work with "mixed" units such as "millis," "micros," and "kilos" all in the same formula. In this case 7.0 milliamperes is 0.007 amperes. Likewise, 1.25 kilohms is 1,250 ohms. Now use the current and resistance version of the magic circle for the equation $P = I^2 \times R$. $P = 0.007^2 \times 1250$. This gives the answer in WATTS – 0.06125 watts. Now you may convert the unit into milliwatts by multiplying by 1000 for the correct answer of *61 milliwatts*. Calculator key strokes are: Clear, 0.007 $\times$ 0.007 $\times$ 1250 = 0.06125 (in watts). **ANSWER A.**

G5B07 What value of an AC signal produces the same power dissipation in a resistor as a DC voltage of the same value?

A. The peak-to-peak value.
B. The peak value.

C. The RMS value.
D. The reciprocal of the RMS value.

Root Mean Square (RMS) measurement of an AC signal (also called the effective value of an AC voltage) is the same as a DC voltage of the same value. **ANSWER C.**

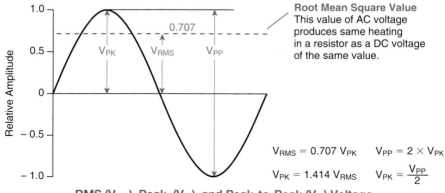

Root Mean Square Value
This value of AC voltage produces same heating in a resistor as a DC voltage of the same value.

$V_{RMS} = 0.707\ V_{PK}$ $V_{PP} = 2 \times V_{PK}$

$V_{PK} = 1.414\ V_{RMS}$ $V_{PK} = \dfrac{V_{PP}}{2}$

RMS (V_{RMS}), Peak, (V_{PK}), and Peak-to-Peak (V_{PP}) Voltage

G5B09 What is the RMS voltage of a sine wave with a value of 17 volts peak?

    A. 8.5 volts.   C. 24 volts.

    B. 12 volts.   D. 34 volts.

This question simply works the formula backwards. From the formulas shown in the figure for Root Mean Square Value we see that peak voltage (the value we have in the question) is equal to $1.414 \times$ RMS voltage (the value the question is asking for):

$$V_{pk} = 1.414 \times V_{rms}$$
$$17 = 1.414 \times V_{rms}$$
$$V_{rms} = 17 \div 1.414 = 12.0226 \text{ or about } \textit{12 volts.} \textbf{ ANSWER B.}$$

G7A08 Which of the following is an advantage of a switch mode power supply as compared to a linear power supply?

    A. Faster switching time makes higher output voltage possible.

    B. Fewer circuit components are required.

    C. High frequency operation allows the use of smaller components.

    D. All of these choices are correct.

The switching power supply uses a relatively *high-frequency* oscillator at a frequency where *small, light-weight, low-cost miniature transformers* create relatively smooth DC power output. These units are smaller and lighter than older units that use large, heavy traditional transformers. One concern of the switching power supply is its proximity to your high-frequency antenna system. The antenna system must be 10 feet or more away from the switching power supply so that broad-band noise from the unit is not picked up by the antenna. **ANSWER C.**

Modern switching power supplies incorporate "crowbar protection" to provide overvoltage protection.

G7A05 What portion of the AC cycle is converted to DC by a half-wave rectifier?

    A. 90 degrees.   C. 270 degrees.

    B. 180 degrees.   D. 360 degrees.

The half-wave rectifier uses only half of the cycle, which is *180 degrees.* **ANSWER B.**

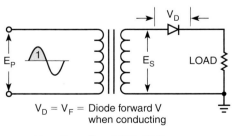

Conducts only on positive cycle.
No conduction on negative cycle.

Reverse voltage across diode is E_{SPK}, the peak voltage of the secondary voltage.

$V_D = V_F =$ Diode forward V when conducting

$V_D = V_R = E_{SPK}$ when diode is not conducting

Half-Wave Rectifier

G7A06 What portion of the AC cycle is converted to DC by a full-wave rectifier?
- A. 90 degrees.
- C. 270 degrees.
- B. 180 degrees.
- D. 360 degrees.

A full-wave rectifier is much more efficient because it uses all *360 degrees* of the AC cycle. The output of a full-wave rectifier is much easier to filter to provide pure DC voltage. **ANSWER D.**

G7A07 What is the output waveform of an unfiltered full-wave rectifier connected to a resistive load?
- A. A series of DC pulses at twice the frequency of the AC input.
- B. A series of DC pulses at the same frequency as the AC input.
- C. A sine wave at half the frequency of the AC input.
- D. A steady DC voltage.

A full-wave rectifier gives a much smoother *pulsating DC* than a half-wave rectifier because the full-wave rectified half sine waves are *double the frequency of the AC line input*. **ANSWER A.**

G7A03 What is the peak-inverse-voltage across the rectifiers in a full-wave bridge power supply?
- A. One-quarter the normal output voltage of the power supply.
- B. Half the normal output voltage of the power supply.
- C. Double the normal peak output voltage of the power supply.
- D. Equal to the normal peak output voltage of the power supply.

The full-wave bridge rectifier circuit offers an output of pulsating DC that is far easier to smooth out than either a single-diode half-wave circuit or a two-diode full-wave center tap rectifier circuit. This full wave bridge develops a Peak Inverse Voltage across the 4 rectifier diodes that is nearly *equal to the normal peak output of the power supply*. **ANSWER D.**

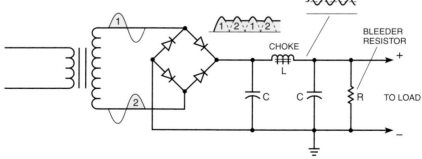

Full-Wave Bridge Power Supply with Bleeder Resistor

G7A04 What is the peak-inverse-voltage across the rectifier in a half-wave power supply?
- A. One-half the normal peak output voltage of the power supply.
- B. One-half the normal output voltage of the power supply.
- C. Equal to the normal output voltage of the power supply.
- D. Two times the normal peak output voltage of the power supply.

In the half-wave rectifier power supply, the voltage across that single hard-working rectifier is two times the normal peak output voltage. The smoothing output capacitor will hold the peak voltage during the negative half of the cycle, while the transformer is at the negative peak, letting the rectifier see *twice the normal peak output voltage* across it! **ANSWER D.**

G7A02 Which of the following components are used in a power supply filter network?
A. Diodes.
B. Transformers and transducers.
C. Quartz crystals.
D. Capacitors and inductors.

In power supplies, transformers supply the voltage and current, diodes rectify, *capacitors and inductors filter*, and a bleeder resistor protects. **ANSWER D.**

An inductor is a coil of wire that opposes AC current trapped in its magnetic field. Your new radio is loaded with many types of inductor coils used in different stages throughout the radio.

G6A15 Which of the following is an advantage of an electrolytic capacitor?
A. Tight tolerance.
B. Much less leakage than any other type.
C. High capacitance for a given volume.
D. Inexpensive RF capacitor.

We usually find the electrolytic capacitor in the power supply section of our new rig. The electrolytic capacitor is polarized with a positive and negative connection point and offers *high capacitance for given volume* (volume = size). **ANSWER C.**

Electrolytic capacitors are used in just about every power supply as they can contain a lot of capacitance in a small space.

G6A13 Why is the polarity of applied voltages important for polarized capacitors?
A. Incorrect polarity can cause the capacitor to short-circuit.
B. Reverse voltages can destroy the dielectric layer of an electrolytic capacitor.
C. The capacitor could overheat and explode.
D. All of these choices are correct.

Most electrolytic capacitors are polarized, meaning they care deeply about which way you wire them up. You just haven't lived until you've been "shot" by an exploding metal can wet-slug tantalum capacitor! They bear striking resemblance to blasting caps and have approximately the same effect if you wire them up backwards! Check the polarity before installing them in any circuit. *All of the answer choices are correct*. **ANSWER D.**

This electrolytic capacitor has clearly marked polarity.

G7A01 What useful feature does a power supply bleeder resistor provide?
 A. It acts as a fuse for excess voltage.
 B. It ensures that the filter capacitors are discharged when power is removed.
 C. It removes shock hazards from the induction coils.
 D. It eliminates ground loop current.

When you turn off your big rig, it dims down and then cycles off completely. This slow decay of voltage is from the *filter capacitors* that are slowly *being discharged by the bleeder resistors.* This is a safety feature that also helps provide voltage regulation. See the illustration at **G7A03**, page 136. **ANSWER B.**

G4B06 What is an advantage of a digital voltmeter as compared to an analog voltmeter?
 A. Better for measuring computer circuits.
 B. Better for RF measurements.
 C. Better precision for most uses.
 D. Faster response.

Your buddy discovers you are a brand new General and gives you several gel-cell 12 volt batteries. To see which one has the absolute best charge, use a digital volt meter to get a *more precise digital readout* of the battery voltage. A neat little analog volt meter might not show you subtle changes in battery terminal voltage. **ANSWER C.**

G4B14 What is an instance in which the use of an instrument with analog readout may be preferred over an instrument with a digital readout?
 A. When testing logic circuits.
 B. When high precision is desired.
 C. When measuring the frequency of an oscillator.
 D. When adjusting tuned circuits.

Don't throw away that old Simpson model 260 needle meter. The analog needle movement can give you the "feel," visually, of *tuned circuits*, as long as that particular tuned circuit does not call for specialized, non-loading measurements. That old needle readout may be less affected by strong nearby signals up at the repeater site, too! **ANSWER D.**

Analog multimeter.

G4B05 Why is high input impedance desirable for a voltmeter?
 A. It improves the frequency response.
 B. It decreases battery consumption in the meter.
 C. It improves the resolution of the readings.
 D. It decreases the loading on circuits being measured.

New digital volt meters have a relatively *high input impedance to avoid loading* down *the circuit being measured*. If you are measuring a fraction of a volt, you don't want to use an older volt meter that might significantly add load to the circuit and result in a bogus reading. **ANSWER D.**

G6A01 What is the minimum allowable discharge voltage for maximum life of a standard 12 volt lead acid battery?

A. 6 volts.
B. 8.5 volts.

C. 10.5 volts.
D. 12 volts.

When operating your equipment with a 12 volt lead acid automobile battery during Field Day, make sure you never pull your battery below *10.5 volts*. If you do, you will shorten the maximum life of that battery. An indication that you are reaching that minimum is that any transmitter running at 10.5 volts (instead of 12 volts) usually sounds distorted on high frequencies. **ANSWER C.**

G6A04 When is it acceptable to recharge a carbon-zinc primary cell?

A. As long as the voltage has not been allowed to drop below 1.0 volt.
B. When the cell is kept warm during the recharging period.
C. When a constant current charger is used.
D. Never.

Disposable flashlight "D" cells are *never* intended to be *recharged*. Attempts to recharge carbon zinc primary cells or newer alkaline batteries may lead to the battery venting dangerous gas. Unless the battery specifically states "rechargeable," do not try to recharge it. **ANSWER D.**

The common "D" cell carbon-zinc battery is non-rechargeable.

G6A02 What is an advantage of the low internal resistance of nickel-cadmium batteries?

A. Long life.
B. High discharge current.

C. High voltage.
D. Rapid recharge.

The Nickel Cadmium battery is a low-cost, rechargeable voltage source for handheld radios as well as for some QRP (low power output) high frequency transceivers. The low internal resistance of the nickel cadmium battery allows for *high discharge current* when transmitting. The disadvantage of low internal resistance is the slight self-discharge between uses of your radio equipment. So before going out on Field Day, be sure to cycle your nickel cadmium battery pack several times, and end the cycle with a good charge. **ANSWER B.**

Always check the polarity of your batteries. Many "dead" radios are simply the result of one or more batteries being installed backwards!

G4E08 What is the name of the process by which sunlight is changed directly into electricity?

A. Photovoltaic conversion.
B. Photon emission.

C. Photosynthesis.
D. Photon decomposition.

You can change sunlight into voltage, and notice the word "volt" in the term *photovoltaic conversion*. **ANSWER A.**

G4E09 What is the approximate open-circuit voltage from a fully illuminated silicon photovoltaic cell?
  A. 0.02 VDC.   C. 0.2 VDC.
  B. 0.5 VDC.   D. 1.38 VDC.

A complete photovoltaic cell will yield *0.5 volts* direct current. A solar panel is made up of a series-parallel connection of these cells in order to charge your storage battery system.
ANSWER B.

Solar Panel array for
Charging Storage Batteries

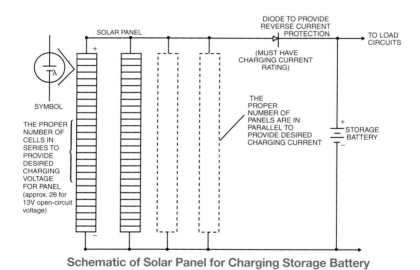

Schematic of Solar Panel for Charging Storage Battery

G4E10 What is the reason that a series diode is connected between a solar panel and a storage battery that is being charged by the panel?
  A. The diode serves to regulate the charging voltage to prevent overcharge.
  B. The diode prevents self-discharge of the battery though the panel during times of low or no illumination.
  C. The diode limits the current flowing from the panel to a safe value.
  D. The diode greatly increases the efficiency during times of high illumination.

I always like to monitor solar power charging with a small amp meter in series with the red lead. You can really see how a single shadow will decrease output. Then one night you check the panel and its actually showing a discharge on your battery. There probably was no series diode to prevent the panel from slightly discharging your battery. Newer panels usually have the diodes in place. But some older panels, or scavenged panels without a controller, could really use that *reverse current diode to prevent battery discharge*. **ANSWER B.**

G4E11 Which of the following is a disadvantage of using wind as the primary source of power for an emergency station?

A. The conversion efficiency from mechanical energy to electrical energy is less than 2 percent.

B. The voltage and current ratings of such systems are not compatible with amateur equipment.

C. A large energy storage system is needed to supply power when the wind is not blowing.

D. All of these choices are correct.

The wind doesn't blow all the time, so wind power is not a good primary source for your emergency communications station. When the wind isn't blowing, you need a *huge bank of batteries* to keep your station on the air. **ANSWER C.**

This small wind generator can keep a charge on a portable battery system as long as the wind is greater than 5 mph.

G4E03 Which of the following direct, fused power connections would be the best for a 100 watt HF mobile installation?

A. To the battery using heavy gauge wire.

B. To the alternator or generator using heavy gauge wire.

C. To the battery using resistor wire.

D. To the alternator or generator using resistor wire.

As a General Class operator, you'll probably be running a 100-watt, HF mobile transceiver in your car. You cannot rely on the car's 12-volt accessory or "power port" socket wiring to support the necessary 20-amp (minimum) power demands from your HF radio. Wire your red and black power leads *directly to the battery using heavy-gauge wire*. Fuse both the red and the black power leads close to the battery connection point. **ANSWER A.**

G4E04 Why is it best NOT to draw the DC power for a 100 watt HF transceiver from a vehicle's auxiliary power socket?

A. The socket is not wired with an RF-shielded power cable.

B. The socket's wiring may be inadequate for the current drawn by the transceiver.

C. The DC polarity of the socket is reversed from the polarity of modern HF transceivers.

D. Drawing more than 50 watts from this socket could cause the engine to overheat.

While you might be tempted to grab 12 volts from an automobile auxiliary power socket, don't! Sure, the radio will work for a few minutes, but after a little bit of transmitting the auxiliary power receptacle wiring will get red hot from *over-drawing the current*, and quite possibly cause a fire in your dashboard! **ANSWER B.**

Elmer Point: To go mobile with your 100-watt HF ham transceiver, you'll need to run the red and black power wires directly to the positive and negative terminals on your car or truck battery. You should have separate fuses right next to the battery terminal connections for safety. While automotive sound systems sometimes use the vehicle chassis as the negative black wire return, commercial two-way radio installers always say it's best to run directly to the positive and negative terminals on the battery. The chassis of your HF radio also should be well grounded to your vehicle frame.

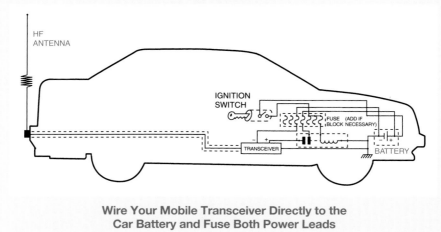

Wire Your Mobile Transceiver Directly to the Car Battery and Fuse Both Power Leads

G6B15 What is the main reason to use keyed connectors instead of non-keyed types?
  A. Prevention of use by unauthorized persons.
  B. Reduced chance of incorrect mating.
  C. Higher current carrying capacity.
  D. All of these choices are correct.

Many plugs that attach to receptacles on your radio, including the metal microphone plugs and jacks, have a protruding ridge or a channel so that the plug fits properly into the receptacle. They call this a "keyed" connector. It *reduces the chance* of accidentally *bending fragile pins* when you plug in to the receptacle.
ANSWER B.

Keyed Connector.

Elmer Point: *Want to learn more about electricity and how electronics work? Here are two books we recommend highly for your self-education!*

Getting Started in Electronics by Forrest M. Mims III is a true classic. It is used by a wide range of people – from junior-high teachers to the U.S. Army to teach the fundamentals of electricity and electronics.

Basic Electronics by Alvis J. Evans and Gene McWhorter goes a little deeper into the topic, and includes end of chapter quizzes and worked-out problems to teach you in detail the various aspects of electronics.

Either book – or both – will give you a solid grounding in the theory, science, and practical applications of electronics. You can get your copies of the books at your local ham radio store, on line at www.w5yi.org, or by calling The W5YI Group at 800-669-9594.

Website Resources

▼ IF YOU'RE LOOKING FOR	▼ THEN VISIT
equipment reviews	www.hamoperator.com
Call sign lookups and more	www.qrz.com
ham radio gear, call sign look-ups	www.hamcall.net
QSO's and more	www.hamgallery.com
ham radio resources	www.dxzone.com
articles, reviews, etc.	www.eham.net
used equipment ads and more	www.qth.com
operating tips from Calgary hams	www.cara.ampr.org
directional antennas	www.arrowantennas.com
direction finding tips and more	www.homingin.com
free e-mail service for hams	www.qsl.net
ham radio for people with disabilities	www.handiham.org
Canada's amateur radio society	www.rac.ca
operating tips, ham news	www.hamquick.com
FCC amateur radio enforcement log	www.rainreport.com
California club with good tech articles	www.cvarc.org/faq.htm
antennas and related gear	www.natcommgroup.com
every ham accessory known to man	www.mfjenterprises.com
CQ Magazine's website	www.cq-amateur-radio.com
radio propagation reports	www.dxworld.com/50prop.html
news & science reports about space	www.spacetoday.org
mobile antennas and accessories	www.hiqantennas.com
educational resources and links	www.ecjones.org
antennas, connectors, and more	www.cq73.com
linking ham radio via the internet	www.winlink.org
inductive components for RFI	www.amidoncorp.com
HF amplifiers, antennas, and more	www.ameritron.com
feedlines, connectors, & wire galore	www.cablexperts.com
copper ground strap, antenna masts	www.metal-cable.com
all kinds of antennas & accessories	www.antennaworld.com
antenna site with good technical data	www.cushcraft.com
excellent RF safety calculator	http://n5xu.ae.utexas.edu/rfsafety
technical resources for hams	www.csvhfs.org
old instruction manuals	http://bama.sbc.edu
RF safety calculator	http://hintlink.com/power_density.htm

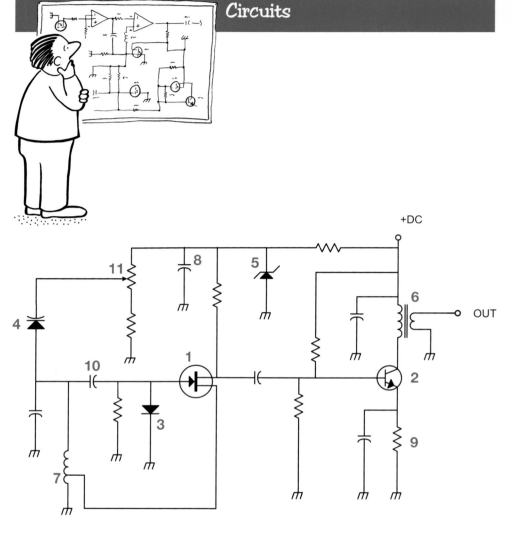

Look at Figure G7-1. On your exam, it may appear on the last page of the examination sheets or may appear for a single question about the components. We can identify this circuit as a Hartley oscillator, with symbol 7 as the telltale tapped coil. This is a voltage-controlled Hartley oscillator, seen by the varactor, symbol 4. Symbol 11 is a variable potentiometer, and symbol 8 is a bypass capacitor. Symbol 10 is a blocking capacitor, isolating out DC. Symbol 1 is a field effect transistor (JFET) with symbol 5 being a Zener diode for voltage regulation. Symbol 6 is the oscillator's companion amplifier output transformer, and symbol 2 is an NPN transistor. Symbol 9 is a fixed resistor, and symbol 3 is a diode. Now, let's see what they're going to ask on the exam.

G7A09 Which symbol in figure G7-1 represents a field effect transistor?

A. Symbol 2.   C. Symbol 1.
B. Symbol 5.   D. Symbol 4.

Symbol 1 is the Field Effect Transistor. The schematic symbol in the diagram is an N channel FET. We know it's an N Channel, because the arrow is pointing "Nwards." (Bad puns are always a great way to remember electronic principles!) **ANSWER C.**

Symbol 1

G7A10 Which symbol in figure G7-1 represents a Zener diode?

A. Symbol 4.   C. Symbol 11.
B. Symbol 1.   D. Symbol 5.

Symbol 5 is the Zener diode, used for voltage regulation. The cathode end of a Zener symbol is somewhat Z shaped. And always remember, in nearly every case the Zener diode is in the circuit backwards from a normal diode.
ANSWER D.

Symbol 5

G7A11 Which symbol in figure G7-1 represents an NPN junction transistor?

A. Symbol 1.   C. Symbol 7.
B. Symbol 2.   D. Symbol 11.

See the transistor all the way to the right, *symbol 2*? The arrow is Not Pointing In so it is an NPN junction transistor. **ANSWER B.**

Symbol 2

G7A12 Which symbol in Figure G7-1 represents a multiple-winding transformer?

A. Symbol 4.   C. Symbol 6.
B. Symbol 7.   D. Symbol 1.

It's easy to spot the transformer – we find it at *symbol 6*. The 2 vertical lines indicate an iron core. Sometimes you'll see a dot near the ends of the windings. The dots indicate the relative phasing of the transformer. This is more common in radio frequency transformers such as baluns and transmission line transformers. **ANSWER C.**

Symbol 6

G7A13 Which symbol in Figure G7-1 represents a tapped inductor?

A. Symbol 7.   C. Symbol 6.
B. Symbol 11.   D. Symbol 1.

This is what gives away the Hartley oscillator; *symbol 7*, the tapped inductor. This provides us with the feedback necessary to keep the oscillator oscillating! The tapped inductor actually functions as a step up autotransformer.
ANSWER A.

Symbol 7

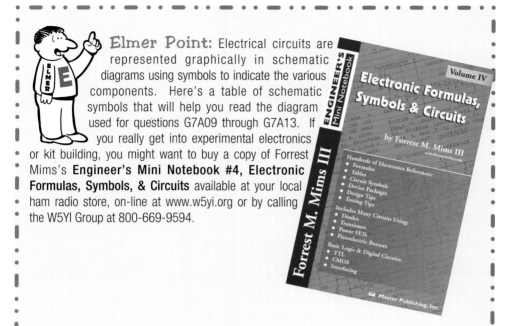

Elmer Point: Electrical circuits are represented graphically in schematic diagrams using symbols to indicate the various components. Here's a table of schematic symbols that will help you read the diagram used for questions G7A09 through G7A13. If you really get into experimental electronics or kit building, you might want to buy a copy of Forrest Mims's **Engineer's Mini Notebook #4, Electronic Formulas, Symbols, & Circuits** available at your local ham radio store, on-line at www.w5yi.org or by calling the W5YI Group at 800-669-9594.

SCHEMATIC SYMBOLS

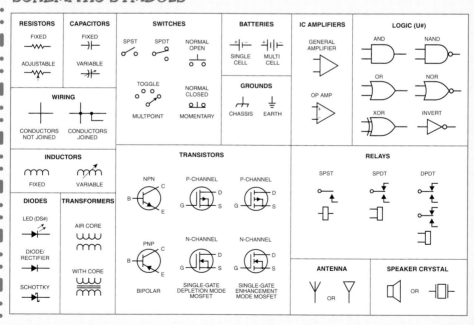

G5C04 What is the total resistance of three 100 ohm resistors in parallel?
    A. 0.30 ohms.
    B. 0.33 ohms.
    C. 33.3 ohms.
    D. 300 ohms.

If we have three equal value resistors in parallel, we will have three individual paths for current to flow, decreasing each like resistor's ohmic resistance by 1/3. You can do this one in your head: 1/3 the resistance of each 100 ohm resistor is *33.3 ohms*. If you want to do it the long way, here is the formula:

$$R_T = 1 \div (1/R_1 + 1/R_2 + 1/R_3).$$

ANSWER C.

Here we have a bouquet of high power resistors. Don't expect to see your normal color code on these. They're big enough to have the resistance values spelled right out.

G6A16 What will happen to the resistance if the temperature of a resistor is increased?
    A. It will change depending on the resistor's reactance coefficient.
    B. It will stay the same.
    C. It will change depending on the resistor's temperature coefficient.
    D. It will become time dependent.

Heating a resistor always decreases its resistance. The amount of change for any particular temperature change depends on the *resistor's temperature coefficient*, which depends on the materials used in the resistor's construction. **ANSWER C.**

G5B02 How does the total current relate to the individual currents in each branch of a purely resistive parallel circuit?
    A. It equals the average of each branch current.
    B. It decreases as more parallel branches are added to the circuit.
    C. It equals the sum of the currents through each branch.
    D. It is the sum of the reciprocal of each individual voltage drop.

If you *add up the current* in each branch of a parallel circuit, you will come up with the total current in the circuit. **ANSWER C.**

G5C05 If three equal value resistors in series produce 450 ohms, what is the value of each resistor?
    A. 1500 ohms.
    B. 90 ohms.
    C. 150 ohms.
    D.175 ohms.

If we have 3 same-value resistors in series whose total resistance adds up to 450 ohms, each resistor will have a value of 1/3rd of 450 ohms. 450 divided by 3 = *150 ohms*. Now let's check our answer:
        R1 + R2 + R3 = R total. 150 + 150 + 150 = 450 ohms! **ANSWER C.**

Elmer Point: Here is a set of questions that asks about the total value of resistors, capacitors, and inductors connected in SERIES and in PARALLEL. Resistors (R) and Inductors (L) act the same way. Capacitors (C) act in the opposite way. Here are the formulas to calculate the total value of these components:

Resistors in SERIES simply add up: $R_{total} = R_1 + R_2 + R_3$

Inductors in SERIES simply add up: $L_{total} = L_1 + L_2 + L_3$

Resistors and Inductors in PARALLEL combine with a resulting total value that is always LESS than the value of the lowest value resistor in parallel, for easy problem solving! Here are the formulas:

when there are 2 resistors or inductors: $R_{total} = \dfrac{R_1 \times R_2}{R_1 + R_2}$ or $L_{total} = \dfrac{L_1 \times L_2}{L_1 + L_2}$

when there are 3 or more resistors: $R_{total} = \dfrac{1}{\dfrac{1}{R_1} + \dfrac{1}{R_2} + \dfrac{1}{R_3}}$ or $L_{total} = \dfrac{1}{\dfrac{1}{L_1} + \dfrac{1}{L_2} + \dfrac{1}{L_3}}$

Capacitors in PARALLEL simply add up: $C_{total} = C_1 + C_2 + C_3$

Capacitors in SERIES combine with a resulting total value that is always LESS than the value of the lowest value capacitor in series, for easy problem solving! Here is the formula:

when there are 2 capacitors: $C_{total} = \dfrac{C_1 \times C_2}{C_1 + C_2}$

when there are 3 or more capacitors: $C_{total} = \dfrac{1}{\dfrac{1}{C_1} + \dfrac{1}{C_2} + \dfrac{1}{C_3}}$

G5C15 What is the total resistance of a 10 ohm, a 20 ohm, and a 50 ohm resistor connected in parallel?

A. 5.9 ohms.
B. 0.17 ohms.
C. 10000 ohms.
D. 80 ohms.

While you can solve this problem with a big formula, always remember that with unlike resistors in parallel, just like unlike capacitors in series, the resulting answer will always be less than the smallest value component. *5.9 ohms* is a logical answer to solve for when you work the big long formula all the way out. **ANSWER A.**

$R_T = 1 \div (1/R_1 + 1/R_2 + 1/R_3)$

G5C03 **Which of the following components should be added to an existing resistor to increase the resistance?**

A. A resistor in parallel.
B. A resistor in series.
C. A capacitor in series.
D. A capacitor in parallel.

Another easy one here – to add more resistance to a circuit, we *add resistor(s) in series.* **ANSWER B.**

G5C08 **What is the equivalent capacitance of two 5.0 nanofarad capacitors and one 750 picofarad capacitor connected in parallel?**

A. 576.9 nanofarads.
B. 1733 picofarads.
C. 3583 picofarads.
D. 10.750 nanofarads.

Capacitors in parallel add up, similar to resistors in series: $C1 + C2 + C3 = C$ total. But hold on, they have mixed in one picofarad capacitor with two same-size nanofarad capacitors! This is easy. Let's take the 750 picofard capacitor, and determine what its value is as a matching nanofarad capacitor!

One nanofarad $= 10^{-9}$ of a farad.
One picofarad $= 10^{-12}$ of a farad.

So to convert the picofarad to the equivalent nanofarad value, we move the decimal point three places to the left. The 750 picofarad capacitor equals 0.750 nanofarads. Now we can do the easy math for the 3 capacitors in parallel:
$5.0 + 5.0 + 0.750 = 10.750$ nanofarads. **ANSWER D.**

Handy hint: In a test you can encounter mixed units as in this question, such as milliwatts and microwatts. If working with metric prefixes isn't second nature, always convert the values to their fundamental units first! In other words, rewrite the numbers as watts or ohms or farads, not nanofarads or picofarads. Then when you're all done with the calculations, go back and give the answer in the units they want! You'll save yourself a lot of heartburn.

G5C09 **What is the capacitance of three 100 microfarad capacitors connected in series?**

A. 0.30 microfarads.
B. 0.33 microfarads.
C. 33.3 microfarads.
D. 300 microfarads.

We have three like capacitors in series – since they are in series, just like resistors in parallel, total capacitance will be 1/3 of each of the 100 microfarad capacitors. *33.3 microfarads* is an answer you can do in your head! The formula is:
$$C_T = 1 \div (1/C_1 + 1/C_2 + 1/C_3.)$$ **ANSWER C.**

G5C12 **What is the capacitance of a 20 microfarad capacitor connected in series with a 50 microfarad capacitor?**

A. 0.07 microfarads.
B. 14.3 microfarads.
C. 70 microfarads.
D. 1000 microfarads.

Calculating for total capacitance of unlike capacitors in series is much like the formula for calculating unlike resistors in parallel: $(C_1 \times C_2) \div (C_1 + C_2)$. In this  equation, the total capacitance will always be less than the smaller capacitor, so *14.3 microfarads* can be confirmed as the correct answer by working through the formula. **ANSWER B.**

Capacitors on a circuit board, mounted on-end to conserve space.

G5C17 What is the value in nanofarads (nF) of a 22,000 pF capacitor?

A. 0.22 nF.
B. 2.2 nF.
C. 22 nF.
D. 220 nF.

Metric prefixes come in groups of three decimal places. Starting three places to the right of the decimal point we have: milli, micro, nano, and pico, or thousandths, millionths, billionths, and trillionths, respectively. There are 1,000 picos in a nano, so *22,000 picofarads ÷ 1000 = 22 nanofarads or 22nF*. As minuscule as a picofarad may seem, it's a very common unit in radio work! **ANSWER C.**

G5C18 What is the value in microfarads of a 4700 nanofarad (nF) capacitor?

A. 47 µF.
B. 0.47 µF.
C. 47,000 µF.
D. 4.7 µF.

Each metric prefix represents a 1,000:1 ratio of the prefix next door. We have 1,000 millis to a single unit, 1,000 micros to a milli, 1,000 nanos to a micro, and 1,000 picos to a nano. Since there is a 1,000:1 ratio between "nanos" and "micros" we can *divide 4700 nanofarads by 1,000 to come up with 4.7 microfarads (4.7 µF).* Always remember, the smaller the unit, the more of them you need, hence the larger the "answer" and vice versa. **ANSWER D.**

G5C13 Which of the following components should be added to a capacitor to increase the capacitance?

A. An inductor in series.
B. A resistor in series.
C. A capacitor in parallel.
D. A capacitor in series.

If we need to add some additional capacitance to a circuit which already has a fixed capacitor, we would add a second *capacitor in PARALLEL.* **ANSWER C.**

G5C14 Which of the following components should be added to an inductor to increase the inductance?

A. A capacitor in series.
B. A resistor in parallel.
C. An inductor in parallel.
D. An inductor in series.

If we need to increase the inductance (L) of a circuit, we would simply add another *inductor in series.* **ANSWER D.**

G5C10 What is the inductance of three 10 millihenry inductors connected in parallel?

A. 0.30 henrys.
B. 3.3 henrys.
C. 3.3 millihenrys.
D. 30 millihenrys.

Treat inductors like resistors when working either a series or parallel problem. This one you can do in your head. Three 10 millihenry inductors in parallel, total inductance will be 1/3 or *3.3 millihenrys* when connected in parallel. **ANSWER C.**

These open air coils mounted on a circuit board are held in place with some blobs of hot glue to retain their precise inductance.

G5C11 What is the inductance of a 20 millihenry inductor connected in series with a 50 millihenry inductor?
    A. 0.07 millihenrys.
    B. 14.3 millihenrys.
    C. 70 millihenrys.
    D. 1000 millihenrys.
Easy one. Just like resistors add up in series, inductors add up in series. $20 + 50 = $ **70 millihenrys. ANSWER C.**

G5A02 What is reactance?
    A. Opposition to the flow of direct current caused by resistance.
    B. Opposition to the flow of alternating current caused by capacitance or inductance.
    C. A property of ideal resistors in AC circuits.
    D. A large spark produced at switch contacts when an inductor is de-energized.
Inductive *reactance is the opposition to AC* caused by inductors. Capacitive reactance is the opposition to AC caused by capacitors. Both reactances vary with frequency. When there are an inductor and a capacitor in the same circuit, there is a special frequency, called the resonant frequency, where the inductive reactance equals the capacitive reactance. **ANSWER B.**

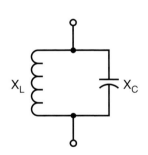

$$X_L = 2\pi fL$$

$$X_C = \frac{1}{2\pi fC}$$

The resonant frequency of a circuit is:

$$f_r = \frac{1}{2\pi \sqrt{LC}}$$

The resonant frequency is the frequency where $X_L = X_C$.

$$\therefore 2\pi fL = \frac{1}{2\pi fC}$$

$$f^2 = \frac{1}{(2\pi L)(2\pi C)}$$

$$f^2 = \frac{1}{(2\pi)^2 LC}$$

$$\therefore f_r = \frac{1}{2\pi \sqrt{LC}}$$

Resonant Frequency

G5A03 Which of the following causes opposition to the flow of alternating current in an inductor?
    A. Conductance.   C. Admittance.
    B. Reluctance.   D. Reactance.
Think of an inductor as a coil of wire. Its opposition to AC is called inductive *reactance*, which is calculated as $X_L = 2\pi fL$ where f is the frequency in hertz and L is the inductance in henries. X_L increases as frequency increases. **ANSWER D.**

G5A09 What unit is used to measure reactance?
    A. Farad.   C. Ampere.
    B. Ohm.   D. Siemens.
The *ohm* is the unit of measurement for reactance as well as resistance. **ANSWER B.**

G5A04 Which of the following causes opposition to the flow of alternating current in a capacitor?

A. Conductance.
B. Reluctance.
C. Reactance.
D. Admittance.

A capacitor has plates separated by an insulating dielectric. Its opposition to AC is called capacitive **reactance**, which is calculated as $X_c = 1 \div 2\pi fC$ where f is the frequency in hertz and C is the capacitance in farads. X_c decreases as frequency increases. **ANSWER C.**

G5A06 How does a capacitor react to AC?

A. As the frequency of the applied AC increases, the reactance decreases.
B. As the frequency of the applied AC increases, the reactance increases.
C. As the amplitude of the applied AC increases, the reactance increases.
D. As the amplitude of the applied AC increases, the reactance decreases.

Capacitors offer reactance to AC inversely proportional to the frequency. Capacitors have high reactance at low frequencies and *low reactance at high frequencies*. Remember, as f increases, X_c decreases ($X_c = 1 \div 2\pi fC$). **ANSWER A.**

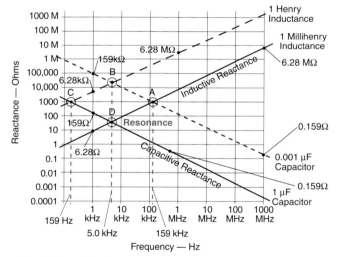

Variation of inductance and capacitive reactance with frequency (illustration not to exact log-log scale).

Source: *Basic Communications Electronics,* © 1999 Master Publishing, Inc., Niles, IL

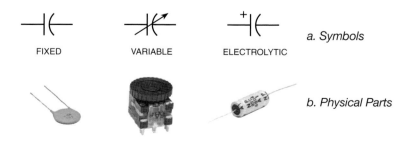

a. Symbols

FIXED VARIABLE ELECTROLYTIC

b. Physical Parts

Capacitors

G5A05 How does an inductor react to AC?

A. As the frequency of the applied AC increases, the reactance decreases.

B. As the amplitude of the applied AC increases, the reactance increases.

C. As the amplitude of the applied AC increases, the reactance decreases.

D. As the frequency of the applied AC increases, the reactance increases.

Inductors (coils) are effective in reducing alternator whine in high-frequency mobile installations. The *higher* the alternator whine *frequency*, the *greater* the *reactance* from the inductor. Remember, as f increases, X_L increases ($X_L = 2\pi fL$). **ANSWER D.**

G5A01 What is impedance?

A. The electric charge stored by a capacitor.

B. The inverse of resistance.

C. The opposition to the flow of current in an AC circuit.

D. The force of repulsion between two similar electric fields.

The term *impedance* means the *opposition to the flow of alternating current in a circuit*. Impedance to AC can be made up of resistance only, reactance only, or both resistance and reactance. You can create impedance to AC by winding a wire around a pencil to create a coil. This handy "choke" might minimize the alternator whine that may come in on your new worldwide mobile high-frequency station temporarily mounted in your vehicle. **ANSWER C.**

These coils were in place to test a mobile antenna's feed point impedance on different bands.

G5A10 What unit is used to measure impedance?

A. Volt.

B. Ohm.

C. Ampere.

D. Watt.

The *ohm* is also used for measuring impedance. Thus, the ohm may mean impedance, reactance, or resistance. **ANSWER B.**

G5A11 Which of the following describes one method of impedance matching between two AC circuits?

A. Insert an LC network between the two circuits.

B. Reduce the power output of the first circuit.

C. Increase the power output of the first circuit.

D. Insert a circulator between the two circuits.

Two AC circuits might be impedance matched by *using coils and capacitors (LC) between the two circuits*. **ANSWER A.**

G5A12 What is one reason to use an impedance matching transformer?
    A. To minimize transmitter power output.
    B. To maximize the transfer of power.
    C. To reduce power supply ripple.
    D. To minimize radiation resistance.
When impedances are matched, we have the greatest amount of power transfer. An *impedance matching transformer* allows us to precisely match radio stages for the *maximum transfer of power*. Always remember the NFL principle of transformers: No Free Lunch. While a properly matched transformer can minimize losses, you never get any more power out of it than you put into it. The product of voltage and current on the output can never be more than the product of voltage and current on the input. If you step up the voltage, the current must go down, and vice versa. **ANSWER B.**

G5A08 Why is impedance matching important?
    A. So the source can deliver maximum power to the load.
    B. So the load will draw minimum power from the source.
    C. To ensure that there is less resistance than reactance in the circuit.
    D. To ensure that the resistance and reactance in the circuit are equal.
In order to transmit maximum power from a source (such as a transmitter) to a load (such as an antenna) there must be an impedance match. This means that the internal resistance of the transmitter and the antenna resistance need to be the same, typically 50 ohms in a modern ham radio situation. However, remember that impedance is not a simple resistance, but also includes any reactance, which we can't simply ignore. The simplest solution is to operate on the antenna's resonant frequency, in which case the reactance is zero. When *source and load impedances* are *matched, maximum power* will be delivered to the load. Most new ham HF radios will automatically reduce power output when there is an impedance mismatch. **ANSWER A.**

G5A13 Which of the following devices can be used for impedance matching at radio frequencies?
    A. A transformer.   C. A length of transmission line.
    B. A Pi-network.   D. All of these choices are correct.
There are plenty of ways we can match impedances at radio frequencies. Up at the antenna, we sometimes will use fractional wavelength impedance-matching transmission lines. In a radio RF output stage, we might use an impedance-matching Pi-network. And within the radio, small transformers will allow us to impedance match. *All of these* are great ways for providing the maximum transfer of radio frequency energy. **ANSWER D.**

G5A07 What happens when the impedance of an electrical load is equal to the output impedance of a power source, assuming both impedances are resistive?
    A. The source delivers minimum power to the load.
    B. The electrical load is shorted.
    C. No current can flow through the circuit.
    D. The source can deliver maximum power to the load.
Always make sure your worldwide antenna systems have an impedance of around 50 ohms for *maximum power transfer*. Some HF ham transceivers have built-in automatic impedance-matching antenna tuner networks. **ANSWER D.**

G7C06 **What should be the impedance of a low-pass filter as compared to the impedance of the transmission line into which it is inserted?**

A. Substantially higher.
B. About the same.
C. Substantially lower.
D. Twice the transmission line impedance.

As we discussed earlier, impedances should always be the same for maximum transfer of power. Therefore, you want the low-pass filter to have the *same impedance* as both the transmission line and the ham transceiver to which it is connected. **ANSWER B.**

G6A17 **Which of the following is a reason not to use wire-wound resistors in an RF circuit?**

A. The resistor's tolerance value would not be adequate for such a circuit.
B. The resistor's inductance could make circuit performance unpredictable.
C. The resistor could overheat.
D. The resistor's internal capacitance would detune the circuit.

If you were able to scrape off the brown glaze coating on a *wire-wound resistor*, you would quickly see it looks exactly like a coil with evenly spaced turns. Actually, it IS an inductor and would not be suitable in any circuit that *could accidentally make the circuit performance unpredictable* through the use of the wrong component. Normally, we find wire-wound resistors in simple DC

applications where we need to drop a small amount of voltage with relatively high current being passed. **ANSWER B.**

Here we see the inner workings of a wire-wound resistor. Most resistors of this sort are wound with nichrome wire or other resistance wire, which has much more resistance than copper. It's the same stuff used for the heating elements in your toaster.

G6A14 **Which of the following is an advantage of ceramic capacitors as compared to other types of capacitors?**

A. Tight tolerance.
B. High stability.
C. High capacitance for given volume.
D. Comparatively low cost.

The ceramic capacitor is the workhorse in ham radio equipment. Their reliability is very good, and their *comparatively low cost* helps to keep ham radio equipment reasonably priced. **ANSWER D.**

G6A18 What is an advantage of using a ferrite core toroidal inductor?

A. Large values of inductance may be obtained.
B. The magnetic properties of the core may be optimized for a specific range of frequencies.
C. Most of the magnetic field is contained in the core.
D. All of these choices are correct.

When you pass this exam and earn General Class privileges, you may begin to operate HF. A couple of rigs actually have their batteries on the inside! With any portable transceiver, including VHF/UHF handhelds, make sure they never get dropped! Dropping radio equipment can fracture the brittle iron cores within a toroidal inductor. The ferrite core within a toroidal inductor offers large values of inductance, with most of the magnetic field contained within the core so it does not affect other nearby components. The toroidal inductor may be used in applications where core saturation is desirable, so *all of the answer choices are correct*. **ANSWER D.**

A transformer wound around a ferrite toroid core is a common component in modern radio gear. Such cores allow a lot of inductance to be provided in a small space.

G6A19 How should the winding axes of two solenoid inductors be oriented to minimize their mutual inductance?

A. In line.
B. Parallel to each other.
C. At right angles to each other.
D. Interleaved.

Solenoid inductors will interact if they are placed side by side, due to mutual inductance. To minimize this, 2 solenoid inductors should be placed at right angles to their winding axes to minimize unwanted mutual inductance. Just think of how a transformer winding FAVORS mutual inductance, but placing them *"at right angles"* will MINIMIZE the effect. **ANSWER C.**

Inductors are placed at right angles to each other to minimize mutual inductance.

G5C01 What causes a voltage to appear across the secondary winding of a transformer when an AC voltage source is connected across its primary winding?

A. Capacitive coupling.
B. Displacement current coupling.
C. Mutual inductance.
D. Mutual capacitance.

Think of a transformer with interlaced coils. Through mutual inductance within the transformer, voltage applied to the primary will also appear across the secondary. *Mutual inductance.* **ANSWER C.**

G5C16 Why is the conductor of the primary winding of many voltage step up transformers larger in diameter than the conductor of the secondary winding?

A. To improve the coupling between the primary and secondary.
B. To accommodate the higher current of the primary.
C. To prevent parasitic oscillations due to resistive losses in the primary.
D. To insure that the volume of the primary winding is equal to the volume of the secondary winding.

On any ideal transformer, the product of the primary voltage and current has to equal the product of the secondary voltage and current. This is the "no free lunch" principle of transformers. You can never get any more power out than you put in. A step up transformer will have low voltage/high current on the primary side and high voltage/low current on the secondary side. *The primary winding needs to have larger wire to handle the higher current.* **ANSWER B.**

G5C06 What is the RMS voltage across a 500-turn secondary winding in a transformer if the 2250-turn primary is connected to 120 VAC?

A. 2370 volts.
B. 540 volts.
C. 26.7 volts.
D. 5.9 volts.

This is a turns ratio problem, and is relatively easy to solve using the following equation:

$$E_S = E_P \times \frac{N_S}{N_P} = \frac{E_P \times N_S}{N_P}$$

It means the voltage of the secondary is equal to the voltage of the primary times the number of turns of the secondary divided by the number of turns of the primary. It is derived from the equation that says that the ratio of the secondary voltage, E_S, to the primary voltage, E_P, is equal to the ratio of the turns on the secondary, N_S, to the turns on the primary, N_P.

$$\frac{E_S}{E_P} = \frac{N_S}{N_P}$$

Multiply 120 (E_P) times 500 (N_S), and then divide your answer by 2250. This gives you 26.7 volts. Calculator keystrokes are: Clear, 120 × 500 ÷ 2250 = and the answer is *26.7 volts*. **ANSWER C.**

G5C02 What happens if you reverse the primary and secondary windings of a 4:1 voltage step down transformer?

A. The secondary voltage becomes 4 times the primary voltage.
B. The transformer no longer functions as it is a unidirectional device.
C. Additional resistance must be added in series with the primary to prevent overload.
D. Additional resistance must be added in parallel with the secondary to prevent overload.

A transformer consists of two or more windings of wire that are magnetically coupled. The ratio of voltages of any transformer is proportional to the turns ratio. A transformer with 10 turns on the primary side and 100 turns on the secondary side is a 10:1 step up transformer. Likewise, a transformer in this question with 400 turns on the primary side and 100 turns on the secondary side is a 4:1 step-down transformer. Whatever voltage you put across the primary winding will be divided by 4 on the secondary. Going back through the transformer the other way, *the input voltage is multiplied by 4*. Important note: While a transformer can have a tremendous amount of voltage step up, there is no free lunch! The power out of any transformer is only equal to the power going into the transformer (minus some losses). A 4:1 voltage step down transformer will have a 4:1 CURRENT step UP. The product of the input voltage and current must always equal the product of the output voltage and current. **ANSWER A.**

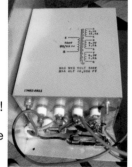

Transformer from a RADAR.

G5C07 What is the turns ratio of a transformer used to match an audio amplifier having 600 ohm output impedance to a speaker having 4 ohm impedance?

A. 12.2 to 1.
B. 24.4 to 1.
C. 150 to 1.
D. 300 to 1.

The equation that applies is:

$$\frac{N_P}{N_S} = \sqrt{\frac{Z_P}{Z_S}}$$

The ratio of the turns on the primary, N_P, to the turns on the secondary, N_S, is equal to the square root of the ratio of the primary impedance, Z_P, to the secondary impedance, Z_S. Remember that this turns ratio is primary to secondary.

Don't worry if you have forgotten about square roots. There's an easy way to solve the problem. The primary impedance, Z_P, of the transformer must match the 600-ohms output impedance of the amplifier; therefore, Z_P is 600 ohms. Divide 600 ohms by 4 ohms, the speaker load impedance on the secondary, and you end up with 150.

Now you need to find the square root of 150. You know that a square root multiplied by itself gives you the number you want. You can do it by approximation. Since 12 × 12 = 144 and 13 × 13 = 169, you know that the square root of 150 is between 12 and 13. The only answer given that is close is 12.2. Choose it and you have the correct answer. See, you didn't have to remember how to do square roots. The calculator keystrokes are: Clear, *600 ÷ 4 = 150, then press the square root key to produce the answer, 12.25.* **ANSWER A.**

Advancing the Radio Art

One of the primary reasons radio amateurs have retained valuable frequency allocations is so that we may "advance the state of the radio art." Countless advances in science and technology – not all of them directly related to communications – have come about by amateur radio experimentation.

If you're a new radio amateur, you might feel the need to be a rocket scientist to contribute anything new to the radio art. Not so! There is still a great deal to be learned about such matters as radio propagation, which can easily be investigated by anyone with an amateur radio license. All that is required is insatiable curiosity, an observant eye and ear, and systematic record keeping. Your amateur radio log book can be a valuable scientific instrument! Give honest signal reports and keep good station notes. Experiment with odd radio modes. Explore some of our unused bands. Do some homebrewing. Write some technical articles. Spend a lot of time on the air. You are quite likely to stumble across something nobody has seen or heard before!

One area where the opportunity to explore is wide open are our 12 microwave bands! For the most part, these bands are unused by radio amateurs. Granted, there may not be a lot of "ready-made" amateur gear for some of these bands, but that lack provides a great opportunity to exercise your home brewing skills. These are prime bands for experimenting. Remember, one of the reasons we exist as amateur operators is to "advance the state of the radio art," and that advancement comes through our experimentation.

If you want some more encouragement, read Eric's book *Radio Science for the Radio Amateur*. You can get a copy from The W5YI Group by calling 800-669-9594 or visit www.w5yi.org.

Good Grounds

G4C05 What might be the problem if you receive an RF burn when touching your equipment while transmitting on an HF band, assuming the equipment is connected to a ground rod?
  A. Flat braid rather than round wire has been used for the ground wire.
  B. Insulated wire has been used for the ground wire.
  C. The ground rod is resonant.
  D. The ground wire has high impedance on that frequency.

Nothing worse than petting Fido while going on the air with your new high frequency installation and seeing a blue arc from your D-104 microphone to his metal nametag, accompanied by a yelp! Welcome to RF floating along the chassis ground of your equipment. Using wire to ground HF equipment may create an antenna-like circuit that looks like an open circuit to earth ground. Round ground wires may also behave like wire coils, developing a reactance at specific frequencies, thus blocking the ground connection to that cold water pipe. This blocking action is called *impedance*. Always ground your equipment with flat braid or copper foil, using the shortest run possible to an actual earth ground. In some cases, this may not be possible. In such a situation you might try a device called an artificial ground, which makes a low impedance, series resonant circuit out of any ground wire you do have. Sometimes acquiring a good RF ground is an art form and may require patience and persistence. **ANSWER D.**

G4C07 What is one good way to avoid unwanted effects of stray RF energy in an amateur station?
  A. Connect all equipment grounds together.
  B. Install an RF filter in series with the ground wire.
  C. Use a ground loop for best conductivity.
  D. Install a few ferrite beads on the ground wire where it connects to your station.

A safe way to keep all of your equipment at the same potential is to run a strip of copper foil at the rear of your station operating desk, and then small, one inch wide copper foil tags going to each radio and accessory. These tags should

---

be long enough to allow you to pull out the equipment for servicing, and then accordion-up when you push the gear back into place. *Connecting all of your equipment grounds together* in this way (a procedure known as *bonding*) will help keep stray RF out of your station. **ANSWER A.**

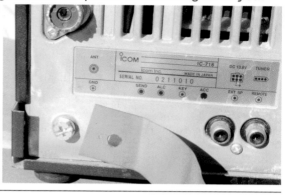

Flat copper foil attached to the rear of an HF transceiver. Never use wire for RF grounding.

G4C09 How can a ground loop be avoided?
    A. Connect all ground conductors in series.
    B. Connect the AC neutral conductor to the ground wire.
    C. Avoid using lock washers and star washers when making ground connections.
    D. Connect all ground conductors to a single point.

I have several HF transceivers at the shack, and *all* copper foil *ground connections go to a single ground point*. From that point, the flattened copper pipe goes through the wall and into the earth. Grounding to a single point will minimize ground loops. If you ever have a new fancy audio stereo system installed in your vehicle, the savvy tech will run all component grounds to a single ground point to minimize ground loops. **ANSWER D.**

G4C10 What could be a symptom of a ground loop somewhere in your station?
    A. You receive reports of "hum" on your station's transmitted signal.
    B. The SWR reading for one or more antennas is suddenly very high.
    C. An item of station equipment starts to draw excessive amounts of current.
    D. You receive reports of harmonic interference from your station.

You are on the air for the first time and everyone reports you sound loud and sort of clear, but with a *hum behind your signal*. Sounds like a ground loop to me. This can be cured with good copper foil grounding interconnected to each and every piece of metal equipment you have on your desk. This includes that big computer, too. **ANSWER A.**

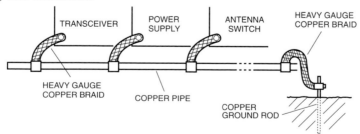

Grounding Equipment

G4C06 What effect can be caused by a resonant ground connection?
   A. Overheating of ground straps.
   B. Corrosion of the ground rod.
   C. High RF voltages on the enclosures of station equipment.
   D. A ground loop.

If you notice a tingle when you touch anything metal on your equipment during transmit, it is a sign that a *resonant ground connection* is *causing high voltages* to back up *onto the case of the radio*. Time to switch over to some 3-inch wide copper foil. That's what Gordo and Eric use at their stations.
ANSWER C.

Copper foil ground strap
provides a good surface
area ground.

GROUND FOIL FACTS:
To receive a sample of 3″ wide 3 mil copper foil used for grounding, enclose $5.00 in stamps or currency, and mail your request to:
   Metal-Cable Corp.
   PO Box 117
   Twinsburg, OH 44087
Foil in 25' and 50' sections are available at ham radio stores. Longer rolls of foil for extended ground runs are available direct from Metal-Cable Corporation.

G4A15 Which of the following can be a symptom of transmitted RF being picked up by an audio cable carrying AFSK data signals between a computer and a transceiver?
   A. The VOX circuit does not un-key the transmitter.
   B. The transmitter signal is distorted.
   C. Frequent connection timeouts.
   D. All of these choices are correct.

Not only can radio frequency interference potentially cause problems with your neighbors' electronics, but sometimes you can cause interference to yourself. This interferrence can manifest itself in a number of unexpected and "interesting" ways! "RF in the shack" is the general term used to describe a whole catalog of undesired symptoms. But they can usually be resolved with some logic and persistence. The two main ingredients of harmful RF are an antenna of some sort and a rectifier "detector" of some sort. These components may not be obvious. Any conductor, such as a microphone cable, computer data cable, or your transmission line (if it's not properly decoupled from your transmitting antenna), can be an antenna. A detector can be anything from a microphone preamplifier to a cold solder connection. When RF in a conductor encounters a detector, a DC or audio voltage is created, which looks just like "real" audio to your transmitter. This *audio can keep your VOX keyed, create distortion, or do "a number" on digital signals*. A few ferrite beads slipped over suspect cables can do wonders to tame RF in the shack. Sometimes just rearranging cables can fix things, too.
ANSWER D.

G4C01 Which of the following might be useful in reducing RF interference to audio frequency devices?
A. Bypass inductor.
B. Bypass capacitor.
C. Forward-biased diode.
D. Reverse-biased diode.

When you begin operating on General Class frequencies, your powerful, high-frequency SSB transceiver fed into a roof-top antenna system will probably create audio-frequency interference to your own home electronics and those of your neighbors. Bypass capacitors – usually 0.01 µf – will sometimes help minimize this problem when strategically placed across and onto speaker wires and wiring harnesses inside the affected home electronic systems. It's not a cure-all, but *bypass capacitors* are your first step in resolving interference complaints on a case-by-case basis. **ANSWER B.**

G4C08 Which of the following would reduce RF interference caused by common-mode current on an audio cable?
A. Placing a ferrite choke around the cable.
B. Adding series capacitors to the conductors.
C. Adding shunt inductors to the conductors.
D. Adding an additional insulating jacket to the cable.

You can get some terrific audio DSP speakers to add on to older equipment that does not have audio DSP capability. If the speakers are amplified, sometimes RF

transmit sounds come out over the speaker itself. You can minimize this common-mode current on the audio cable by *placing ferrite beads around the cable*. Use ferrite beads around all the computer and data cables, too. **ANSWER A.**

Snap-on ferrite choke.

G4C03 What sound is heard from an audio device or telephone if there is interference from a nearby single sideband phone transmitter?
A. A steady hum whenever the transmitter is on the air.
B. On-and-off humming or clicking.
C. Distorted speech.
D. Clearly audible speech.

Single-sideband sounds like distorted speech coming over a public address system or certain home electronics. However, double sideband AM CB radio transmissions usually come through loud and clear, so these are easily distinguished from SSB ham transmissions. If someone says you are causing interference, ask the big question: "Does it sound clear, or does it sound garbled?" **ANSWER C.**

G4C04 What is the effect on an audio device or telephone system if there is interference from a nearby CW transmitter?
A. On-and-off humming or clicking.
B. A CW signal at a nearly pure audio frequency.
C. A chirpy CW signal.
D. Severely distorted audio.
CW transmissions come over a PA or home electronics system as *on-and-off humming or clicking sounds*. There is no mistaking the sound of CW.
ANSWER A.

G4C02 Which of the following could be a cause of interference covering a wide range of frequencies?
A. Not using a balun or line isolator to feed balanced antennas.
B. Lack of rectification of the transmitter's signal in power conductors.
C. Arcing at a poor electrical connection.
D. Using a balun to feed an unbalanced antenna.
About once every 6 months I go around and tighten up all connections on my ham equipment. Most important is the tightening-up of the copper ground foil connections to the back of my rig. An *intermittent RF ground* will sometimes create *broadband radio frequency noise* that will magically go away as soon as you give that nut a little clockwise crank. **ANSWER C.**

G4E07 Which of the following may cause interference to be heard in the receiver of an HF radio installed in a recent model vehicle?
A. The battery charging system.
B. The fuel delivery system.
C. The vehicle control computer.
D. All of these choices are correct.
The noise blankers on most HF mobile transceivers do a nice job of getting rid of sparkplug pops. But right where you want to operate on the "Gordo net" frequency at 7250 kHz you hear a steady, raspy carrier that only goes away when you shut off the ignition. Guess what? This steady carrier may be from your vehicle's computer system. The whistle sound that changes pitch when you rev up the engine could be from your alternator. And ticking sounds all over the band could be from your vehicle's electric fuel pump. *All of these choices* are possible sources of vehicle noise that may creep in to your mobile HF radio setup. Some can be cured with in-line DC filters, but suspect all of these as noise sources that disappear when you turn off the ignition on newer vehicles. **ANSWER D.**

G9B10 What is the approximate length for a 1/2 wave dipole antenna cut for 14.250 MHz?
    A. 8 feet.
    B. 16 feet.
    C. 24 feet.
    D. 32 feet.

To calculate the length, in feet, of a half-wavelength dipole antenna, divide 468 by the antenna's operating frequency in MHz. Just remember: "2-**4-6-8**, who do we appreciate?" if you want your results in **feet**. This calculation is easy with the calculator you brought to the exam session. Divide 468 by the frequency in MHz, 14.250 to get 32.842 feet, rounded to *32 feet*. **ANSWER D.**

G9B11 What is the approximate length for a 1/2 wave dipole antenna cut for 3.550 MHz?
    A. 42 feet.
    B. 84 feet.
    C. 131 feet.
    D. 263 feet.

Let's do the math: 468 ÷ 3.55 = 131.8 feet! Rounded to *131 feet*. Easy, huh?
ANSWER C.

Elmer Point:

In case you're wondering where this 468 comes from, let's look at the speed of light in feet per second. The speed of light in free space is 186,292 miles per second. If we multiply that by 5280 feet per statute mile, we get 984,000,000 feet per second (rounded to three significant digits). If we divide that by 1 million, we get feet per *microsecond*, or 984. Okay, now what frequency radio wave has a *period* of 1 microsecond. Period is the reciprocal of frequency. The answer is 1 MHz. 984 is the wavelength in space, in feet, of a 1 MHz signal. But we know that a dipole is only ½ wavelength. So a dipole for 1 MHz is going to be 984/2 feet, or 492 feet. Well, 492 is *sort of* 468, but not quite. There's about a 5% error. What gives? As it turns out, radio waves don't quite travel in a wire at the speed of light in free space. There are a number of contributing effects, but they're all lumped into this mysterious entity called "end effect," which is really just a mathematical construct that gives you a bonus of 5% increase in effective length for a wire. The end effect is greater for fat conductors, such as tubing used for Yagi antennas and the like.

Now for those of you who have been "metricated" we can apply the same calculations, except using the speed of light in meters per second, which comes out to be almost exactly 300,000,000. Or 300 meters per *microsecond*. Again, this gives you the free space full wavelength of a 1 MHz signal. To find the actual length of a dipole, you want to divide this by a little over 2.

The half-wavelength dipole antenna offers no compromise when transmitting and receiving long-range signals. A half-wave dipole usually will outperform multi-band medium length verticals and excel above a fancy $800 mobile, big-coil whip. Dipoles are simple to construct and you can pull up the center section with a rope to configure it as an inverted vee. The only thing that beats a dipole is a big 3-element beam or a quad.

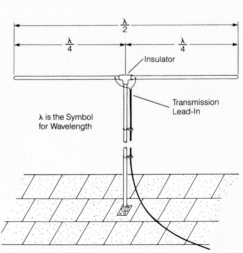

G9B09 Which of the following is an advantage of a horizontally polarized as compared to a vertically polarized HF antenna?
A. Lower ground reflection losses.   C. Shorter Radials.
B. Lower feed point impedance.   D. Lower radiation resistance.

The well-constructed and properly-elevated 1/2 wave dipole that is horizontally polarized will generally outperform a ground mounted vertical antenna. This is because the ground mounted vertical antenna usually encounters *ground reflection losses* from everything close to its base. **ANSWER A.**

G3C11 **Which of the following antenna types will be most effective for skip communications on 40-meters during the day?**
A. A vertical antenna.
B. A horizontal dipole placed between 1/8 and 1/4 wavelength above the ground.
C. A left-hand circularly polarized antenna.
D. A right-hand circularly polarized antenna.

A simple *dipole antenna, placed between 1/8 and 1/4 wavelength* above the ground, will give you powerful daytime skywave communications on the 40 meter band. To reach out further, elevate it. To "pull in" your first hop, lower it slightly!
ANSWER B.

G9B07 **How does the feed point impedance of a 1/2 wave dipole antenna change as the antenna is lowered below 1/4 wave above ground?**
A. It steadily increases.
B. It steadily decreases.
C. It peaks at about 1/8 wavelength above ground.
D. It is unaffected by the height above ground.

The 1/2 wave dipole is an outstanding antenna system that will cost you little to build. This antenna elevated to roof level will generally outperform expensive, high-frequency mobile whips, expensive trap vertical antennas, and pricey automatic-tuner-fed long wires. But get the 1/2 wave dipole up high. If it is less than 1/4 wavelength above ground, the *feed point impedance will dramatically decrease*, and your radiation pattern goes whacko, not to mention that you now have a source to load impedance mismatch that will affect your output power.
ANSWER B.

Have antenna will travel! Here is a portable half-wave dipole system that gives good results on shorter wavelengths. The plot to the right shows a typical dipole radiation pattern.

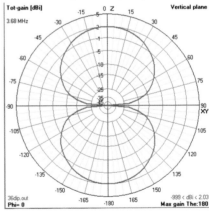

G9B08 **How does the feed point impedance of a 1/2 wave dipole change as the feed point is moved from the center toward the ends?**
A. It steadily increases.
B. It steadily decreases.
C. It peaks at about 1/8 wavelength from the end.
D. It is unaffected by the location of the feed point.

If you try to offset the feed point of a 1/2 wave dipole from the center toward the ends, *feed point impedance will rise* well above 50 ohms and your rig's automatic antenna tuner may have a hard time correcting to an SWR of 1:1.
ANSWER A.

G9B04 What is the radiation pattern of a dipole antenna in free space in the plane of the conductor?

A. It is a figure-eight at right angles to the antenna.
B. It is a figure-eight off both ends of the antenna.
C. It is a circle (equal radiation in all directions).
D. It has a pair of lobes on one side of the antenna and a single lobe on the other side.

The dipole gives you a *figure eight pattern at right angles to the antenna* wire. Reception and transmission are minimal off the ends of the wire. **ANSWER A.**

G9B05 How does antenna height affect the horizontal (azimuthal) radiation pattern of a horizontal dipole HF antenna?

A. If the antenna is too high, the pattern becomes unpredictable.
B. Antenna height has no effect on the pattern.
C. If the antenna is less than 1/2 wavelength high, the azimuthal pattern is almost omnidirectional.
D. If the antenna is less than 1/2 wavelength high, radiation off the ends of the wire is eliminated.

Never mount a dipole antenna less than 1/2 wavelength above the ground for long-range DX. Any lower and you may have signal distortion, an *omnidirectional radiation pattern*, and most of your signal going straight up. **ANSWER C.**

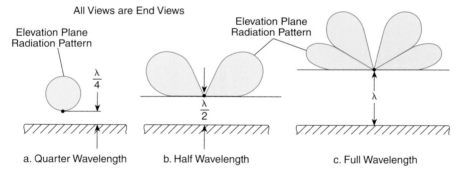

The radiation pattern of an antenna changes as height above ground is varied.
Source: *Antennas*, A.J. Evans, K.E. Britain, © 1998, Master Publishing, Niles, Illinois

G3C13 What is Near Vertical Incidence Sky-wave (NVIS) propagation?

A. Propagation near the MUF.
B. Short distance MF or HF propagation using high elevation angles.
C. Long path HF propagation at sunrise and sunset.
D. Double hop propagation near the LUF.

Let's imagine you go out on a camping trip into a valley 200 miles away from your buddy's house. With a normal dipole up about 1/2 wave length, your 40 meter signal literally skips over his location. A neat way to "pull in" your first skywave hop is to lower your dipole so it is just high enough that no one can touch it. You will find that your first skywave hop now arrives at your friend's house loud and clear. Dramatically *lowering an antenna* will develop a higher elevation angle of radiation, causing your skip distance to "pull in," which establishes *shorter-than-normal skywave communications*. **ANSWER B.**

G9D01 What does the term NVIS mean as related to antennas?
A. Nearly Vertical Inductance System.
B. Non-Varying Indicated SWR.
C. Non-Varying Impedance Smoothing.
D. Near Vertical Incidence Skywave.

The dipole antenna is fun to play with when strung between two trees using two pulleys. String it way up high and your angle of radiation lowers, yielding a longer distance skip. However, if you want to talk with your Granddad who is about 300 miles away, try lowering the dipole real close to the ground and notice that the distant skywave skip will fade out and good old Granddad's signal just a few hundred miles away now comes in stronger. This is because your *skywave is nearly vertical*. **ANSWER D.**

G9D03 At what height above ground is an NVIS antenna typically installed?
A. As close to 1/2 wavelength as possible.
B. As close to one wavelength as possible.
C. Height is not critical as long as it is significantly more than 1/2 wavelength.
D. Between 1/10 and 1/4 wavelength.

To get your dipole to operate like an NVIS antenna, start near ground level and work up from *1/10 to 1/4 wavelength*. Listen with each change in height as closer stations get dramatically stronger. **ANSWER D.**

G9D02 Which of the following is an advantage of an NVIS antenna?
A. Low vertical angle radiation for working stations out to ranges of several thousand kilometers.
B. High vertical angle radiation for working stations within a radius of a few hundred kilometers.
C. High forward gain.
D. All of these choices are correct.

The military and emergency communicators will use NVIS dipoles mounted just a few feet above the ground. This configuration causes the *signals* to take off in an almost *vertical direction* into the ionosphere. The signal comes back down *much closer* than with a regular dipole up 1/2 wavelength. This is great for short skip during the day. **ANSWER B.**

G9B03 What happens to the feed point impedance of a ground plane antenna when its radials are changed from horizontal to sloping downward?
A. It decreases.
B. It increases.
C. It stays the same.
D. It reaches a maximum at an angle of 45 degrees.

The feed point *impedance increases* from 25 ohms to 50 ohms *when you bend the radials downward*. Remember, most General Class transceivers are designed for a 50 ohm impedance match. **ANSWER B.**

The white fiberglass ground plane antenna is mounted at the very top of this mast. Notice the ground radials are slightly sloping down to achieve 50 ohms impedance.

G9B12 What is the approximate length for a 1/4 wave vertical antenna cut for 28.5 MHz?
    A. 8 feet.
    B. 11 feet.
    C. 16 feet.
    D. 21 feet.

Let's say you want to operate 10 meters mobile. When you operate mobile, the metal frame of the vehicle makes up 1/4 wavelength of your antenna system, and the other 1/4 wavelength is the vertical radiating antenna. Think of your vertical whip as one side of a dipole and the vehicle chassis as the other. To calculate the length, in **feet**, of a 1/4 -wavelength vertical antenna, first find the length of a 1/2 wavelength in feet then take half of that. To find 1/2 wavelength, divide 468 by the antenna's operating frequency in MHz. Just remember: "2-**4-6-8**, who do we appreciate?" if you want your results in **feet**. This calculation is easy with the calculator you brought to the exam session. Divide 468 by the frequency in MHz, 28.5 to get 16.42 feet. Then 16.42 ÷ 2 = 8.2 *rounded to 8 feet*. **ANSWER A.**

G9B06 Where should the radial wires of a ground-mounted vertical antenna system be placed?
    A. As high as possible above the ground.
    B. Parallel to the antenna element.
    C. On the surface of the Earth or buried a few inches below the ground.
    D. At the center of the antenna.

Ground radial wires are important for the ground-mounted vertical antenna to establish its own counterpoise. To hear any real difference when you already have a few radials laid out per band, you must double the number of radials. If you have 2 per band, try 4. If you have 4, try 8. If you need more ground plane than 8 radials per band, try mounting your antenna on the aluminum shed in the backyard and use the roof of the shed as a substitute for the radials! The more ground radials you have on a ground plane antenna, the lower the takeoff angle of radiation, which means more DX. Get out the shovel, and *start digging to install more ground radials*! **ANSWER C.**

G2D11 Which HF antenna would be the best to use for minimizing interference?
    A. A quarter-wave vertical antenna.
    B. An isotropic antenna.
    C. A directional antenna.
    D. An omnidirectional antenna.

An antenna with appreciable gain in one direction (a "beam" antenna) always has an equivalent null or nulls in some other direction(s). All beam antennas, such as Yagis, function by redistributing the power that's applied. As in every other situation we've encountered, NFL (No Free Lunch) applies. An antenna can only increase signal strength in one direction at the expense of a decrease somewhere else, which is not necessarily a bad thing. Deep nulls off the back or sides of a *directional antenna can greatly minimize interference*. **ANSWER C.**

G9C03 Which statement about a three-element, single-band Yagi antenna is true?
    A. The reflector is normally the shortest element.
    B. The director is normally the shortest element.
    C. The driven element is the longest element.
    D. Low feed point impedance increases bandwidth.
On a three-element beam, the *director is shorter* than the driven element, and the reflector is longer than the driven element. **ANSWER B.**

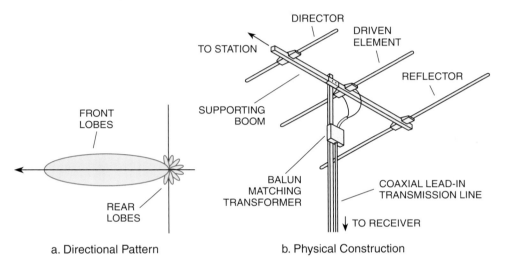

a. Directional Pattern   b. Physical Construction

A 3 element beam antenna – the Yagi antenna

Source: *Antennas - Selection and Installation,*©`1986 Master Publishing, Inc., Niles, IL

G9C02 What is the approximate length of the driven element of a Yagi antenna?
    A. 1/4 wavelength.
    B. 1/2 wavelength.
    C. 3/4 wavelength.
    D. 1 wavelength.
Since the Yagi antenna is a series of dipoles affixed to a boom in the same plane, the *driven element is about 1/2 wavelength long*. The reflector is a little longer. The directors a little bit shorter. **ANSWER B.**

G9C04 Which statement about a three-element, single-band Yagi antenna is true?
    A. The reflector is normally the longest element.
    B. The director is normally the longest element.
    C. The reflector is normally the shortest element.
    D. All of the elements must be the same length.
You can always figure out which way to point a 3 element Yagi by seeing which elements on the boom are the shortest. The *reflector is* normally the *longest* parasitic element. The directors are usually 5% shorter than the driven element. The shortest elements of the Yagi always point in the general direction of the distant station. Most worldwide Yagis are horizontally polarized, too. **ANSWER A.**

G9C05 How does increasing boom length and adding directors affect a Yagi antenna?
A. Gain increases.
B. Beamwidth increases.
C. Front to back ratio decreases.
D. Front to side ratio decreases.

On a Yagi antenna, *boom length* determines the amount of *gain*. The number of elements and the diameter of the elements influence the directivity and bandwidth of the antenna. **ANSWER A.**

G9C08 What is meant by the "main lobe" of a directive antenna?
A. The magnitude of the maximum vertical angle of radiation.
B. The point of maximum current in a radiating antenna element.
C. The maximum voltage standing wave point on a radiating element.
D. The direction of maximum radiated field strength from the antenna.

The *main lobe* is the *main radiating direction* of the signal. Use a field strength meter to determine the main lobe of most directional antennas. Incidentally, many

beam antennas such as broadside arrays, curtain arrays, unterminated rhombics, Vee beams, and even quad loops are bidirectional, with two equal-gain lobes 180 degrees apart. **ANSWER D.**

It's hard to beat the beach for great antenna performance – even more so if you have a respectable antenna to start with, such as this three element Yagi at a reasonable height. Famed DXer Chip, K7JA, regularly works the world on 10 meters using his homebrew 3 element beam down at the beach!

G9C07 What does "front-to-back ratio" mean in reference to a Yagi antenna?
A. The number of directors versus the number of reflectors.
B. The relative position of the driven element with respect to the reflectors and directors.
C. The power radiated in the major radiation lobe compared to the power radiated in exactly the opposite direction.
D. The ratio of forward gain to dipole gain.

The Yagi antenna gives you an excellent front-to-back ratio. This means that the *majority of the power is radiated out of the front* of the antenna with *little signal wasted to the back* or sides. **ANSWER C.**

G9C10 Which of the following is a Yagi antenna design variable that could be adjusted to optimize forward gain, front-to-back ratio, or SWR bandwidth?

A. The physical length of the boom.
B. The number of elements on the boom.
C. The spacing of each element along the boom.
D. All of these choices are correct.

Any time you begin lengthening the boom, adding or subtracting elements along the boom, or spacing the elements differently on a Yagi antenna, you will affect gain, front to back ratios, and SWR bandwidth. So, *all of the choices are correct.* **ANSWER D.**

The larger your antennas and the higher they are mounted on your tower, the better your range to distant DX stations!

G9C01 Which of the following would increase the bandwidth of a Yagi antenna?

A. Larger diameter elements.
B. Closer element spacing.
C. Loading coils in series with the element.
D. Tapered-diameter elements.

The *greater the diameter of the elements*, the *greater the bandwidth*. This is why a wire beam antenna does not offer as much bandwidth as one constructed of large aluminum tubes. **ANSWER A.**

G9C11 What is the purpose of a gamma match used with Yagi antennas?

A. To match the relatively low feed point impedance to 50 ohms.
B. To match the relatively high feed point impedance to 50 ohms.
C. To increase the front-to-back ratio.
D. To increase the main lobe gain.

If you decide to construct your own 3 element beam, chances are you will need to develop a feed point connection that will take the relatively *low feed point impedance up to 50 ohms to match the impedance of your coax*. The gamma match is a line matching system that lets you tap the driven element at a preferred 50 ohm feed point. The gamma match may look like a short circuit to an ohm meter – but to your radio signal it will look like a perfect match! **ANSWER A.**

Eric's unusual homebrew VHF "Q-Pole" antenna uses the principle of the gamma match for precise impedance matching.

G9C12 Which of the following is an advantage of using a gamma match for impedance matching of a Yagi antenna to 50 ohm coax feed line?
A. It does not require that the elements be insulated from the boom.
B. It does not require any inductors or capacitors.
C. It is useful for matching multiband antennas.
D. All of these choices are correct.

High frequency Yagi antennas may achieve a more predictable radiation pattern by insulating all elements from the boom. Big improvements in those element insulators keep them from cracking when a giant crow lands on one of them. Some high frequency antennas *couple the elements directly to the boom through stainless steel hardware and alignment brackets*. This simplifies the matching network to the popular gamma match. With the gamma match in place, you can hook up the Yagi antenna directly to a 50-ohm coax feed. While the pattern may not be quite as predictable, the gamma match metal-to-boom high frequency antenna is a solid performer. **ANSWER A.**

G9D05 What is an advantage of vertical stacking of horizontally polarized Yagi antennas?
A. It allows quick selection of vertical or horizontal polarization.
B. It allows simultaneous vertical and horizontal polarization.
C. It narrows the main lobe in azimuth.
D. It narrows the main lobe in elevation.

Vertically stacking horizontal Yagis helps *concentrate the main lobe in elevation* for added signal strength to the desired station. **ANSWER D.**

A pair of long-boom beam antennas on Gordo's tower add 3dB over a single antenna of the same type.

G9C09 How does the gain of two 3-element horizontally polarized Yagi antennas spaced vertically 1/2 wavelength apart typically compare to the gain of a single 3-element Yagi?
A. Approximately 1.5 dB higher.   C. Approximately 6 dB higher.
B. Approximately 3 dB higher.   D. Approximately 9 dB higher.

You don't need a linear amplifier to boost your effective radiated power output or increase reception. You could stack a pair of Yagis about 1/2 wavelength apart and double your transmit and receive gain. Remember, 2 times the gain is *3 dB*. **ANSWER B.**

G9D04 What is the primary purpose of antenna traps?
    A. To permit multiband operation.
    B. To notch spurious frequencies.
    C. To provide balanced feed point impedance.
    D. To prevent out of band operation.
A great way to get started on 40, 20, 15, and 10 meters is with a trap dipole, a trap beam antenna, or a trap vertical antenna. The traps allow the antenna to naturally tune to specific ham bands. Gordo operates a 4-element, 4-band beam antenna. The *traps* work great to give him high frequency operation on *multiple ham bands with only one antenna*.
ANSWER A.

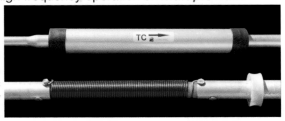

The inner workings of a typical multiband Yagi trap consist of a parallel coil and capacitor. In this case, the capacitor is formed by concentric aluminum tubing.

G9D11 Which of the following is a disadvantage of multiband antennas?
    A. They present low impedance on all design frequencies.
    B. They must be used with an antenna tuner.
    C. They must be fed with open wire line.
    D. They have poor harmonic rejection.
Newer high frequency radios have internal band pass filters to minimize harmonics. A harmonic is a multiple of your fundamental frequency that causes problems when you realize you are transmitting on two frequencies at once. If you are transmitting on 7 MHz, you want to minimize any harmonic on 14 MHz that would interfere with nearby hams on that frequency. Unfortunately, while *multiband antennas* have many advantages, they have the disadvantage of *poor harmonic rejection*. **ANSWER D.**

G9B01 What is one disadvantage of a directly fed random-wire HF antenna?
    A. It must be longer than 1 wavelength.
    B. You may experience RF burns when touching metal objects in your station.
    C. It produces only vertically polarized radiation.
    D. It is more effective on the lower HF bands than on the higher bands.
Unless you use a remote-mounted automatic antenna tuner, the random-wire antenna can put a lot of *RF feedback* in your station. **ANSWER B.**

G4A06 What type of device is often used to match transmitter output impedance to an impedance not equal to 50 ohms?
    A. Balanced modulator.   C. Antenna coupler or antenna tuner.
    B. SWR Bridge.   D. Q Multiplier.
Most antenna tuners built into today's HF transceivers have a limited tuning and matching range and are incapable of efficiently handling gross mismatches. On the other hand, a large, high-quality external antenna tuner can handle "just about anything you can throw at it." Many hams like the versatility of using open wire feed lines with an external *antenna coupler or tuner* that can handle just about any kind of mismatch with negligible loss. If you anticipate using open wire feed line, a good external tuner is a must. Your transmitter will never "see" what's on the other side of the tuner. It will just see a *50 ohm load*. **ANSWER C.**

Don't Dread the Decibel!

As hard as it may be to believe, a lot of the mathematical concepts we use in electronics and Amateur Radio were developed to make life EASIER, not to serve as some medieval torture device! One of these concepts is the decibel.

In radio we work with both extremely large and extremely small values. For example, a very weak UHF signal may be only a few femtowatts at the input of a receiver. A femtowatt is 0.000000000000001 watts. That's a whole lot of zeros to keep track of, especially if you're doing calculations that involve very large numbers, too. The decibel is a tool that shrinks the difference between those huge and minuscule numbers to a manageable size. When we work with decibels we're comparing two values. From a practical standpoint, we want to know if what we're doing is making something worse or better, and by how much.

If we want to know how much smaller a femtowatt is than a watt, without a truckload of zeros, we can use the decibel formula: $dB = 10 \log(P1/P2)$. P1 is 0.000000000000001 watts. P2 is 1 watt. So let's first divide P1 by P2, which gives us 0.000000000000001. Notice at this point there are no UNITS, since this is a ratio. Taking the logarithm of 0.000000000000001 gives us -15. Finally, we multiply that by 10, to give us -150 (decibels). -150dB is certainly a lot easier to manage than 0.000000000000001, isn't it? The minus sign simply tells us that the value is smaller. A femtowatt is 150 decibels smaller than a watt.

One final thing remains to tie things up. -150 dB needs to be associated with a unit to give it relevance. In this example, Watt is the unit. We put W with the dB figure to tell the whole story. So, a femtowatt is -150 dbW. Similarly, dbm, which uses the milliwatt as the basic unit, is a common unit in radio work.

Another way the decibel (dB) simplifies life is when we have a complex system with several GAINS and LOSSES. A good example of this is a radio circuit with a 10 dB antenna at each end and a 60 dB path loss in between. If each of these values is expressed in decibels, the calculations become a simple matter of addition and subtraction. We add the gains and subtract the losses to find the total SYSTEM gain (or loss). In this example, $+10 +10 -60 = -40db$, a total system loss since the result is negative. From the chart below you see that the signal power at the end of the system is 1/10,000 of the power it started out with. Looks like it's time to work on the system or get a really big amplifier! Nothing to it!

DB	P1/P2	DB	P1/P2
1	1.3	-1	0.794
2	1.6	-2	0.631
3	2	-3	0.5
6	4	-6	0.390
10	10	-10	0.1
20	100	-20	0.01
30	1,000	-30	0.001
40	10,000	-40	0.0001
50	100,000	-50	0.00001
60	1,000,000	-60	0.000001

The decibel was invented to make life easier. This calculator makes it doubly easy to work with decibels, whether you're working with power or voltage.
https://itunes.apple.com/us/app/dbcalculator/id489100786?mt=8

G9C20 What is meant by the terms dBi and dBd when referring to antenna gain?

A. dBi refers to an isotropic antenna, dBd refers to a dipole antenna.
B. dBi refers to an ionospheric reflecting antenna, dBd refers to a dissipative antenna.
C. dBi refers to an inverted-vee antenna, dBd refers to a downward reflecting antenna.
D. dBi refers to an isometric antenna, dBd refers to a discone antenna.

The decibel is a unit of comparison, which is somewhat meaningless unless you have a reference point to compare it with. In the antenna business we have two common references, the isotropic radiator and the dipole antenna. The isotropic antenna doesn't exist in real life, but if it did its gain would be 0 *dBi (decibels referenced to an isotropic radiator)*. The dipole antenna has a gain of 2.15 dBi over the isotropic radiator, and it has a gain of 0 *dBd (decibels referred to a dipole)*. It doesn't matter which reference you use, as long as you know what that reference is. If an antenna is specified by its gain in dBi, that figure will be 2.15 dB greater than if it's specified in dBd. **ANSWER A.**

G9C19 How does antenna gain stated in dBi compare to gain stated in dBd for the same antenna?

A. dBi gain figures are 2.15 dB lower then dBd gain figures.
B. dBi gain figures are 2.15 dB higher than dBd gain figures.
C. dBi gain figures are the same as the square root of dBd gain figures multiplied by 2.15.
D. dBi gain figures are the reciprocal of dBd gain figures + 2.15 dB.

Remember the decibel is a figure of comparison, so unless we know what we're comparing it is a meaningless figure. In antenna work, there are actually two commonly used decibel references, one is the *isotropic radiator (dBi)*, and the other is the *dipole antenna (dBd)*. A *dipole already has a gain of 2.15 dB over an isotropic radiator* (about twice the power). So, let's say a manufacturer sells you an antenna with a gain of 4 dBd. To know what its gain is in dBi simply add the 2.15 dB gain that the dipole already has. An antenna with 4dBd will have a gain of 6.15 dBi. Note: you will never see an actual isotropic radiator; it is a theoretical reference point that is commonly used in antenna work. **ANSWER B.**

G9C13 Approximately how long is each side of the driven element of a quad antenna?

A. 1/4 wavelength.   C. 3/4 wavelength.
B. 1/2 wavelength.   D. 1 wavelength.

The cubical-quad antenna is a four-sided wire antenna system that incorporates a full-wavelength for the band. Its performance is identical to or slightly better than a Yagi. *Each side of the cubicle quad is 1/4 wavelength*. Use the following formula to determine the length of wire needed for each side of the driven element of a quad antenna.

$$\text{Each side of the driven element (in feet)} = \frac{1005}{f\ (MHz)} \div 4$$

The math is easy to do on that calculator you bring to the exam session. **ANSWER A.**

Quad antenna.

G9C14 How does the forward gain of a two-element quad antenna compare to the forward gain of a three-element Yagi antenna?

A. About 2/3 as much.
B. About the same.
C. About 1.5 times as much.
D. About twice as much.

The 2 element cubicle quad antenna is constructed of wire and fiberglass spreaders while a 3 element Yagi antenna is constructed of aluminum tubing. The cubicle quad is much more fragile and subject to damage from wind, ice, or snow. If you live in the northeast where severe icing might quickly destroy the 2 element cubicle quad, or if you are planning to leave this antenna in place for an extended time, it's best to consider a 3 element Yagi over the 2 element cubicle quad. *The gain is about the same*. **ANSWER B.**

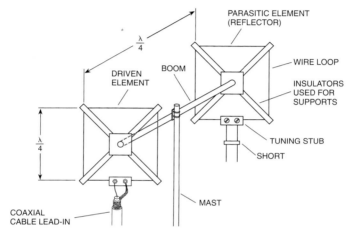

A two-element cubical quad antenna - horizontally polarized
Source: *Antennas—Selection and Installation*, © 1986 Master Publishing, Inc., Niles, IL

G9C06 What configuration of the loops of a two-element quad antenna must be used for the antenna to operate as a beam antenna, assuming one of the elements is used as a reflector?

A. The driven element must be fed with a balun transformer.
B. There must be an open circuit in the driven element at the point opposite the feed point.
C. The reflector element must be approximately 5 percent shorter than the driven element.
D. The reflector element must be approximately 5 percent longer than the driven element.

Remember, *reflectors are generally 5% longer* than the driven element, and director elements are 5% shorter. You want to catch all of the reflection (ergo bigger reflector) and concentrate it as you point it so it goes farther (ergo smaller director). **ANSWER D.**

G9C15 Approximately how long is each side of the reflector element of a quad antenna?

A. Slightly less than 1/4 wavelength.
B. Slightly more than 1/4 wavelength.
C. Slightly less than 1/2 wavelength.
D. Slightly more than 1/2 wavelength.

Since the quad antenna is a full wave loop, each side of any of the elements is about 1/4 wavelength. The *reflector element is always slightly longer* than the driven and director elements of the quad antenna. This same principle holds true for any type of parasitic array, such as a Yagi. The reflector, being slightly longer, is slightly below resonance and thus re-radiates a phase shifted signal which reinforces the signal from the driven element at a distance (constructive interference). This same phase shift causes destructive interference toward the rear of the antenna causing more of your signal to radiate in the direction of your DX contact **ANSWER B.**

G9C18 What happens when the feed point of a quad antenna of any shape is moved from the midpoint of the top or bottom to the midpoint of either side?
    A. The polarization of the radiated signal changes from horizontal to vertical.
    B. The polarization of the radiated signal changes from vertical to horizontal.
    C. There is no change in polarization.
    D. The radiated signal becomes circularly polarized.
What a work of art – you built your own cubicle quad antenna for the band of your choice. If you feed coax cable to the center of the horizontal side, the signal will be horizontally polarized. If you decide to feed the quad in the center of the *vertical side*, guess what? The signal will leave the antenna *vertically polarized*. Will all this work of changing from the horizontal to the vertical make any big difference via skywaves? Probably not. **ANSWER A.**

G9C17 Approximately how long is each leg of a symmetrical delta-loop antenna?
    A. 1/4 wavelength.   C. 1/2 wavelength.
    B. 1/3 wavelength.   D. 2/3 wavelength.
The delta-loop is another version of a full-wavelength antenna system. The beauty of the delta-loop is you can put the apex of the loop way up at the top of a tree. *Each side* of the symmetrical delta-loop antenna is *1/3 wavelength long*. Use the formula:

$$\text{Each side of the driven element (in feet)} = \frac{1005}{f \text{ (MHz)}} \div 3$$

Just as you did for the quad, divide 1005 by the frequency in MHz. Then divide by 3 since the delta loop is a triangle with 3 sides. **ANSWER B.**

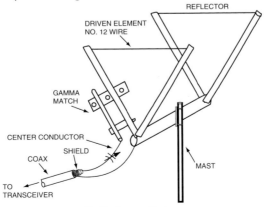

Delta Loop Antenna

G9C16 How does the gain of a two-element delta-loop beam compare to the gain of a two-element quad antenna?
A. 3 dB higher.
B. 3 dB lower.
C. 2.54 dB higher.
D. About the same.

The delta loop beam antenna looks like a triangle with each side being 1/3 wavelength long. When compared to the 4 sided cubicle quad antenna, the gain *is almost identical*. **ANSWER D.**

G9D07 Which of the following describes a log periodic antenna?
A. Length and spacing of the elements increase logarithmically from one end of the boom to the other.
B. Impedance varies periodically as a function of frequency.
C. Gain varies logarithmically as a function of frequency.
D. SWR varies periodically as a function of boom length.

They call this monster antenna a "logarithmic" periodic antenna because the *length and spacing of the elements increase logarithmically from one end of the boom to the other*. These are very big antennas with limited applications for specific ham radio bands. Best to go with a multiband dipole or a multiband beam long before you ever consider the monster "log!" **ANSWER A.**

G9D06 Which of the following is an advantage of a log periodic antenna?
A. Wide bandwidth.
B. Higher gain per element than a Yagi antenna.
C. Harmonic suppression.
D. Polarization diversity.

Some military stations may use an antenna system called a "log periodic." The elements get progressively shorter on a very long boom, allowing for a *wide bandwidth* over many MHz of radio bands. SWR remains flat on a high frequency log periodic antenna from 10 MHz all the way up to 50 MHz! The only problem with a log antenna is the low forward gain achieved with such a monster in the air. **ANSWER A.**

Log periodic antenna

G9D10 Which of the following describes a Beverage antenna?
A. A vertical antenna.
B. A broad-band mobile antenna.
C. A helical antenna for space reception.
D. A very long and low directional receiving antenna.

If you have plenty of real estate, the *low and long* Beverage antenna can achieve some great directionality. This antenna lets you either home-in on a specific signal or minimize noise coming off a nearby power line. **ANSWER D.**

G9D09 Which of the following is an application for a Beverage antenna?
A. Directional transmitting for low HF bands.
B. Directional receiving for low HF bands.
C. Portable direction finding at higher HF frequencies.
D. Portable direction finding at lower HF frequencies.

Some of the larger high frequency base station rigs have a separate antenna port for an optional *receive antenna*. This would be perfect for a Beverage antenna that you can build yourself out of wire. **ANSWER B.**

G9D08 Why is a Beverage antenna not used for transmitting?
A. Its impedance is too low for effective matching.
B. It has high losses compared to other types of antennas.
C. It has poor directivity.
D. All of these choices are correct.

Sounds like a soft drink, but the Beverage antenna is actually a fabulous shortwave receive antenna. It is excellent at pulling in distant stations with minimal atmospheric noise. However, use it as a receive-only antenna because its *transmit losses are high* when compared to the common dipole. **ANSWER B.**

G4E05 Which of the following most limits the effectiveness of an HF mobile transceiver operating in the 75-meter band?
A. "Picket Fencing" signal variation.
B. The wire gauge of the DC power line to the transceiver.
C. The antenna system.
D. FCC rules limiting mobile output power on the 75-meter band.

75 meters is a great night-time band for talking more than 1,000 miles away. However, to get on 75 meters with a mobile unit you need a monster *antenna system*. Getting all the parts of that system mounted and working properly will be your biggest challenge when operating mobile on 75 meters. **ANSWER C.**

Effective HF Mobile

Operating HF mobile is one of the most fun activities in all of Amateur Radio. Having an effective mobile HF station is not only invaluable in emergencies, but can be an effective DX station as well. Many hams in antenna restricted or noisy home environments can evade those issues by taking their mobile station to quiet, secluded areas where they can operate to their heart's content! More than one ham has earned the coveted DXCC award entirely from a mobile station!

There are challenges to building an effective mobile HF station. Unlike 2-meter mobile, where you can simply plop a mag mount antenna on the roof of your car and have a great station, an effective HF mobile installation takes some planning. Mobile HF antennas, especially on the low bands, are by nature quite inefficient. But you can still do some great hamming if that antenna is installed and tuned properly. The famous "Texas Bugcatcher" design, while big and ungainly, is the most effective configuration for operating low band mobile. 40 meters has always been a popular mobile band, as it gives good regional coverage day and night. There are many 40 meter regional mobile nets that cater to just this kind of operation. Give mobile HF a try!

G4E06 What is one disadvantage of using a shortened mobile antenna as opposed to a full size antenna?
    A. Short antennas are more likely to cause distortion of transmitted signals.
    B. Short antennas can only receive circularly polarized signals.
    C. Operating bandwidth may be very limited.
    D. Harmonic radiation may increase.

Lightweight, fiberglass/stainless steel high frequency mobile whips provide some amazing performance. However, *the resonant bandwidth of these antennas may be only 20 or 30 kHz wide*. On 40 meters, the mobile whip will need to be tuned to either the top of the voice band or the bottom of the CW band. On 75 meters, the mobile whip needs to be tuned to a specific frequency where you want to operate. Mount the whips as high as possible on the vehicle for a good impedance match and good radiation. **ANSWER C.**

G4E01 What is the purpose of a capacitance hat on a mobile antenna?
    A. To increase the power handling capacity of a whip antenna.
    B. To allow automatic band changing.
    C. To electrically lengthen a physically short antenna.
    D. To allow remote tuning.

What's that eggbeater do-dad on top of my 40 meter high frequency antenna? That's a *capacitance hat*, which makes my *antenna look electrically longer*

than it physically is. On 40, 75, and 160 meters, when operating mobile, you really need a good capacitance hat to gain a little bit more radiation capability. **ANSWER C.**

Capacitance hats can take a multitude of forms ranging from elegant to whimsical. The idea is to get as much capacitance as possible without too much wind loading. This one looks strange, but it makes a big coil mobile antenna work better on 75 meters.

G4E02 What is the purpose of a corona ball on a HF mobile antenna?
    A. To narrow the operating bandwidth of the antenna.
    B. To increase the "Q" of the antenna.
    C. To reduce the chance of damage if the antenna should strike an object.
    D. To reduce high voltage discharge from the tip of the antenna.

When transmitting, the high frequency mobile antenna carries some very high voltage at the tip of the whip. A big *corona ball* at the tip of the mobile antenna will help *minimize sparks coming off the tip* when you transmit. Caution: never operate a mobile antenna in close proximity to trees. Even at 100 watts the signal could arc from the tip of a mobile antenna, with or without a coronal ball, to a nearby tree branch.
ANSWER D.

Corona is the formation of a plasma (electric arc) due to a high voltage gradient caused by sharp conductors. This corona ball helps prevent sparks flying off the tip of the whip antenna on high power transmit.

G4B11 Which of the following must be connected to an antenna analyzer when it is being used for SWR measurements?
A. Receiver.
B. Transmitter.
C. Antenna and feed line.
D. All of these choices are correct.

Invention of the portable antenna analyzer was a real improvement for anyone working with antennas. It allows you to test the SWR of the antenna without risking your expensive HF gear. The analyzer is hooked up only to the *antenna and feed line* to determine a standing wave ratio (SWR) measurement. **ANSWER C.**

The antenna analyzer is a must-have accessory when working with mobile and fixed antenna systems. It is battery powered and works from 160 meters through the VHF and UHF bands.

G4B13 What is a use for an antenna analyzer other than measuring the SWR of an antenna system?
A. Measuring the front to back ratio of an antenna.
B. Measuring the turns ratio of a power transformer.
C. Determining the impedance of an unknown or unmarked coaxial cable.
D. Determining the gain of a directional antenna.

There is plenty one can do with an antenna analyzer, such as "wringing out" coax cable for opens and shorts, determining the resonant frequency of an antenna, or *determining the impedance of that unmarked coax cable* you bought at a local swap meet. **ANSWER C.**

G4B12 What problem can occur when making measurements on an antenna system with an antenna analyzer?
A. Permanent damage to the analyzer may occur if it is operated into a high SWR.
B. Strong signals from nearby transmitters can affect the accuracy of measurements.
C. The analyzer can be damaged if measurements outside the ham bands are attempted.
D. Connecting the analyzer to an antenna can cause it to absorb harmonics.

This happened to Gordo this past weekend – he was doing some SWR analyzer checks of his 3 element beam after a big rainstorm and for the first 30 seconds there was a perfect dip right at 14.250 MHz. All of a sudden, his SWR analyzer showed intermittent spikes in the standing wave ratio, looking like some sort of intermittent connection. There were short spikes and long spikes. Hmmmmm, maybe he could even read them as Morse code! It was his neighbor across the street, Jim, N6JF, operating CW on 20 meters with just enough power to cause his SWR analyzer to dance around with dots and dashes. As soon as he stopped transmitting, things settled down to normal. Fact: most SWR analyzers will freeze up and/or become erratic when trying to measure an antenna at a repeater site because other *strong signals interfere with the antenna being tested*.
ANSWER B.

G4B08 **Which of the following instruments may be used to monitor relative RF output when making antenna and transmitter adjustments?**
A. A field strength meter.
B. An antenna noise bridge.
C. A multimeter.
D. A Q meter.

For relative transmitter output checks, an inexpensive *field-strength meter* is a good addition to any ham station. **ANSWER A.**

A simple field strength meter can give you a fast check that your rig is transmitting power out of the antenna system high on your tower.

G4B09 **Which of the following can be determined with a field strength meter?**
A. The radiation resistance of an antenna.
B. The radiation pattern of an antenna.
C. The presence and amount of phase distortion of a transmitter.
D. The presence and amount of amplitude distortion of a transmitter.

A well-calibrated *field-strength meter* might be used to determine *radiation patterns* off that brand-new ground plane antenna you just built. But in the real world of radio, the only way to properly measure antenna pattern field strengths is out in the middle of a 5-acre field where the ground is absolutely flat and there are no buildings or structures to reflect the signal. The antenna is then rotated with the field-strength measurements at a specific fixed spot. Forget about trying to calculate antenna patterns of a vertical antenna in your neighborhood – it just won't work. **ANSWER B.**

After completing antenna work and you're safely down off the tower, use a field strength meter to check relative antenna patterns from the main lobe.

Effective Radiated Power (ERP)

One of the guiding principles in all that we do in radio is NFL – No Free Lunch – meaning that we never get something for nothing. Every improvement in radio performance comes at a cost. Nowhere is this more glaringly evident than when dealing with antennas.

An antenna can never put out more than you put into it; and in many cases, what we get out of an antenna is a great deal less than what we put into it. An antenna with gain gets the gain by subtracting radiation in some directions to concentrate it in other directions. This is where the concept of an isotropic radiator comes in. You will never see a true isotropic radiator (it is theoretical and cannot be built), but you can approach the behavior of one by shrinking a dipole antenna to near the vanishing point. A very very short (in terms of wavelength) antenna "radiates poorly in all directions," like an incandescent light bulb.

In order for an antenna to have gain, we need to take the radiation pattern of an isotropic radiator (which basically emits rays in all directions like the quills on a porcupine) and rearrange those rays so they all point in a useful direction. (Don't try rearranging the quills on a porcupine; they object strenuously to this!) Obviously, the more rays we have pointing in one direction, the fewer we have pointing in another.

Now, as useful in concept as an isotropic radiator is, since we can't build one we need to use the next best thing as a reference, the familiar dipole antenna. A dipole antenna squishes the spherical pattern of an isotropic radiator into sort of a doughnut shape. We sacrifice a lot of radiation off the ends and reorganize the rays to radiate at right angles from the center of the wire. The rearrangement of rays that the dipole provides gives us a gain of 2.15 dB over the theoretical isotropic radiator, or a power gain of a little over 1.6:1. This means that if we feed one watt of power into a dipole, the field strength broadside to the dipole is the same as putting a little over 1.6 watts into an isotropic radiator.

Is there something magic or "special" about a dipole? Not at all; it's just a very convenient reference. It's something we can actually make as opposed to the theoretically precise isotropic radiator.

To tie this all together, we have Effective Radiated Power, or ERP, a useful figure for calculating transmitted power based on the RF power put into an antenna, less any losses incurred in the process, plus the antenna gain. By convention, when calculating ERP, we use the antenna gain relative to the dipole or dBd. ERP is a reliable indicator of transmitted power in the direction of maximum radiation.

So, if we have a transmitter with 1500 watts output power, and an antenna gain of 7dBd (a reasonable figure for a moderately large Yagi), we have an ERP of about 7500 watts. Using the formula $dB = 10 \log P1/P2$, let's work backwards and determine the power ratios:

First, take our dB number, 7, and divide by 10, since the last thing we did to get this was multiplying by 10. This gives us 0.7. Now, let's take the antilog of this. If you're using a typical scientific calculator, this is the 10x key. Plug in 0.7, press that key, and we come up with 5.011 and some loose change. Rounding off to 5, we have a 5:1 power ratio (increase). Multiplying 1500 by 5 we get 7500 W.

Is this legal? Absolutely! Unlike commercial radio regulations, amateur radio rules place no restrictions whatsoever on effective radiated power. The only restrictions we have are found in what we can physically build! (Other than the 1500 watt transmitter output power limit, of course).

What have we sacrificed to get those 7500 watts ERP? Well, an antenna with that kind of gain has far less gain than a dipole in most directions other than that of the main lobe, and probably some nulls where the power level goes to almost nothing. So the cost we incur is the necessity of rotating the antenna to point it where we want to concentrate our signal, thus restricting our transmissions to one direction!

▼ IF YOU'RE LOOKING FOR	▼ THEN VISIT
Roll Your Own Antenna	www.cebik.com
Portable Satellite Beams	www.arrowantennas.com
HF Antennas	www.AORUSA.com
	www.directivesystems.com
	www.MFJEnterprises.com
	www.M2INC.com
	www.NEW-Tronics.com
	www.DiamondAntenna.com
	www.Cushcraft.com
	www.Cubex.com
	www.Radioworks.com
	www.Radiowavz.com
	www.alphadelta.com
	www.hiqantennas.com
	www.cq73.com
Coax Cable	www.cableexperts.com
	www.coaxial.com

Coax Cable

G9A02 What are the typical characteristic impedances of coaxial cables used for antenna feed lines at amateur stations?

A. 25 and 30 ohms.   C. 80 and 100 ohms.

B. 50 and 75 ohms.   D. 500 and 750 ohms.

Amateur Radio coax cable usually is rated at *50 ohms* impedance. We have talked about the 50 ohm impedance that ham radios are designed for. Most cable TV coax is rated at *75 ohms*. This type of 75 ohm antenna feed line is used for special antennas in certain applications for the amateur radio operator. **ANSWER B.**

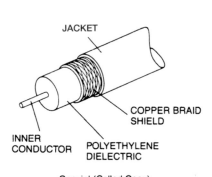

JACKET

COPPER BRAID SHIELD

INNER CONDUCTOR

POLYETHYLENE DIELECTRIC

Coaxial (Called Coax)

This photo shows the different inside construction of various brands of coax cable.

G9A05 How does the attenuation of coaxial cable change as the frequency of the signal it is carrying increases?
   A. Attenuation is independent of frequency.
   B. Attenuation increases.
   C. Attenuation decreases.
   D. Attenuation reaches a maximum at approximately 18 MHz.
The *higher* you go in *frequency*, the *greater the attenuation* of the transmission line. This is why it's very important to always use the largest size coax cable available for VHF and UHF frequencies. **ANSWER B.**

G9A06 In what units is RF feed line loss usually expressed?
   A. Ohms per 1000 feet.   C. Ohms per 100 feet.
   B. Decibels per 1000 feet.   D. Decibels per 100 feet.
RF feed line losses are usually expressed in *decibels (dB) per 100 feet*. See the decibels explanation and chart on page 178. **ANSWER D.**

Attenuation	
Frequency (MHz)	(dB/100 ft.)
2	0.21
10	0.5
20	0.71
100	1.7
200	2.4
1000	5.7

Attenuation of RG-8 coax with foam dielectric

G5B10 What percentage of power loss would result from a transmission line loss of 1 dB?
   A. 10.9 percent.   C. 20.5 percent.
   B. 12.2 percent.   D. 25.9 percent.
On your examination, it will be expected that certain things are committed to memory. In the real world of ham radio there are charts available for this information. In this question, they ask the percentage loss from a transmission line of 1 dB. *One dB of loss* results in 0.795 (79.5%) of the energy making it through the coax, leading to 20.5% getting lost in the transmission line (100% - 79.5% = *20.5% loss*). **ANSWER C.**

G9A03 What is the characteristic impedance of flat ribbon TV type twinlead?
   A. 50 ohms.   C. 100 ohms.
   B. 75 ohms.   D. 300 ohms.
Hams who operate their high frequency equipment into an external, manual antenna tuner may reduce SWR losses to a non-resonant antenna by using the manual tuner's parallel conductor output setting. Parallel feed lines, like the old *TV twin lead (rated at 300 ohms)*, minimize SWR losses and allow a manual tuner to tune most any type of wire antenna, such as loops, quads, delta loops, and rhombics! The flat two-conductor feed line must be kept away from anything else metal or it may arc over. Being too close to anything metal could also create an electrical imbalance of voltage and currents in the feel line. **ANSWER D.**

Elmer Point: The characteristic impedance of a transmission line is impossible to measure directly. The best definition of characteristic impedance is given in the March 1956 *QST* article, "My Feedline Tunes My Antenna," by Byron Goodman, W1DX. "The characteristic impedance of a transmission line is the value of resistance that, when used as a termination for the line, makes the impedance of the line independent of the electrical length of the line."

Practically speaking, the thinner and farther apart the conductors are, the higher the characteristic impedance. This applies to coaxial cable or parallel transmission lines.

When most radio amateurs think of transmission lines, they think of coaxial cable. The reality is that coaxial cable is a "Johnny Come Lately" development, almost unheard of until after World War II. Before then, open wire feed line or "ladder line" was the nearly universal transmission line. Closely related to ladder line is 450 ohm "window" line and 300 ohm twin lead, which still have advantages over coax in many instances. Coaxial cable is fairly limited with regard to SWR tolerance, while open wire feed line doesn't care. In fact in many systems, a high SWR is necessary for the system to work. A good example is the classic end-fed Zepp antenna which uses a ¼ wave length of open wire feed line, operating with nearly infinite SWR. This transmission line acts as a matching transformer by the very virtue of it having a large standing wave ratio.

In most modern implementations of parallel transmission lines, an open wire antenna coupler is used as a go-between for a 50 ohm transmitter and a random impedance load on the other side. This results in a very versatile and robust system.

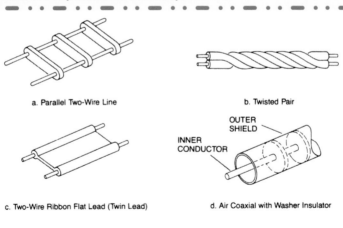

a. Parallel Two-Wire Line

b. Twisted Pair

c. Two-Wire Ribbon Flat Lead (Twin Lead)

d. Air Coaxial with Washer Insulator

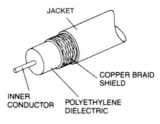

f. Coaxial (Called Coax)

Different transmission lines
Source: *Antennas – Selection and Installation*, © 1986 Master Publishing, Inc., Niles, IL

G9A01 Which of the following factors determine the characteristic impedance of a parallel conductor antenna feed line?
A. The distance between the centers of the conductors and the radius of the conductors.
B. The distance between the centers of the conductors and the length of the line.
C. The radius of the conductors and the frequency of the signal.
D. The frequency of the signal and the length of the line.

The characteristic impedance of parallel conductor antenna feed line is most influenced by the *distance between the center of the conductors*, and slightly influenced by actual *radius of the conductors*. An impedance "bump" is caused when the parallel conductor feed line twists and kinks in the wind, dramatically changing the distance between the conductors. Until the feed line gets straightened out, the impedance will no longer be constant. If you are running parallel conductor feed line, keep it absolutely un-kinked, keep it away from metal masts and, if that parallel conductor antenna feed line is part of the vertical radiator, make sure it hangs straight down and never coiled up on itself. **ANSWER A.**

G9A07 What must be done to prevent standing waves on an antenna feed line?
A. The antenna feed point must be at DC ground potential.
B. The feed line must be cut to a length equal to an odd number of electrical quarter wavelengths.
C. The feed line must be cut to a length equal to an even number of physical half wavelengths.
D. The antenna feed point impedance must be matched to the characteristic impedance of the feed line.

Always try to *match feed point impedance* of the antenna to the characteristic impedance of the feed line for maximum power transfer and minimum SWR. **ANSWER D.**

G4B10 Which of the following can be determined with a directional wattmeter?
A. Standing wave ratio.   C. RF interference.
B. Antenna front-to-back ratio.   D. Radio wave propagation.

A directional watt meter makes a dandy *standing wave ratio* checker. Maximum forward power with minimum reflected power will indicate an acceptably low SWR. **ANSWER A.**

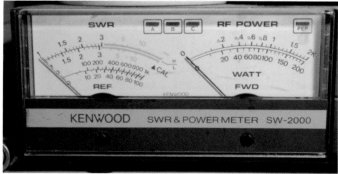

DIrectional Watt Meter

G9A04 What might cause reflected power at the point where a feed line connects to an antenna?
   A. Operating an antenna at its resonant frequency.
   B. Using more transmitter power than the antenna can handle.
   C. A difference between feed line impedance and antenna feed point impedance.
   D. Feeding the antenna with unbalanced feed line.

Keep the impedances of your feed line and antenna the same for minimum standing wave ratio. Standing waves are set-up on the feed line because power is being reflected back due to an *impedance mismatch*. **ANSWER C.**

G9A11 What standing wave ratio will result when connecting a 50 ohm feed line to a non-reactive load having 50 ohm impedance?
   A. 2:1.   C. 50:50.
   B. 1:1.   D. 0:0.

50 into 50 is a perfect match, so your *SWR would be 1:1*. **ANSWER B.**

Here's a homebrew, brute force choke balun made out of good quality coax. It is an effective means of preventing your transmission line from radiating and causing other unpredictable behavior. It's sometimes called an "ugly balun," but if assembled neatly like this one it doesn't have to be ugly at all.

G9A14 What is the interaction between high standing wave ratio (SWR) and transmission line loss?
   A. There is no interaction between transmission line loss and SWR.
   B. If a transmission line is lossy, high SWR will increase the loss.
   C. High SWR makes it difficult to measure transmission line loss.
   D. High SWR reduces the relative effect of transmission line loss.

In a transmission line that has measurable loss, *the loss will increase as the SWR increases.* Therefore, in most cases, it's beneficial to reduce the SWR as much as possible by careful impedance matching at the load end. However, very low loss transmission lines such as open wire feed line are capable of operating efficiently with very high SWR values. They are useful when great flexibility takes precedence over a small amount of loss, such as when operating a random length doublet antenna on multiple bands. **ANSWER B.**

G9A15 What is the effect of transmission line loss on SWR measured at the input to the line?
   A. The higher the transmission line loss, the more the SWR will read artificially low.
   B. The higher the transmission line loss, the more the SWR will read artificially high.
   C. The higher the transmission line loss, the more accurate the SWR measurement will be.
   D. Transmission line loss does not affect the SWR measurement.

This is one of many cases in Amateur Radio where a little information can be a dangerous thing. A very low SWR can mean you have a very good antenna, or a very effective dummy load! If at all possible, SWR should be measured at the antenna. The reason for this is that if the transmission line is lossy, the reflected power will be attenuated, just like the forward power. Since SWR is calculated (indirectly) by looking at the ratio of reflected power to forward power, the *SWR will always be lower at the input end of a lossy transmission line*. At UHF frequencies, the losses can be so great in low-grade coax that even with no antenna connected the SWR will read 1:1 or nearly so. All this is telling you is that the transmission line is absorbing all the power! So we need to understand what we're really measuring. An SWR meter is a handy tool, but it doesn't tell the whole story! Use it with discrimination. **ANSWER A.**

G9A12 What standing wave ratio will result when connecting a 50 ohm feed line to a non-reactive load having 25 ohm impedance?
    A. 2:1.
    B. 2.5:1.
    C. 1.25:1.
    D. You cannot determine SWR from impedance values.
It's relatively easy to build a 10- or 15-meter ground plane antenna out of copper tubing. The radiating element is one-quarter wavelength long, and the ground radials are also one-quarter wavelength long. The ground radials must be bent down at an approximately 45-degree angle in order to bring the impedance up to 50 ohms, which is the normal impedance of coax cable. If the ground plane copper tubes extend straight out at 90 degrees from the base of the ground plane, the impedance might look like 25 ohms instead of 50 ohms. This would result in an *SWR reading of about 2:1*, acceptable, but easily improved by simply bending the ground radials down at a 45-degree angle. **ANSWER A.**

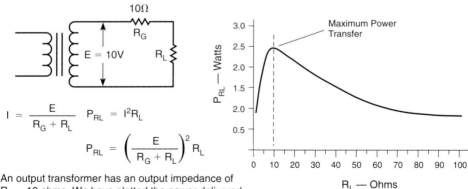

10Ω

R_G

$E = 10V$ R_L

P_{RL} — Watts

$$I = \frac{E}{R_G + R_L} \qquad P_{RL} = I^2 R_L$$

$$P_{RL} = \left(\frac{E}{R_G + R_L}\right)^2 R_L$$

Maximum Power Transfer

R_L — Ohms

An output transformer has an output impedance of R_G = 10 ohms. We have plotted the power delivered to R_L as R_L varies when E = 10V.
The values for the curve are calculated by substituting different values of R_L into the formula when E = 10V and R_G = 10 .
Maximum power is transferred when $R_G = R_L$.

Maximum power transfer

G9B02 Which of the following is a common way to adjust the feed point impedance of a quarter wave ground plane vertical antenna to be approximately 50 ohms?
  A. Slope the radials upward.
  B. Slope the radials downward.
  C. Lengthen the radials.
  D. Shorten the radials.

A "perfect" ¼ wave ground plane antenna (one with a quarter wave vertical section and an infinite number of ¼ wave horizontal radials) will have an impedance of 36 ohms, exactly half that of a dipole in free space (72 ohms). While this antenna will work quite well with no modification, you can achieve *a better match to 50 ohms by slanting the radials downward.* (Your ground plane antenna will probably not have an infinite number of radials, usually four, so this job is pretty easy!)
ANSWER B.

G9A09 What standing wave ratio will result when connecting a 50 ohm feed line to a non-reactive load having 200 ohm impedance?
  A. 4:1.
  B. 1:4.
  C. 2:1.
  D. 1:2.

50 goes into 200 4 times, so the impedance of the mismatch is *4:1*. 1:4 is not the correct answer, even though it looks correct. Whichever value is larger is the numerator, which means that SWR by definition will always be equal to or greater than 1:1. **ANSWER A.**

G9A10 What standing wave ratio will result when connecting a 50 ohm feed line to a non-reactive load having 10 ohm impedance?
  A. 2:1.
  B. 50:1.
  C. 1:5.
  D. 5:1.

By definition, a perfect match is an SWR of 1:1, which is the lowest value possible. To calculate SWR, always divide the larger impedance by the smaller one. 10 goes into 50 5 times, so the mismatch is *5:1*. 1:5 is not correct. **ANSWER D.**

G9A13 What standing wave ratio will result when connecting a 50 ohm feed line to an antenna that has a purely resistive 300 ohm feed point impedance?
  A. 1.5:1.
  B. 3:1.
  C. 6:1.
  D. You cannot determine SWR from impedance values.

The folded dipole has a characteristic impedance of about 300 ohms. This is why it is often fed with twin lead and the impedance transformed with the use of a manual antenna tuner. If you tried to hook up 50-ohm coax cable directly to a 300-ohm feed point, your SWR would be an unacceptable *6:1.* Divide 50 ohms into 300 ohms to calculate the 6:1 ratio. **ANSWER C.**

G9A08 If the SWR on an antenna feed line is 5 to 1, and a matching network at the transmitter end of the feed line is adjusted to 1 to 1 SWR, what is the resulting SWR on the feed line?

A. 1 to 1.

B. 5 to 1.

C. Between 1 to 1 and 5 to 1 depending on the characteristic impedance of the line.

D. Between 1 to 1 and 5 to 1 depending on the reflected power at the transmitter.

SWR is determined only by the load impedance. The SWR will still be 5 to 1. An antenna tuner or coupler will only change the input impedance (the impedance your transmitter sees). Let's show how the system as a whole still delivers full power to the load, assuming the transmission line is not too lossy itself, and the antenna tuner is of high quality. Using some standard charts, we see that a 6:1 SWR results in 51% power being reflected from the load. (For simplicity, we'll round this down to 50%). This means that with no further action taken, with a 100 watt transmitter, 50 watts will be delivered to the load. (We'll assume the transmitter has no protective circuitry to back off the power). Now, let's put a GOOD antenna tuner in line, near the transmitter, and adjust the tuner until the transmitter "sees" 50 ohms. The transmitter is once again delivering 100 watts into the antenna tuner. Now, if we were to take a good directional wattmeter and put it on the OUTPUT side of the tuner, we would see 100 watts reflected from the load. This may seem a bit odd, since we know we're only reflecting 50% of the power from the mismatched load. Now remember, SWR is determined only by the load. So, where is that missing 100 watts going? Is it somehow lost in the tuner? No way! Let's switch our trusty Bird wattmeter to the forward direction. What do we see? 200 WATTS forward power! Well, now the numbers add up, but what's happening? What we're seeing is a DOUBLE reflection. When we adjust the tuner to create a 50 ohm load on the INPUT, we create a CONJUGATE match on the OUTPUT, which causes the reflected power to be re-reflected and ADDED to the power passing THROUGH the tuner. Subtracting 100 Watts reflected from 200 Watts forward, still gives us 100 Watts to the antenna. Pretty neat! Now, in all fairness, we need to mention that coax cable generally should not be operated with a 6:1 SWR, as any loss that coax has will be increased with high SWR. But as a general rule, most decent antenna tuners have very small losses, and can greatly increase your operating flexibility. **ANSWER B.**

Close up of an automatic antenna tuner control switches. Besides the "Auto" mode, you can make small changes in inductance (L) and capacitance (C) to fine-tune your antenna system.

G6B16 Which of the following describes a type N connector?
A. A moisture-resistant RF connector useful to 10 GHz.
B. A small bayonet connector used for data circuits.
C. A threaded connector used for hydraulic systems.
D. An audio connector used in surround-sound installations.

As a licensed Technician Class operator, chances are you encountered the type N connector when working with UHF and microwave equipment. The *type N*

connector is great at VHF and UHF antenna feed points because it is *moisture resistant* and it works well all the way up to *10 GHz.* When working with your high frequency transceiver, it is doubtful you will need a type N connector. **ANSWER A.**

Shown left to right are the BNC, PL-259, "N", SMA, and TV connectors.

G6B18 What is a type SMA connector?
A. A large bayonet connector usable at power levels in excess of 1 KW.
B. A small threaded connector suitable for signals up to several GHz.
C. A connector designed for serial multiple access signals.
D. A type of push-on connector intended for high voltage applications.

The modern handheld has switched from an antenna connector called BNC to the *threaded antenna connector called SMA*. Even the microwave operators up at 10,000 MHz use SMA connectors. They are good for several GHz! **ANSWER B.**

SMA connector

G6B13 Which of these connector types is commonly used for RF connections at frequencies up to 150 MHz?
A. Octal.   C. PL-259.
B. RJ-11.   D. DB-25 .

The most common antenna connector for HF radios operating up to 150 MHz (the 2 meter band) is the *PL-259.* **ANSWER C.**

Elmer Point: The common UHF jack on the back of your new HF transceiver will accept the coax cable PL-259 connector, which is the common coax connector for high frequency use. However, the PL-259 is NOT waterproof. If you use an antenna feed point that takes a PL-259, make absolutely sure to completely waterproof the connection with flexible sealant, as well as an added wrap of self-vulcanizing tape. The number one reason why ham radio antenna systems fail is water migrating into the PL-259 and killing the feed point connection. When I visit your QTH, I don't want to see any exposed PL-259 connectors on the coax at the antenna feed point!

G1B01 What is the maximum height above ground to which an antenna structure may be erected without requiring notification to the FAA and registration with the FCC, provided it is not at or near a public use airport?

A. 50 feet.

B. 100 feet.

C. 200 feet.

D. 300 feet.

The FCC works closely with the FAA when it comes to towers taller than 200 feet. Although you do not need FCC approval for towers less than *200 feet tall*, you may need approval from your city or homeowner's association. [97.15(a)]

ANSWER C.

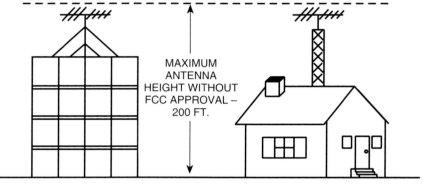

MAXIMUM ANTENNA HEIGHT WITHOUT FCC APPROVAL – 200 FT.

Maximum antenna height

Coaxing R.F. Without Coax

Although most radio amateurs rely on coaxial cable transmission lines to get their signals from their shacks to their antennas (and vice versa), this is not the only way to accomplish this crucial task.

Long before coaxial cable was even thought of, most radio amateurs used open wire feedlines. An open wire feedline is simply two parallel wires separated by appropriate spacers. Although open wire feedline is not as convenient to install as coaxial cable, it is capable of excellent performance and flexibility. It can operate with extremely high standing wave ratios with very low loss. And best of all, it's very cheap if you roll your own! Yes, generations of hams used to do this. There are "snap in" insulator/spacers available to make this easy! One source of the spacers can be found on-line at: www.73cnc.com/product_p/ls100.htm

Open wire feedline is becoming quite popular again, and a number of commercial antenna tuners have provisions for attaching these "old-fangled" transmission lines. Check out the amateur radio literature for hints on how to install and use open wire feedline systems.

Also, if you get a chance, check out "Ladder Line to Eternity: SWR Meters Make You Stupid" in the appendix of *The Opus of Amateur Radio Knowledge and Lore* for the full story on transmission lines.

RF & Electrical Safety

G0A12 What precaution should you take whenever you make adjustments or repairs to an antenna?
A. Ensure that you and the antenna structure are grounded.
B. Turn off the transmitter and disconnect the feed line.
C. Wear a radiation badge.
D. All of these choices are correct.

While working on an antenna system, *turn off the transmitter and disconnect the feed line* from it so there is absolutely no way that someone could accidentally transmit while you are making the repairs. **ANSWER B.**

G0B08 What should be done by any person preparing to climb a tower that supports electrically powered devices?
A. Notify the electric company that a person will be working on the tower.
B. Make sure all circuits that supply power to the tower are locked out and tagged.
C. Unground the base of the tower.
D. All of these choices are correct.

To insure that no one starts rotating a beam antenna using the electric powered rotator, double check that the rotator control unit is *unplugged and tagged "climber aloft."* **ANSWER B.**

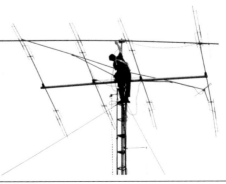

Our tower climber needs a hard hat and safety glasses, too. And, yes, he's wearing a full-body safety harness to keep him safe for this long reach!

G0B07 Which of these choices should be observed when climbing a tower using a safety belt or harness?
  A. Never lean back and rely on the belt alone to support your weight.
  B. Confirm that the belt is rated for the weight of the climber and that it is within its allowable service life.
  C. Ensure that all heavy tools are securely fastened to the belt D-ring.
  D. All of these choices are correct.

Preventing falls from a tower is best achieved with a professional safety harness. Always be sure that the *belt is rated for the weight of the climber and is within its service life.* It's good practice to attach the belt's safety hook to the "D" ring with the hook opening always away from the tower. We also recommend that you regularly inspect the safety harness as an added measure to prevent an accident. **ANSWER B.**

We're sending up your required hard hat and safety glasses!

G0A08 Which of the following steps must an amateur operator take to ensure compliance with RF safety regulations when transmitter power exceeds levels specified in FCC Part 97.13?
  A. Post a copy of FCC Part 97.13 in the station.
  B. Post a copy of OET Bulletin 65 in the station.
  C. Perform a routine RF exposure evaluation.
  D. All of these choices are correct.

Performing a *routine RF exposure evaluation* is a good idea for all amateurs to ensure compliance with RF safety regulations and that you and your neighbors are not being "overexposed" to RF radiation. **ANSWER C.**

G0A11 What precaution should you take if you install an indoor transmitting antenna?
  A. Locate the antenna close to your operating position to minimize feed line radiation.
  B. Position the antenna along the edge of a wall to reduce parasitic radiation.
  C. Make sure that MPE limits are not exceeded in occupied areas.
  D. Make sure the antenna is properly shielded.

It is always a good idea to locate an antenna as far away as possible from living spaces that will be occupied when you are transmitting. If you're just receiving, no problem – but when you're transmitting, get your antenna away from everyone to minimize RF exposure! This will help ensure that Maximum Permissible Exposure *(MPE) limits are not exceeded.* **ANSWER C.**

G0A01 What is one way that RF energy can affect human body tissue?
   A. It heats body tissue.
   B. It causes radiation poisoning.
   C. It causes the blood count to reach a dangerously low level.
   D. It cools body tissue.

If RF energy from your antenna system is concentrated on the human body, it *heats the body tissue* just like your microwave oven heats your leftovers. RF burns are a very real thing. They include those experienced from poor grounding of the equipment to those received from touching or standing too close to an antenna while someone is transmitting. **ANSWER A.**

Speeding motorists don't need to panic! Gordo's on the 10,000 MHz X band working stations 300 miles away using his dish antenna. Always stand behind or well to the sides of a dish or horn antenna to avoid RF exposure.

G0A03 How can you determine that your station complies with FCC RF exposure regulations?
   A. By calculation based on FCC OET Bulletin 65.
   B. By calculation based on computer modeling.
   C. By measurement of field strength using calibrated equipment.
   D. All of these choices are correct.

You can determine how your station complies with FCC RF exposure regulations by using The W5YI RF Safety Tables in the Appendix of this book. These tables can be used to estimate safe distances based on FCC OET Bulletin No. 65. These distances can also be determined using your own calculations based on computer modeling. Alternately, you can actually go out there and measure the power density levels with a field strength meter making sure to use calibrated equipment. *All of these choices* are good ways to determine whether or not you are going to unnecessarily expose yourself or your neighbors to RF energy. [97.13(c)(1)] **ANSWER D.**

G0A04 What does "time averaging" mean in reference to RF radiation exposure?
A. The average amount of power developed by the transmitter over a specific 24 hour period.
B. The average time it takes RF radiation to have any long-term effect on the body.
C. The total time of the exposure.
D. The total RF exposure averaged over a certain time.

Time-averaging is a method of *calculating* an individual's *total exposure to RF radiation over a given period of time*. The premise of time-averaging is that the human body can tolerate larger amounts of RF radiation if the exposure is received in short "bursts" as compared to a constant exposure at the same high level of RF radiation. As depicted here, total exposure to various levels of radiation is averaged over a 6-minute period. On a time-averaged basis, the amount of thermal load on the body is equal in all cases. **ANSWER D.**

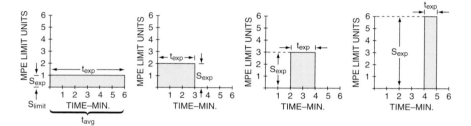

The general equation for time averaging exposure equivalence is: $S_{exp}\ t_{exp} = S_{limit}\ t_{avg}$

G0A07 What effect does transmitter duty cycle have when evaluating RF exposure?
A. A lower transmitter duty cycle permits greater short-term exposure levels.
B. A higher transmitter duty cycle permits greater short-term exposure levels.
C. Low duty cycle transmitters are exempt from RF exposure evaluation requirements.
D. High duty cycle transmitters are exempt from RF exposure requirements .

Duty cycle is the percentage of time the transmitter is actually sending out energy. If you hold down your telegraph key for continuous full-transmit-power output, the equipment would be operating at100% duty cycle. If the space in between each dit were equal to the duration of the transmitted signal, the equipment would be operating at 50% duty cycle. The *lower duty cycle permits greater short-term exposure levels to RF radiation*. **ANSWER A.**

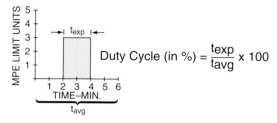

$$\text{Duty Cycle (in \%)} = \frac{t_{exp}}{t_{avg}} \times 100$$

Duty Cycle

G0A02 Which of the following properties is important in estimating whether an RF signal exceeds the maximum permissible exposure (MPE)?
A. Its duty cycle.
B. Its frequency.
C. Its power density.
D. All of these choices are correct.

There is a lot to do before you can consider your station safe and be sure you are not exceeding the maximum permissible exposure (MPE) limits. *Do all of these steps*. **ANSWER D.**

G0A05 What must you do if an evaluation of your station shows RF energy radiated from your station exceeds permissible limits?
A. Take action to prevent human exposure to the excessive RF fields.
B. File an Environmental Impact Statement (EIS-97) with the FCC.
C. Secure written permission from your neighbors to operate above the controlled MPE limits.
D. All of these choices are correct.

In Section 97.13, the FCC rules state that if your station's RF exceeds permissible limits, you "must *take action to prevent human exposure* to such RF electromagnetic fields." If your station exceeds permissible limits, you need to make changes to solve the problem. **ANSWER A.**

G0A09 What type of instrument can be used to accurately measure an RF field?
A. A receiver with an S meter.
B. A calibrated field strength meter with a calibrated antenna.
C. An SWR meter with a peak-reading function.
D. An oscilloscope with a high-stability crystal marker generator.

Although a simple field-strength meter can show the presence of radio frequency emissions, it takes a precisely *calibrated field-strength meter with a calibrated antenna* to make accurate measurements of the RF field. **ANSWER B.**

G0A06 What precaution should be taken when installing a ground-mounted antenna?
A. It should not be installed higher than you can reach.
B. It should not be installed in a wet area.
C. It should limited to 10 feet in height.
D. It should be installed such that it is protected against unauthorized access.

There are all sorts of great 5-band and 7-band trap vertical antennas that work nicely mounted on the ground or on a metal shed just above the ground. When you're looking for a spot to mount an antenna, keep in mind maximum permissible exposure limits. *Install it so that no one can actually walk up to it* or stand near it when you are transmitting. This goes for your pets, too. Don't fry Fido or Furball by leaving a ground-mounted vertical antenna unfenced. **ANSWER D.**

Ground-mounted antennas, like this 10GHz EME dish in Alaska, should be surrounded by a wood safety fence. And make sure to stay a safe distance away from any antenna on transmit!

G0A10 What is one thing that can be done if evaluation shows that a neighbor might receive more than the allowable limit of RF exposure from the main lobe of a directional antenna?
    A. Change to a non-polarized antenna with higher gain.
    B. Post a warning sign that is clearly visible to the neighbor.
    C. Use an antenna with a higher front-to-back ratio.
    D. Take precautions to ensure that the antenna cannot be pointed in their direction.
If your calculations indicate that you may be exposing your neighbors to too much RF, you need to relocate your entire antenna system, or take precautions to *ensure it cannot be pointed in their direction* when transmitting. **ANSWER D.**

G0B14 Which of the following is covered by the National Electrical Code?
    A. Acceptable bandwidth limits.
    B. Acceptable modulation limits.
    C. Electrical safety inside the ham shack.
    D. RF exposure limits of the human body.
The *National Electrical Code* covers *electrical safety standards* as they relate to conductors and wiring inside your ham shack. RF exposure limits to the human body are covered by ANSI, not by the NEC. **ANSWER C.**

G0B05 Which of the following conditions will cause a Ground Fault Circuit Interrupter (GFCI) to disconnect the 120 or 240 Volt AC line power to a device?
    A. Current flowing from one or more of the voltage-carrying wires to the neutral wire.
    B. Current flowing from one or more of the voltage-carrying wires directly to ground.
    C. Overvoltage on the voltage-carrying wires.
    D. All of these choices are correct.
Ground fault circuit interrupters are found in newer electrical plug outlets. They instantly open a circuit to halt current flow when they detect *current flowing from the hot wire to ground*. **ANSWER B.**

Ground fault receptacle

G0B06 Why must the metal enclosure of every item of station equipment be grounded?
    A. It prevents a blown fuse in the event of an internal short circuit.
    B. It prevents signal overload.
    C. It ensures that the neutral wire is grounded.
    D. It ensures that hazardous voltages cannot appear on the chassis.
Good station grounding ensures that *no hazardous* or dangerous *voltages* appear *on the metal chassis* of your equipment. Without good grounding you could be shocked when you touch a piece of equipment. **ANSWER D.**

G0B01 Which wire or wires in a four-conductor connection should be attached to fuses or circuit breakers in a device operated from a 240 VAC single phase source?

A. Only the two wires carrying voltage.
B. Only the neutral wire.
C. Only the ground wire.
D. All wires.

Most ham transceivers run on 12 volts DC. Some base stations may have their own 110 VAC power supplies built-in. However, linear amplifiers may require 240 VAC. For single phase *240 VAC, fuse both the black and red hot wires.* NEVER fuse the neutral white wire or the neutral ground bare copper wire. Most amplifiers already have the fuse circuits built in. **ANSWER A.**

G0B03 Which size of fuse or circuit breaker would be appropriate to use with a circuit that uses AWG number 14 wiring?

A. 100 amperes.   C. 30 amperes.
B. 60 amperes.   D. 15 amperes.

Based on the American Wire Gauge (AWG) information shown, 14 gauge wire handles 15 amperes. The easy way to remember this is with the "F" for "Fourteen" (14 gauge) wiring will handle *Fifteen (15) amps*. **ANSWER D.**

Wire Size A.W.G. (B&S)	Current-Amps (Continuous Duty)	
	Single Wire	Bundled Wire
8	73	46
10	55	33
12	41	23
14	32	17
16	22	13
18	16	10

American Wire Gauge (AWG) wire size vs. current capability

G0B02 What is the minimum wire size that may be safely used for a circuit that draws up to 20 amperes of continuous current?

A. AWG number 20.   C. AWG number 12.
B. AWG number 16.   D. AWG number 8.

Based on the American Wire Gauge (AWG) information shown, *20 amperes* of continuous current requires a wire size of *AWG #12*. The easy way to remember this is with the "T" for "Twenty" (20 amperes) current requires AWG number 12 ("T" for twelve). Don't confuse the "T" for twenty in the answers, current flow and wire size don't match like that. **ANSWER C.**

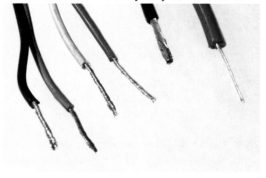

Thick or thin insulation can be misleading about the actual wire size! You need to strip off the insulation from unmarked wire to determine which gauge wire you are working with.

G0B12 What is the purpose of a power supply interlock?

A. To prevent unauthorized changes to the circuit that would void the manufacturer's warranty.
B. To shut down the unit if it becomes too hot.
C. To ensure that dangerous voltages are removed if the cabinet is opened.
D. To shut off the power supply if too much voltage is produced.

Linear amplifiers using vacuum tubes will likely have a power supply interlock switch. If the equipment is on and *the power supply door is opened*, the equipment will either *instantly power off*, or you will hear a loud "bang" when the high voltage gets shorted to ground tripping an internal fuse or breaker. This protects you and the equipment from a high voltage shock. **ANSWER C.**

G0B10 Which of the following is a danger from lead-tin solder?

A. Lead can contaminate food if hands are not washed carefully after handling the solder.
B. High voltages can cause lead-tin solder to disintegrate suddenly.
C. Tin in the solder can "cold flow" causing shorts in the circuit.
D. RF energy can convert the lead into a poisonous gas.

Any time you are working on radio equipment innards, *wash your hands* when you finish to remove any lead that might be contained in that roll of old solder before you grab a sandwich. **ANSWER A.**

G0B11 Which of the following is good practice for lightning protection grounds?

A. They must be bonded to all buried water and gas lines.
B. Bends in ground wires must be made as close as possible to a right angle.
C. Lightning grounds must be connected to all ungrounded wiring.
D. They must be bonded together with all other grounds.

Good engineering practice for a lightning ground indicates that *all grounds be bonded together* with all other grounds. **ANSWER D.**

G0B09 Why should soldered joints not be used with the wires that connect the base of a tower to a system of ground rods?

A. The resistance of solder is too high.
B. Solder flux will prevent a low conductivity connection.
C. Solder has too high a dielectric constant to provide adequate lightning protection.
D. A soldered joint will likely be destroyed by the heat of a lightning strike.

Carefully inspect tower grounding circuits and you will find that all the ground connections have been swaged rather than soldered. *Solder might melt on a direct lightning strike* destroying the route to ground. **ANSWER D.**

G0B04 Which of the following is a primary reason for not placing a gasoline-fueled generator inside an occupied area?

A. Danger of carbon monoxide poisoning.
B. Danger of engine over torque.
C. Lack of oxygen for adequate combustion.
D. Lack of nitrogen for adequate combustion.

The running generator exhaust contains *carbon monoxide* that can accumulate inside a closed space. This could become lethal. Always think "fresh air" safety when operating with a generator running. **ANSWER A.**

G0B13 What must you do when powering your house from an emergency generator?

  A. Disconnect the incoming utility power feed.
  B. Insure that the generator is not grounded.
  C. Insure that all lightning grounds are disconnected.
  D. All of these choices are correct.

In an emergency when you look around and see nothing but downed power poles and know it is going to be several days – or weeks – before electricity is restored, you might power your house with your RV generator. Any time you connect a generator into your home, you MUST ABSOLUTELY trip all of the breakers to *disconnect the incoming utility power feed.* This ensures you are not sending voltage back into the grid through your electrical panel, which could prove dangerous for anyone working on the lines. Disconnecting the utility power feed at the panel will also prevent damage to the generator when the power is restored. **ANSWER A.**

G0B15 Which of the following is true of an emergency generator installation?

  A. The generator should be located in a well-ventilated area.
  B. The generator must be insulated from ground.
  C. Fuel should be stored near the generator for rapid refueling in case of an emergency.
  D. All of these choices are correct.

Any time you use a generator for power, make sure the generator is *located in a well-ventilated area*; not where someone could inhale the toxic exhaust. The generator should be properly grounded, and always store the generator's fuel in a safe place away from any inhabited area. **ANSWER A.**

Portable generators must be placed well away from an operating position, have good ventilation, and never be operated with a container of gasoline nearby. In this picture, the generator is in storage, with no gas in the container.

HOORAY!!
YOU FINISHED THE Q & A!

4

Taking the General Class Examination

Get ready for worldwide skywave band privileges! As soon as you pass your General Class theory exam you'll be licensed to transmit on frequency bands that regularly offer skywave excitement every hour of the day and all through the night. This chapter tells you how the examination will be given, who is qualified to administer the General Class exam, and what happens after you successfully complete the written exam.

IMPORTANT NOTE: In order to receive credit for Technician Class, a prerequisite to the Element 3 General Class examination, you must bring a photocopy of your original, signed, valid Technician Class license to the examination site. You also will need 2 forms of identification, one of which must be a photo ID (such as your driver's license). If you can't find your Technician Class original license, you can download a copy from the FCC website at **wireless.fcc.gov** and then doing a license search by your call sign or your name. There no longer is any requirement to show a Morse code credit or to take a Morse code test.

If you are brand new to ham radio, you can certainly take both the Technician and General Class exams in one test session as long as you pass the Technician exam first.

THE GENERAL CLASS EXAMINATION

Here is an overview of the General Class examination and what to expect when you go to the test session.

Examination Administration

The General Class exam is given by a team of 3 Volunteer Examiners (VEs) – hams who hold Advanced or Extra Class licenses and who are accredited to administer your exam by a Volunteer Examiner Coordinator (VEC).

Volunteer Examiner teams offer examinations on a regular basis at local sites to serve their communities. Generally, the VECs closely coordinate their activities with one another, so you should be able to find a nearby test site and exam date that is convenient for you. You can obtain information about VECs and exam sessions in your area by checking with your local radio club, ham radio store, or local packet bulletin boards. A list of VECs that was current at the time of publication is given in the Appendix (see page 224).

Once you have found your local VE team, contact them to select a test date and location and pre-register for your examination. They will hold a seat for you at the next available session. Don't be a no-show, and don't be a surprise-show. Call them ahead of time and pre-register!

The Volunteer Examiners are not compensated for their time and skills, but they are permitted to charge you a fee for certain reimbursable expenses incurred in preparing, administering, and processing the examination. The maximum fee is adjusted frequently and currently is about $14.00. When you call to make your exam reservation, ask the VE the current amount of the exam fee.

> *Want to find a test site fast?*
> Visit the W5YI-VEC website at: www.w5yi.org, or call them at 800-669-9594.

EXAM CONTENT

The questions, answers, and distracters for each question of the General Class written examination are public information. The question pool included in this book contains all 462 possible questions that can be used to make up your 35-question Element 3 written examination. The VEC is not permitted to change any of the wording, punctuation or numerical values included in any questions, answers, or distracters. The VEC can change the A-B-C-D order of the answers, if it wishes.

Also, the VEC is required to select one question from each syllabus topic under each subelement so you should expect an exam that contains one question from each syllabus topic within each subelement. Look again at the question pool syllabus on page 230 to see how the test will be constructed.

WHAT TO BRING TO THE SITE

Here's what you'll need to bring with you for your General Class examination:
- The fee of approximately $14.00.
- The original plus two copies of your current Technician license. If your license has not yet arrived, make sure you bring the original plus two copies of your Certificate of Successful Completion of Examination (CSCE) indicating your most current license status.
- A photo identification card – your driver's license is ideal for this purpose.
- Some sharp pencils and fine-tip pens. It's good to have a backup.
- Calculators may be used. However, the examiners may erase the memory before your exam begins.
- Any other items that the VEC asks you to bring.

TAKING THE EXAM

Don't speed read the examination! Read each question carefully. Take your time looking for the correct answer. Some answer choices start out looking correct, but end up wrong. When you finish, go back over every question and double-check your answers. When you are satisfied that you have passed the examination, turn in all of your test papers to the examination team. Make sure to thank your VEs and to let them know how much you appreciate their efforts to help promote our hobby.

AFTER THE EXAM

Wait patiently outside the exam room for your results. Chances are the VEs will greet you with a smile and your CSCE. If you didn't pass, they will tell you what to do next. When you are told you passed the exam, be sure you are given the appropriate paperwork:

- The CSCE, signed by all three examiners.
- Make sure the temporary identifier is filled in so you can use it to immediately go on the air with your new General Class frequency privileges.

COMPLETING NCVEC FORM 605

When you arrive at the examination site, one of the first things you will do is complete the NCVEC Form 605. This form is retained by the Volunteer Exam Coordinator which transfers your printed information to an electronic file and sends it to the FCC for your new or upgrade license. Your application may be delayed or kicked-back to you if the VEC can't read your writing. Make absolutely sure you print as legibly as you can, and carefully follow the instructions on the form.

NCVEC Form 605

Name

If you are upgrading from a current license, it is very important to compare the information on your present license with what you are writing on NCVEC Form 605. Make sure that *everything* on NCVEC Form 605 *is identical* to how your present license reads. Fill in your last name, first name, middle initial, and suffix such as junior or senior. You must stay absolutely consistent with your name on any future Form 605s for upgrades or changes of address. If you start out as "Jack" and end up "John," the computer will throw out your next application. If you decide to use a nickname, this is okay – but down the line when you visit a foreign country, they may ask you for identification that needs to illustrate this same nickname. It is best to stick with the name that is on most of your personal pictured IDs, such as your Driver's License.

Social Security Number & FRN

You are required to write in either your Social Security Number or your FCC Registration Number (FRN) in the designated box. If you are a citizen of another country, put down the country name in this box. Your current Technician Class license should show your FRN. If you do not have an FRN and you prefer not to disclose your Social Security Number, you should obtain an FRN *before* the exam session so that you can complete your Form 605 when you pass your test. To obtain an FCC Registration Number, go to the following website and follow the instructions there. Visit:

☞ **https://fjallfoss.fcc.gov/coresWeb/publicHome.do**

Address

Have you moved? Check your current Technician Class license. Did you write in the same exact address? If so, you are good to go. If your address is different, check the "change" box and list your new address.

e-mail Address

This is optional, but it's a good idea because the amateur radio service is now under the FCC's Universal Licensing System. Once you get your new call sign, you will be able to work with the FCC directly via computer, including change of address, change of name, and license renewals without having to do any paperwork.

Phone Numbers

There are two boxes for phone numbers – one for a daytime contact, and the other for your FAX number. Put both numbers down in just in case the VEC or VE team need to re-contact you because they can't read your writing.

Signature

Sign your name as legibly as possible and include all of the letters that you printed as your name at the top of the form. Don't just put down a squiggle or an initial. You need to sign your name all the way out, including all of the letters that were in your printed name.

Final Check

Finally, double-check that your handwriting is legible. If a single letter in your name can't be read clearly and is misinterpreted, subsequent electronic filings may get returned as no action. Make sure your Form 605 is as clear as a bell to your Volunteer Examination team, who will then forward it to their VEC.

Your Examiners' Portion

The VEC will carefully review your NCVEC Form 605 to ensure that they can read your handwriting and that everything looks okay. They will then enter this information into their computer database, and will most likely file your test passing results electronically to their Volunteer Examiner Coordinator. The VEC will then verify the information and electronically file your results with the FCC.

YOUR UPGRADE TO GENERAL CLASS

Usually, your General Class upgrade or new call sign will be granted within 72 hours of passing an examination if it is electronically filed by the VEC. As noted on page 16, the FCC no longer automatically mails a paper copy of your license. See the information on page 16 to learn how to request a paper license from the FCC.

When you pass your written exam you will be issued a CSCE – Certificate of Successful Completion of Examination. This CSCE allows you to begin using your new privileges *immediately*. After your call sign append the letters "AG" to indicate your upgrade is being processed by the FCC. As soon as you see your upgrade on the electronic database, or receive your new license, you can drop the "AG" at the end of your call sign. Visit the W5YI-VEC website where you will find links to other sites that allow you to look-up your upgrade or new call sign. The address is **www.w5yi.org**.

If you are going from no license to General Class, *you may not operate immediately* with your CSCE because you have no call sign. But thanks to electronic filing, your new call sign should show up on the FCC database in about 3 to 5 days.

GENERAL CLASS CALL SIGNS

The FCC has exhausted the availability of "Group C" Technician and General Class call signs that begin with the letter "N," a number, and three other letters, such as N9ABC.

If you did not check the "Change Call Sign" box on your NCVEC Form 605 application, you will simply keep your current call sign. However, if you do check the "Change Call Sign" box, you will receive an entry-level "Group D" call sign as if you were a newly-licensed amateur. We suggest you don't check the "Change Call Sign" box and stick with your present call sign.

U.S. Call Sign Areas

VANITY CALL SIGNS

You are eligible to replace your computer-generated, no-choice call sign with a vanity call sign of your choosing. This call sign could be made up of your initials, or represent your love of animals (K9DOG) or could be call letters that your late mom or dad had when they got started in ham radio years ago. General Class amateur operators may request a vanity call sign from Group D or Group C. You also may request a call sign that was previously assigned to you that may have expired years ago, as well as a call sign of a close relative or former holder who is now deceased.

There is an additional fee charged by the FCC for vanity call signs and also an additional fee for renewal of a vanity call sign. But thousands of amateur enjoy a call sign that has special meaning to them personally, or just sounds better phonetically. You can file for a vanity call direct with the FCC by mail using the required application Form 605 and remittance form159, or electronically on the FCC web site, if you know your FRN and password to access your license record. Today, the best way to file a vanity application is to file electronically.

To make it easier for you and to insure you get the vanity call sign that you want, the W5YI Group at 800-669-9594 offers a vanity filing service and will electronically file your application for you. For an nominal service fee, they will research when and if a specific call is available, file your application and pay the FCC filing fee for you. You could end up with the exact call sign of your choice using their 99% success rate vanity filing service. You can enter your application and call sign choices right on their web site at www.w5yi.org.

As for Gordo, he's staying with his original-issue WB6NOA call sign. If he changed it, he would be breaking a 50-year tradition!

CONGRATULATIONS! YOU PASSED!

After you pass the written exam and code test, congratulations are in order and we offer you a big welcome to the worldwide privileges of General Class! Day or night, summer or fall, sunshine or rain, there is always a worldwide band open and ready for General Class voice, code, PACTOR, and television communications. Your new worldwide privileges are added to your existing VHF and UHF privileges. Before you go on the air, do a lot of listening. This will assure that you get started on the right foot with your new privileges. Remember, even the worldwide bands have band plans, so make sure you are operating within the plan for your worldwide communications.

An Invitation from Gordo

I also would like you to write me so I can send you an exclusive General Class passing certificate, plus some valuable manufacturers' discount coupons. Send a self-addressed large envelope with 12 first class stamps loose on the inside to: Gordon West, WB6NOA, Radio School, Inc., 2414 College Drive, Costa Mesa, CA 92626.

Once again... *Welcome to General Class!* We hope to work you on one of the worldwide bands very soon. You can catch Gordo mobile in his communications van regularly on 14.240 MHz, and he's a "regular" on 10 meters from his Southern California home at 28.400 MHz.

Your next upgrade is *Extra Class*. For Extra Class, use our 3rd Ham Book, *Extra Class*. Our explanations make the formula problem-solving easy and the learning fun! So start thinking about that upgrade now.

It's been fun teaching you the General Class. Good luck on that upcoming exam – We know you're going to pass!

Gordon West, WB6NOA

Eric P. Nichols, KL7AJ

PS: Keep reading! Chapter 5 will get you started on your journey to learn CW!
Aw, come on – you can do it!!

5

Gordo's Guide to Learning Morse Code

On April 15, 2000, the FCC dropped the 20- and 13-word-per-minute Morse code requirements for worldwide frequency privileges for General and Extra Class operators down to 5 words per minute. On February 23, 2007, the FCC *totally eliminated* the Morse code test as a prerequisite for high frequency operation.

The elimination of the Morse code test for operation on worldwide frequencies conforms to international radio regulations. In 2003, the International Telecommunications Union (ITU) World Radiocommunication Conference voted to allow individual nations to determine whether or not to retain a Morse code test as a requirement to operate on frequencies below 30 MHz.

When the FCC eliminated the Morse code test for Technician Class operators in 1991 for VHF/UHF operating, the ruling was adopted with little opposition. However, the announcement that the FCC was considering total elimination of the Morse code test drew thousands of written comments to the FCC. Many comments supported code test elimination, while a minority urged the FCC to retain a code test because of the strong tradition of CW as a ham radio operating mode.

The Federal Communications Commission concluded that "...this change (eliminating the code test) eliminates an unnecessary burden that may discourage current amateur radio operators from advancing their skills and participating more fully in the benefits of amateur radio." The FCC Commissioners recognized the simple fact that learning Morse code was keeping many very technical, talented hams from obtaining their General and Extra Class licenses. Morse code is much like musical rhythms. Some people are tone deaf, and some people couldn't carry a rhythm in a hand basket.

So for years, the Morse code test was an insurmountable hurdle to many talented Technician Class hams who wanted to upgrade. If I could take these Techs and put them into one of my regular Morse code classes, we usually could get the majority of them through the CW test with outside home study, on the air practice (on 2 meters), and classroom study followed by the code test. But throughout the country, Morse code classes were few and far between and it is tough to learn new music and a new language without classroom instruction.

Technician Class operators could not practice on the worldwide airwaves to learn the code because these bands were reserved for only those operators who had already passed the code test. Running Morse code practice on a local 2 meter repeater was one option, but nothing beats the excitement of practicing code on the worldwide bands and hooking up with another station thousands of miles away.

As of February 23, 2007, we can now take new General Class operators and introduce them to Morse code on the exciting worldwide bands!

Morse code is the ham radio operator's most basic language of short and long sounds, dits and dahs, or dots and dashes. Sailors have pounded SOS when trapped beneath a sailboat hull. In submarines, the tapping of Morse code gets the message through when there is no other way to communicate. Prisoners of war have tapped out Morse code messages, or BLINKED the code when being publicly displayed on television.

Ham operators use the code to get through when noise would otherwise cover up data or voice signals. Years ago, before road rage, fellow hams driving might greet each other by sending on their car horns H-I, a friendly salute to another ham.

So I encourage you to learn code. It is best mastered by sound along with memorizing the Morse code patterns seen on the upcoming pages. The pages show the number of dots and dashes to learn for a specific character, and learning the sound (rhythm) of Morse code is always the best way to practice. Let's see what these short sounds and long sounds are all about.

LOOKING AT MORSE CODE

The International Morse code, originally developed as the American Morse code by Samuel Morse, is truly international — all countries use it, and most commercial worldwide services employ operators who can recognize it. It is made up of short and long duration sounds. Long sounds, called "dahs," are three times longer than short sounds, called "dits." *Figure 2-1* shows the time intervals for Morse code sounds and spaces. *Figure 2-3,* on the next page, indicates the sounds for all the CW characters and symbols.

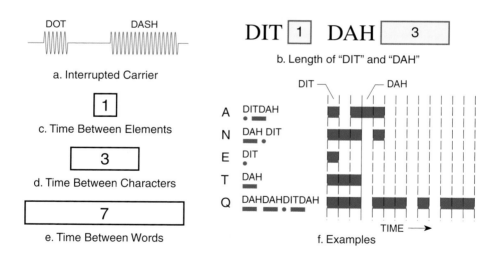

Figure 2-1. Time Intervals for Morse Code

Gordo's Guide to Learning Morse Code

a. Alphabet

LETTER	Composed of:	Sounds like:	LETTER	Composed of:	Sounds like:
A	▪ —	didah	N	— ▪	dahdit
B	— ▪ ▪ ▪	dahdididit	O	— — —	dahdahdah
C	— ▪ — ▪	dahdidahdit	P	▪ — — ▪	didahdahdit
D	— ▪ ▪	dahdidit	Q	— — ▪ —	dahdahdidah
E	▪	dit	R	▪ — ▪	didahdit
F	▪ ▪ — ▪	dididahdit	S	▪ ▪ ▪	dididit
G	— — ▪	dahdahdit	T	—	dah
H	▪ ▪ ▪ ▪	didididit	U	▪ ▪ —	dididah
I	▪ ▪	didit	V	▪ ▪ ▪ —	didididah
J	▪ — — —	didahdahdah	W	▪ — —	ditdahdah
K	— ▪ —	dahdidah	X	— ▪ ▪ —	dahdididah
L	▪ — ▪ ▪	didahdidit	Y	— ▪ — —	dahdidahdah
M	— —	dahdah	Z	— — ▪ ▪	dahdahdidit

b. Special Signals and Punctuation

CHARACTER	Meaning:	Composed of:	Sounds like:
$\overline{AR}$	(end of message)	▪ — ▪ — ▪	didahdidahdit
K	invitation to transmit (go ahead)	— ▪ —	dahdidah
$\overline{SK}$	End of work	▪ ▪ ▪ — ▪ —	didididahdidah
$\overline{SOS}$	International distress call	▪ ▪ ▪ — — — ▪ ▪ ▪	didididahdahdahdididit
V	Test letter (V)	▪ ▪ ▪ —	didididah
R	Received, OK	▪ — ▪	didahdit
$\overline{BT}$	Break or Pause	— ▪ ▪ ▪ —	dahdididih
$\overline{DN}$	Slant Bar	— ▪ ▪ — ▪	dahdididahdit
$\overline{KN}$	Back to You Only	— ▪ — — ▪	dahdidahdahdit
Period		▪ — ▪ — ▪ —	didahdidahdidah
Comma		— — ▪ ▪ — —	dahdahdididahdah
Question mark		▪ ▪ — — ▪ ▪	dididahdahdidit
@	For Web Address	▪ — — ▪ — ▪	didahdahdidahdi

c. Numerals

NUMBER	Composed of:	Sounds like:
1	▪ — — — —	didahdahdahdah
2	▪ ▪ — — —	dididahdahdah
3	▪ ▪ ▪ — —	didididahdah
4	▪ ▪ ▪ ▪ —	dididididah
5	▪ ▪ ▪ ▪ ▪	dididididit
6	— ▪ ▪ ▪ ▪	dahdidididit
7	— — ▪ ▪ ▪	dahdahdididit
8	— — — ▪ ▪	dahdahdahdidit
9	— — — — ▪	dahdahdahdahdit
Ø	— — — — —	dahdahdahdahdah

Figure 2-3. Morse Code and Its Sound

CODE KEY

Morse code is usually sent by using a code key. A typical one is shown in *Figure 2-2a*. Normally it is mounted on a thin piece of wood or plexiglass. Make sure that what you mount it on is thin; if the key is raised too high, it will be uncomfortable to the wrist. The correct sending position for the hand is shown in *Figure 2-2b*.

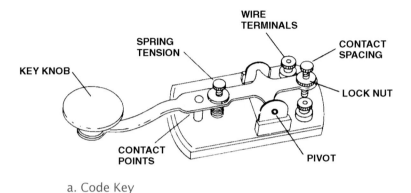

a. Code Key

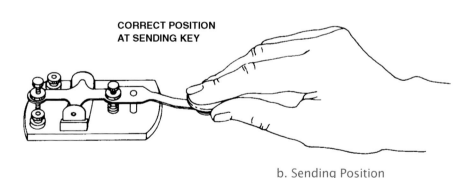

b. Sending Position

Figure 2-2. Code Key for Sending Code

LEARNING MORSE CODE

The reason you are learning the Morse code is to be able to operate all modes on the worldwide bands—including CW. Here are five suggestions (four serious ones) on how to learn the code:

1. Memorize the code from the code charts in this book.
2. Use my fun audio course available at all ham radio stores, and from the W5YI Group.
3. Go out and spend $1,000 and buy a worldwide radio, and listen to the code live and on the air. You don't need to spend that much, but you can listen to Morse code practice on the air, as shown in *Table 2-1*.
4. Use a code key and oscillator to practice sending the code. Believe it or not, someday you're actually going to do code over the live airwaves, using this same code key hooked up to your new megabuck transceiver.
5. Play with code programs on your computer, and *have fun!*

Table 2-1. Radio Frequencies and Times for Code Reception

Pacific	Mountain	Central	Eastern	Mon.	Tue.	Wed.	Thu.	Fri.
6 a.m.	7 a.m.	8 a.m.	9 a.m.		Fast Code	Slow Code	Fast Code	Slow Code
7 a.m. – 1 p.m.	8 a.m. – 2 p.m.	9 a.m. – 3 p.m.	10 a.m. – 4 p.m.	**VISITING OPERATOR TIME**				
1 p.m.	2 p.m.	3 p.m.	4 p.m.	Fast Code	Slow Code	Fast Code	Slow Code	Fast Code
2 p.m.	3 p.m.	4 p.m.	5 p.m.	Code Bulletin				
3 p.m.	4 p.m.	5 p.m.	6 p.m.	Digital Bulletin				
4 p.m.	5 p.m.	6 p.m.	7 p.m.	Slow Code	Fast Code	Slow Code	Fast Code	Slow Code
5 p.m.	6 p.m.	7 p.m.	8 p.m.	Code Bulletin				
6 p.m.	7 p.m.	8 p.m.	9 p.m.	Digital Bulletin				
6:45 p.m.	7:45 p.m.	8:45 p.m.	9:45 p.m.	Voice Bulletin				
7 p.m.	8 p.m.	9 p.m.	10 p.m.	Fast Code	Slow Code	Fast Code	Slow Code	Fast Code
8 p.m.	9 p.m.	10 p.m.	11 p.m.	Code Bulletin				

CW is broadcast on the following MHz frequencies: 1.8025, 3.5815, 7.0475, 14.0475, 18.0975, 21.0675, 28.0675, and 147.555. W1AW schedule courtesy of *QST* magazine.

DATA broadcasts: 3.5975, 7.095, 14.095, 18.1025, 21.095, 28.095 and 147.555 MHz

VOICE broadcasts: 1.855, 3.990, 7.290, 14.290, 18.160, 21.390, 28.590 and 147.555 MHz

CODE COURSES ON CDs AND CASSETTE TAPES

Five words per minute is so slow, and so easy, that many ham radio applicants learn it completely in a single week! You can do it, too, by using the code CDs and tapes mentioned above.

Code courses personally recorded by me make code learning *fun*. They will train you to send and receive the International Morse code in just a few short weeks. They are narrated and parallel the instructions in this book. The CDs have code characters generated at a 15-wpm character rate, spaced out to a 5-wpm word rate. This is known as Farnsworth spacing.

Getting Started

The hardest part of learning the code is taking the first CD out of the case, putting it in your player, and pushing the play button! Try it, and you will be over your biggest hurdle. After that, the CDs will talk you through the code in no time at all.

The CDs make code learning *fun*. You'll hear how humor has been added to the learning process to keep your interest high. Since ham radio is a hobby, there's no reason we can't poke ourselves in the ribs and have a little fun learning the code as part of this hobby experience. Okay, you're still not convinced — you probably have already made up your mind that trying to learn the code will be the hardest part of being a ham. It will not. Give yourself a fair chance. Don't get discouraged. Have patience and remember these important reminders when practicing to learn the Morse code:

- Learn the code by sound. Don't stare at the tiny dots and dashes that we have here in the book — the dit and dah sounds on the CDs and on the air and with your practice keyer will ultimately create an instant letter at your fingertips and into the pencil.
- *Never* scribble down dots or dashes if you forget a letter. Just put a small dash on your paper for a missed letter. You can go back and figure out what the word is by the letters you did copy!
- Practice only with fast code characters; 15-wpm character speed, spaced down to 5-wpm speed, is ideal.
- Practice the code by writing it down whenever possible. This further trains your brain and hand to work together in a subconscious response to the sounds you hear. (Remember Pavlov and his dog "Spot"?)
- Practice only for 15 minutes at a time. The CDs will tell you when to start and when to stop. Your brain and hand will lose that sharp edge once you go beyond 16 minutes of continuous code copy. You will learn much faster with five 15-minute practices per day than a one-hour marathon at night.
- Stay on course with the cassette instructions. Learn the letters, numbers, punctuation marks, and operating signals in the order they are presented. My code teaching system parallels that of the American Radio Relay League, Boy Scouts of America, the Armed Forces, and has worked for thousands in actual classroom instruction.

It was no accident that Samuel Morse gave the single dit for the letter "E" which occurs most often in the English language. He determined the most used letters in the alphabet by counting letters in a printer's type case. He reasoned a printer would have more of the most commonly-used letters. It worked! With just the first lesson, you will be creating simple words and simple sentences with no previous background.

Table 2-2 shows the sequence of letters, punctuation marks, operating signals, and numbers covered in six lessons on the CDs recorded by me.

Table 2-2. Sequence of Lessons on Cassettes

• Lesson 1	E T M A N I S O $\overline{SK}$ Period
• Lesson 2	R U D C 5 Ø $\overline{AR}$ Question Mark
• Lesson 3	K P B G W F H $\overline{BT}$ Comma
• Lesson 4	Q L Y J X V Z $\overline{DN}$ 1 2 3 4 6 7 8 9
• Lesson 5	Random code with narrated answers
• Lesson 6	A typical 5-wpm code test

CODE KEY AND OSCILLATOR – HAM RECEIVER

All worldwide ham transceivers have provisions for a code key to be plugged in for both CW practice off the air as well as CW operating on the air. If you already own a worldwide set, chances are all you will need is a code key for some additional code-sending practice.

Read over your worldwide radio instruction manual where it talks about hooking up the code key. For code practice, read the notes about operating with a "side tone" but not actually going on the air. This "side tone" capability of most worldwide radios will eliminate your need for a separate code oscillator.

Code Key and Oscillator — Separate Unit

Many students may wish to simply buy a complete code key and oscillator set. They are available from local electronic outlets or through advertisements in the ham magazines.

Look again at the code key in *Figure 2-2a*. Note the terminals for the wires. Connect wires to these terminals and tighten the terminals so the wires won't come loose. The two wires will go either to a code oscillator set or to a plug that connects into your ham transceiver. Hook up the wires to the plug as described in your ham transceiver instruction book or the code oscillator set instruction book.

Mount the key firmly, as previously described, then adjust the gap between the contact points. With most new telegraph keys, you will need a pair of pliers to loosen the contact adjustment knob. It's located on the very end of your keyer. First loosen the lock nut, then screw down the adjustment until you get a gap no wider than the thickness of a business card. You want as little space as possible between the points. The contact points are located close to the sending plastic knob.

Now turn on your set or oscillator and listen. If your hear a constant tone, check that the right-hand movable shorting bar is not closed. If it is, swing it open. Adjust the spring tension adjustment screw so that you get a good "feel" each time you push down on the key knob. Adjust it tight enough to keep the contacts from closing while your fingers are resting on the key knob.

Pick up the key by the knob! This is the exact position your fingers should grasp the knob—one or two on top, and one or two on the side of it. Poking at the knob with one finger is unacceptable. Letting your fingers fly off the knob between dots and dashes (dits and dahs) also is not correct. As you are sending, you should be able to instantly pick up the whole key assembly to verify proper finger position.

Your arm and wrist should barely move as you send CW. All the action is in your hand — and it should be almost effortless. Give it a try, and look at *Figure 2-2b* again to double-check your hand position.

Letting someone else use the key to send CW to you will also help you learn the code.

Morse Code Computer Software

The newest way to learn Morse code is through computer-aided instruction. There are many good PC programs on the market that not only teach you the characters, but build speed and allow you to take actual telegraphy examinations, which the computer constructs. Personal computer programs also can be used to make audio tapes on your tape recorder so you can listen to them on the cassette player in your car.

A big advantage of computer-aided Morse code learning is that you can easily customize the program to fit your own needs! You can select the sending speed, Farnsworth character-spacing speed, duration of transmission, number of characters in a random group, tone frequency — and more!

Some have built-in "weighting." That means the software will determine your weaknesses and automatically adjust future sending to give you more study on your problem characters! All Morse code software programs transmit the tone by keying the PC's internal speaker. Some generate a clearer audio tone through the use of external oscillators or internal computer sound cards.

Here are three web addresses of sites that offer Morse code instruction for your computer:

> http://lcwo.net
> http://numorse.com/
> http://www.dxzone.com/catalog/operatingmodes/morsecode/
>   learningmorsecode/

Morse Code Audio Courses

Learn Morse code, CW, with Gordo's narrated audio CD courses. Each course is an 8-CD set in a holder:

- Learn the code at 5 words per minute using his beginner course, GW05.
- Increase your code speed from 5 WPM to 16 WPM using his intermediate courses, GW13.
- Become a CW pro using Gordo's top course to increase your code speed to 28 WPM, GW20.
- Brush up on the CW you remember from your time in the Scouts or Service using Gordo's 2-CD refresher course, GWCT.

These audio CDs play in standard audio/music CD players, or on your computer's audio CD drive. Use your kid's audio CD player, too! Kids love the code!

I hope to hear your CW call on the worldwide bands soon!

Need Gordo's Morse Code Courses?
Call the W5YI Group at 1-800-669-9594, or visit www.w5yi.org

APPENDIX

U.S. VOLUNTEER EXAMINER COORDINATORS IN THE AMATEUR SERVICE

W5YI-VEC
P.O. Box 200065
Arlington, TX 76006-0065
800-669-9594
nb5x@w5yi.org
W5YI-VEC@w5yi.org

Anchorage ARC VEC
PO Box 670616
Anchorage, AK 99567-0616
907-688-0660
e-mail: jwiley@gci.net
Internet: www.kl7aa.net/vec/vecmain.html

American Radio Relay League (ARRL)
225 Main Street
Newington, CT 06111-1494
860-594-0300
860-594-0339
e-mail: vec@arrl.org
Internet: www.arrl.org

Central America CAVEC
1204 Governors Dr. SE
Huntsville, AL 35801-2737
256-653-5007
e-mail: cavec.org@gmail.com

Golden Empire Amateur Radio Society
(GEARS)
P.O. Box 508
Chico, CA 95927-0508
530-893-9211
e-mail: myw6js@gmail.com

Greater L.A. Amateur Radio Group
P.O. Box 500133
Palmdale, CA 93591
661-264-1863
vec@glaarg.org
e-mail: wa6yeo@sbcglobal.net
Internet: www.glaarg.org

Jefferson Amateur Radio Club
P.O. Box 73665
Metairie, LA 70033
504-831-1613
e-mail: w5gad@w5gad.org
Internet: www.w5gad.org

Laurel Amateur Radio Club, Inc.
P.O. Box 146
Laurel, MD 20725-0146
301-937-0394
301-572-5124
e-mail: aa3of@arrl.net
Internet: www.larcmd.org

Milwaukee RAC VEC, Inc.
2505 S. Calhoun Rd., #203
New Berlin, WI 53151
e-mail: MRACVEC@gmail.com
Internet: www.w9rh.org

MO-KAN VEC Coordinator
228 Tennessee Road
Richmond, KS 66080-9174
785-615-1097
e-mail: wo0e@lcwb.coop

Sandarc-VEC
P.O. Box 2446
La Mesa, CA 91943-2446
619-465-3926
e-mail: n6nyx@arrl.net
Internet: http://www.sandarc.net

Sunnyvale VEC Amateur Radio Club, Inc.
P.O. Box 60307
Sunnyvale, CA 94088-0307
408-255-9000
e-mail: vec@amateur-radio.org
Internet: www.amateur-radio.org

W4VEC Volunteer Examiners Club of
America
P. O. Box 482
China Grove, NC 28023-04822
336-249-8734
e-mail: raef@lexcominc.net
Internet: www.w4vec.com

Western Carolina Amateur Radio Society
VEC, Inc.
7 Skyln Ct.
Asheville, NC 28806-3922
828-253-1192
e-mail: wcarsvec@wcarsvec.net

THE W5YI RF SAFETY TABLES

(Developed by Fred Maia, W5YI, working in cooperation with the ARRL.)

There are two ways to determine whether your station's radio frequency signal radiation is within the MPE (Maximum Permissible Exposure) guidelines established by the FCC for *"controlled"* and *"uncontrolled"* environments. One way is direct *"measurement"* of the RF fields. The second way is through *"prediction"* using various antenna modeling, equations and calculation methods described in the FCC's *OET Bulletin 65* and *Supplement B.*

In general, most amateurs will not have access to the appropriate calibrated equipment to make precise field strength/power density measurements. The field-strength meters in common use by amateur operators are inexpensive, hand-held field strength meters that do not provide the accuracy necessary for reliable measurements, especially when different frequencies may be encountered at a given measurement location. It is more practical for amateurs to determine their PEP output power at the antenna and then look up the required distances to the controlled/uncontrolled environments using the following tables, which were developed using the prediction equations supplied by the FCC.

The FCC has determined that radio operators and their families are in the "controlled" environment and your neighbors and passers-by are in the "uncontrolled" environment. The estimated minimum compliance distances are in meters from the transmitting antenna to either the occupational/controlled exposure environment ("Con") or the general population/uncontrolled exposure environment ("Unc") using typical antenna gains for the amateur service and assuming 100% duty cycle and maximum surface reflection. Therefore, these charts represent the worst case scenario. They do not take into consideration compliance distance reductions that would be caused by:

(1) Feed line losses, which reduce power output at the antenna especially at the VHF and higher frequency levels.

(2) Duty cycle caused by the emission type. The emission type factor accounts for the fact that, for some modulated emission types that have a non-constant envelope, the PEP can be considerably larger than the average power. Multiply the distances by 0.4 if you are using CW Morse telegraphy, and by 0.2 for two-way SSB (single sideband) voice. There is no reduction for FM.

(3) Duty cycle caused by on/off time or "time-averaging." The RF safety guidelines permit RF exposures to be averaged over certain periods of time with the average not to exceed the limit for continuous exposure. The averaging time for occupational/controlled exposures is 6 minutes, while the averaging time for general population/uncontrolled exposures is 30 minutes. For example, if the relevant time interval for time-averaging is 6 minutes, an amateur could be exposed to two times the applicable power density limit for three minutes as long as he or she were not exposed at all for the preceding or following three minutes.

A routine evaluation is not required for vehicular mobile or hand-held transceiver stations. Amateur Radio operators should be aware, however, of the potential for exposure to RF electromagnetic fields from these stations, and take measures (such as reducing transmitting power to the minimum necessary, positioning the radiating antenna as far from humans as practical, and limiting continuous transmitting time) to protect themselves and the occupants of their vehicles.

Amateur Radio operators should also be aware that the FCC radio-frequency safety regulations address exposure to people — and not the strength of the signal. Amateurs may exceed the Maximum Permissible Exposure (MPE) limits as long as no one is exposed to the radiation.

How to read the chart: If you are radiating 500 watts from your 10 meter dipole (about a 3 dB gain), there must be at least 4.5 meters (about 15 feet) between you (and your family) and the antenna — and a distance of 10 meters (about 33 feet) between the antenna and your neighbors.

Medium and High Frequency Amateur Bands
All distances are in meters

Freq. (MF/HF) (MHz/Band)	Antenna Gain (dBi)	100 watts		500 watts		1000 watts		1500 watts	
		Con.	Unc.	Con.	Unc.	Con.	Unc.	Con.	Unc.
2.0 (160m)	0	0.1	0.2	0.3	0.5	0.5	0.7	0.6	0.8
2.0 (160m)	3	0.2	0.3	0.5	0.7	0.6	1.06	0.8	1.2
4.0 (75/80m)	0	0.2	0.4	0.4	1.0	0.6	1.3	0.7	1.6
4.0 (75/80m)	3	0.3	0.6	0.6	1.3	0.9	1.9	1.0	2.3
7.3 (40m)	0	0.3	0.8	0.8	1.7	1.1	2.5	1.3	3.0
7.3 (40m)	3	0.5	1.1	1.1	2.5	1.6	3.5	1.9	4.2
7.3 (40m)	6	0.7	1.5	1.5	3.5	2.2	4.9	2.7	6.0
10.15 (30m)	0	0.5	1.1	1.1	2.4	1.5	3.4	1.9	4.2
10.15 (30m)	3	0.7	1.5	1.5	3.4	2.2	4.8	2.6	5.9
10.15 (30m)	6	1.0	2.2	2.2	4.8	3.0	6.8	3.7	8.3
14.35 (20m)	0	0.7	1.5	1.5	3.4	2.2	4.8	2.6	5.9
14.35 (20m)	3	1.0	2.2	2.2	4.8	3.0	6.8	3.7	8.4
14.35 (20m)	6	1.4	3.0	3.0	6.8	4.3	9.6	5.3	11.8
14.35 (20m)	9	1.9	4.3	4.3	9.6	6.1	13.6	7.5	16.7
18.168 (17m)	0	0.9	1.9	1.9	4.3	2.7	6.1	3.3	7.5
18.168 (17m)	3	1.2	2.7	2.7	6.1	3.9	8.6	4.7	10.6
18.168 (17m)	6	1.7	3.9	3.9	8.6	5.5	12.2	6.7	14.9
18.168 (17m)	9	2.4	5.4	5.4	12.2	7.7	17.2	9.4	21.1
21.145 (15m)	0	1.0	2.3	2.3	5.1	3.2	7.2	4.0	8.8
21.145 (15m)	3	1.4	3.2	3.2	7.2	4.6	10.2	5.6	12.5
21.145 (15m)	6	2.0	4.6	4.6	10.2	6.4	14.4	7.9	17.6
21.145 (15m)	9	2.9	6.4	6.4	14.4	9.1	20.3	11.1	24.9
24.99 (12m)	0	1.2	2.7	2.7	5.9	3.8	8.4	4.6	10.3
24.99 (12m)	3	1.7	3.8	3.8	8.4	5.3	11.9	6.5	14.5
24.99 (12m)	6	2.4	5.3	5.3	11.9	7.5	16.8	9.2	20.5
24.99 (12m)	9	3.4	7.5	7.5	16.8	10.6	23.7	13.0	29.0
29.7 (10m)	0	1.4	3.2	3.2	7.1	4.5	10.0	5.5	12.2
29.7 (10m)	3	2.0	4.5	4.5	10.0	6.3	14.1	7.7	17.3
29.7 (10m)	6	2.8	6.3	6.3	14.1	8.9	19.9	10.9	24.4
29.7 (10m)	9	4.0	8.9	8.9	19.9	12.6	28.2	15.4	34.5

VHF/UHF Amateur Bands

All distances are in meters

Freq. (MF/HF) (MHz/Band)	Antenna Gain (dBi)	Peak Envelope Power (watts)							
		50 watts		100 watts		500 watts		1000 watts	
		Con.	Unc.	Con.	Unc.	Con.	Unc.	Con.	Unc.
50 (6m)	0	1.0	2.3	1.4	3.2	3.2	7.1	4.5	10.1
50 (6m)	3	1.4	3.2	2.0	4.5	4.5	10.1	6.4	14.3
50 (6m)	6	2.0	4.5	2.8	6.4	6.4	14.2	9.0	20.1
50 (6m)	9	2.8	6.4	4.0	9.0	9.0	20.1	12.7	28.4
50 (6m)	12	4.0	9.0	5.7	12.7	12.7	28.4	18.0	40.2
50 (6m)	15	5.7	12.7	8.0	18.0	18.0	40.2	25.4	56.8
144 (2m)	0	1.0	2.3	1.4	3.2	3.2	7.1	4.5	10.1
144 (2m)	3	1.4	3.2	2.0	4.5	4.5	10.1	6.4	14.3
144 (2m)	6	2.0	4.5	2.8	6.4	6.4	14.2	9.0	20.1
144 (2m)	9	2.8	6.4	4.0	9.0	9.0	20.1	12.7	28.4
144 (2m)	12	4.0	9.0	5.7	12.7	12.7	28.4	18.0	40.2
144 (2m)	15	5.7	12.7	8.0	18.0	18.0	40.2	25.4	56.8
144 (2m)	20	10.1	22.6	14.3	32.0	32.0	71.4	45.1	101.0
222 (1.25m)	0	1.0	2.3	1.4	3.2	3.2	7.1	4.5	10.1
222 (1.25m)	3	1.4	3.2	2.0	4.5	4.5	10.1	6.4	14.3
222 (1.25m)	6	2.0	4.5	2.8	6.4	6.4	14.2	9.0	20.1
222 (1.25m)	9	2.8	6.4	4.0	9.0	9.0	20.1	12.7	28.4
222 (1.25m)	12	4.0	9.0	5.7	12.7	12.7	28.4	18.0	40.2
222 (1.25m)	15	5.7	12.7	8.0	18.0	18.0	40.2	25.4	56.8
450 (70cm)	0	0.8	1.8	1.2	2.6	2.6	5.8	3.7	8.2
450 (70cm)	3	1.2	2.6	1.6	3.7	3.7	8.2	5.2	11.6
450 (70cm)	6	1.6	3.7	2.3	5.2	5.2	11.6	7.4	16.4
450 (70cm)	9	2.3	5.2	3.3	7.3	7.3	16.4	10.4	23.2
450 (70cm)	12	3.3	7.3	4.6	10.4	10.4	23.2	14.7	32.8
902 (33cm)	0	0.6	1.3	0.8	1.8	1.8	4.1	2.6	5.8
902 (33cm)	3	0.8	1.8	1.2	2.6	2.6	5.8	3.7	8.2
902 (33cm)	6	1.2	2.6	1.6	3.7	3.7	8.2	5.2	11.6
902 (33cm)	9	1.6	3.7	2.3	5.2	5.2	11.6	7.3	16.4
902 (33cm)	12	2.3	5.2	3.3	7.3	7.3	16.4	10.4	23.2
1240 (23cm)	0	0.5	1.1	0.7	1.6	1.6	3.5	2.2	5.0
1240 (23cm)	3	0.7	1.6	1.0	2.2	2.2	5.0	3.1	7.0
1240 (23cm)	6	1.0	2.2	1.4	3.1	3.1	7.0	4.4	9.9
1240 (23cm)	9	1.4	3.1	2.0	4.4	4.4	9.9	6.3	14.0
1240 (23cm)	12	2.0	4.4	2.8	6.2	6.2	14.0	8.8	19.8

All distances are in meters. To convert from meters to feet multiply meters by 3.28. Distance indicated is shortest line-of-sight distance to point where MPE limit for appropriate exposure tier is predicted to occur.

AUTHORIZED FREQUENCY BANDS – AMATEUR SERVICE (for U.S. Amateur Stations operating from ITU-Region 2–North and South America)

Current License Class¹ METERS	Novice	Technician	Tech. w/Code	General	Advanced	Extra Class
Grandfathered²	Novice	Technician	Technician Plus	General	Advanced	Extra Class
160				1800-2000 kHz/All	1800-2000 kHz/All	1800-2000 kHz/All
80/75	3525-3600 kHz/CW		3525-3600 kHz/CW	3525-3600 kHz/CW 3800-4000 kHz/Ph	3525-3600 kHz/CW 3700-4000 kHz/Ph	3500-4000 kHz/CW 3600-4000 kHz/Ph
40	7025-7125 kHz/CW		7025-7125 kHz/CW	7025-7125 kHz/CW 7175-7300 kHz/Ph	7025-7125 kHz/CW 7125-7300 kHz/Ph	7000-7300 kHz/CW 7125-7300 kHz/Ph
30				10.1-10.15 MHz/CW	10.1-10.15 MHz/CW	10.1-10.15 MHz/CW
20				14.025-14.15 MHz/CW 14.225-14.35 MHz/Ph	14.025-14.15 MHz/CW 14.175-14.35 MHz/Ph	14.0-14.35 MHz/CW 14.15-14.35 MHz/Ph
17				18.068-18.11 MHz/CW 18.11-18.168 MHz/Ph	18.068-18.11 MHz/CW 18.11-18.168 MHz/Ph	18.068-18.11 MHz/CW 18.11-18.168 MHz/Ph
15	21.025-21.2 MHz/CW		21.025-21.2 MHz/CW	21.025-21.2 MHz/CW 21.275-21.45 MHz/Ph	21.025-21.2 MHz/CW 21.225-21.45 MHz/Ph	21.0-21.45 MHz/CW 21.2-21.45 MHz/Ph
12				24.89-24.99 MHz/CW 24.93-24.99 MHz/Ph	24.89-24.99 MHz/CW 24.93-24.99 MHz/Ph	24.89-24.99 MHz/CW 24.93-24.99 MHz/Ph
10			28.0-28.5 MHz/CW 28.3-28.5 MHz/Ph	28.0-28.3 MHz/CW 28.3-29.7 MHz/Ph	28.0-28.3 MHz/CW 28.3-29.7 MHz/Ph	28.0-29.7 MHz/CW 28.3-29.7 MHz/Ph
6		50-54 MHz/CW 50.1-54 MHz/Ph	50-54 MHz/CW 50.1-54 MHz/Ph	50-54 MHz/CW 50.1-54 MHz/Ph	50-54 MHz/CW 50.1-54 MHz/Ph	50-54 MHz/CW 50.1-54 MHz/Ph
2		144-148 MHz/CW 144.1-148 MHz/All	144-148 MHz/CW 144.1-148 MHz/All	144-148 MHz/CW 144.1-148 MHz/All	144-148 MHz/CW 144.1-148 MHz/All	144-148 MHz/CW 144.1-148 MHz/All
1.25	222-225 MHz/All	³ 222-225 MHz/All	222-225 MHz/All	222-225 MHz/All	222-225 MHz/All	222-225 MHz/All
0.70		420-450 MHz/All	420-450 MHz/All	420-450 MHz/All	420-450 MHz/All	420-450 MHz/All
0.33		902-928 MHz/All	902-928 MHz/All	902-928 MHz/All	902-928 MHz/All	902-928 MHz/All
0.23	1270-1295 MHz/All	1270-1295 MHz/All	1240-1300 MHz/All	1240-1300 MHz/All	1240-1300 MHz/All	1240-1300 MHz/All

¹ Effective 4-15-00   ² Prior to 4-15-00   ³ Effective 2/1/94 219-220 MHz is authorized for point-to-point fixed digital message forwarding systems.
⁴ 60 meter operation restricted to 5 channels with center frequencies of 5332.0, 5348.0, 5358.5, 5373.0 and 5405.0 kHz, 100 watts PEP. See FCC 97.303.

Note: Morse code (CW, A1A) may be used on any frequency allocated to the amateur service. Telephony emission (abbreviated Ph above) authorized on certain bands as indicated. Higher class licensees may use slow-scan television and facsimile emissions on the Phone bands; radio teletype/digital on the CW bands. All amateur modes and emissions are authorized above 144.1 MHz. In actual practice, the modes/ emissions used are somewhat more complicated than shown above due to the existence of various band plans and "gentlemen's agreements" concerning where certain operations should take place.

Appendix

The following CEPT countries allow U.S. Amateurs to operate in their countries without a reciprocal license. Be sure to carry a copy of your FCC license and FCC Public Notice DA99-1098.

Austria	France & its	Luxembourg	Sweden
Belgium	possessions	Monaco	Switzerland
Bosnia & Herzegovina	Germany	Montenegro	Turkey
Bulgaria	Greenland	Netherlands	United Kingdom & its
Croatia	Hungary	Netherlands Antilles	possessions
Cyprus	Iceland	Norway	
Czech Republic	Ireland	Portugal	
Denmark	Italy	Romania	
Estonia	Latvia	Slovak Republic	
Faroe Islands	Liechtenstein	Slovenia	
Finland	Lithuania	Spain	

List of Countries Permitting Third-Party Traffic

Country	Call Sign Prefix	Country	Call Sign Prefix	Country	Call Sign Prefix
Antigua and Barbuda	V2	El Salvador	YS	Paraguay	ZP
Argentina	LU	The Gambia	C5	Peru	OA
Australia	VK	Ghana	9G	Philippines	DU
Austria, Vienna	4U1VIC	Grenada	J3	St. Christopher & Nevis	V4
Belize	V3	Guatemala	TG	St. Lucia	J6
Bolivia	CP	Guyana	8R	St. Vincent & Grenadines.	. J8
Bosnia-Herzegovina	T9	Haiti	HH	Sierra Leone	9L
Brazil	PY	Honduras	HR	South Africa	ZS
Canada	VE, VO, VY	Israel	4X	Swaziland	3D6
Chile	CE	Jamaica	6Y	Trinidad and Tobago	9Y
Colombia	HK	Jordan	JY	Turkey	TA
Comoros	D6	Liberia	EL	United Kingdom	GB*
Costa Rica	TI	Marshall Is	V6	Uruguay	CX
Cuba	CO	Mexico	XE	Venezuela	YV
Dominica	J7	Micronesia	V6	ITU-Geneva	4U1ITU
Dominican Republic	HI	Nicaragua	YN	VIC-Vienna	4U1VIC
Ecuador	HC	Panama	HP		

Countries Holding U.S. Reciprocal Agreements

Antigua, Barbuda	Chile	Greece	Liberia	Seychelles
Argentina	Colombia	Greenland	Luxembourg	Sierra Leone
Australia	Costa Rica	Grenada	Macedonia	Solomon Islands
Austria	Croatia	Guatemala	Marshall Is.	South Africa
Bahamas	Cyprus	Guyana	Mexico	Spain
Barbados	Denmark	Haiti	Micronesia	St. Lucia
Belgium	Dominica	Honduras	Monaco	St. Vincent and
Belize	Dominican Rep.	Iceland	Netherlands	Grenadines
Bolivia	Ecuador	India	Netherlands Ant.	Surinam
Bosnia-	El Salvador	Indonesia	New Zealand	Sweden
Herzegovina	Fiji	Ireland	Nicaragua	Switzerland
Botswana	Finland	Israel	Norway	Thailand
Brazil	France[2]	Italy	Panama	Trinidad, Tobago
Canada[1]	Germany	Jamaica	Paraguay	Turkey
		Japan	Papua New Guinea	Tuvalu
1. Do not need reciprocal permit		Jordan	Peru	United Kingdom[3]
2. Includes all French Territories		Kiribati	Philippines	Uruguay
3. Includes all British Territories		Kuwait	Portugal	Venezuela

QUESTION POOL SYLLABUS

The syllabus used by the NCVEC Question Pool Committee to develop the question pool is included here as an aid in studying the subelements and topic groups. Reviewing the syllabus will give you an understanding of how the question pool is used to develop the Element 3 General Class written examination. Remember, one question will be taken from each topic group within each subelement to create your exam.

2015-19 Element 3 General Class Syllabus

G1 – Commission's Rules
[5 Exam Questions - 5 Groups]
G1A - General Class control operator frequency privileges; primary and secondary allocations
G1B - Antenna structure limitations; good engineering and good amateur practice; beacon operation; prohibited transmissions; retransmitting radio signals
G1C - Transmitter power regulations; data emission standards
G1D - Volunteer Examiners and Volunteer Examiner Coordinators; temporary identification
G1E - Control categories; repeater regulations; harmful interference; third party rules; ITU regions; automatically controlled digital station

G2 – Operating Procedures
[5 Exam Questions - 5 Groups]
G2A - Phone operating procedures; USB/LSB conventions; procedural signals; breaking into a contact; VOX operation
G2B - Operating courtesy; band plans; emergencies, including drills and emergency communications
G2C - CW operating procedures and procedural signals; Q signals and common abbreviations; full break in
G2D - Amateur Auxiliary; minimizing interference; HF operations
G2E - Digital operating; procedures, procedural signals and common abbreviations

G3 – Radio Wave Propagation
[3 Exam Questions - 3 Groups]
G3A - Sunspots and solar radiation; ionospheric disturbances; propagation forecasting and indices
G3B - Maximum Usable Frequency; Lowest Usable Frequency; propagation
G3C - Ionospheric layers; critical angle and frequency; HF scatter; Near-Vertical Incidence Skywave

G4 – Amateur Radio Practices
[5 Exam Questions-5 groups]
G4A - Station operation and set up
G4B - Test and monitoring equipment; two-tone test
G4C - Interference with consumer electronics; grounding; DSP
G4D - Speech processors; S meters; sideband operation near band edges
G4E - HF mobile radio installations; emergency and battery powered operation

G5 – Electrical Principles
[3 Exam Questions - 3 Groups]
G5A - Reactance; inductance; capacitance; impedance; impedance matching
G5B - The Decibel; current and voltage dividers; electrical power calculations; sine wave root-mean-square (RMS) values; PEP calculations
G5C - Resistors, capacitors, and inductors in series and parallel; transformers

G6 – Circuit Components
[2 Exam Questions - 2 Groups]
G6A - Resistors; Capacitors; Inductors; Rectifiers; solid state diodes and transistors; vacuum tubes; batteries
G6B - Analog and digital integrated circuits (ICs); microprocessors; memory; I/O devices; microwave ICs (MMICs); display devices

G7 – Practical Circuits
[3 Exam Questions - 3 Groups]
G7A - Power supplies; schematic symbols
G7B - Digital circuits; amplifiers and oscillators
G7C - Receivers and transmitters; filters, oscillators

G8 – Signals and Emissions
[3 Exam Questions - 3 Groups]
G8A - Carriers and modulation; AM; FM; single sideband; modulation envelope; digital modulation; over modulation
G8B - Frequency mixing; multiplication; bandwidths of various modes; deviation
G8C - Digital emission modes

G9 – Antennas and Feedlines
[4 Exam Questions - 4 Groups]
G9A - Antenna feed lines; characteristic impedance and attenuation; SWR calculation, measurement and effects; matching networks
G9B - Basic antennas
G9C - Directional antennas
G9D - Specialized antennas

G0 – Electrical and RF Safety
[2 Exam Questions - 2 Groups]
G0A - RF safety principles, rules and guidelines; routine station evaluation
G0B - Safety in the ham shack; electrical shock and treatment, safety grounding, fusing, interlocks, wiring, antenna and tower safety

2015-19 ELEMENT 3 Q&A CROSS REFERENCE

The following cross reference presents all 464 question numbers included in the 2015-19 Element 3 question pool in numerical order, followed by the page number on which the question begins in the book. This will allow you to locate specific questions by question number. Note: two questions were deleted from the pool by the Question Pool Committee resulting in an active pool of 462 questions. The deleted questions do not appear in the book.

Question	Page	Question	Page	Question	Page	Question	Page	Question	Page
G1 – Commission's		G1E01	40	G2D02	35	G3B10	84	G4C01	165
Rules		G1E02	27	G2D03	36	G3B11	87	G4C02	166
G1A01	26	G1E03	69	G2D04	89	G3B12	84	G4C03	165
G1A02	28	G1E04	50	G2D05	39			G4C04	166
G1A03	29	G1E05	40	G2D06	90	G3C01	85	G4C05	162
G1A04	30	G1E06	50	G2D07	30	G3C02	82	G4C06	164
G1A05	29	G1E07	41	G2D08	34	G3C03	81	G4C07	162
G1A06	31	G1E08	41	G2D09	35	G3C04	82	G4C08	165
G1A07	28	G1E09	40	G2D10	49	G3C05	86	G4C09	163
G1A08	31	G1E10	DELETED	G2D11	172	G3C06	89	G4C10	163
G1A09	28		BY QPC			G3C07	88	G4C11	114
G1A10	27	G1E11	69	G2E01	63	G3C08	88	G4C12	113
G1A11	32	G1E12	70	G2E02	73	G3C09	87	G4C13	116
G1A12	31	G1E13	69	G2E03	73	G3C10	89		
G1A13	30			G2E04	62	G3C11	169	G4D01	99
G1A14	29	**G2 – Operating**		G2E05	64	G3C12	85	G4D02	99
		Procedures		G2E06	62	G3C13	170	G4D03	101
G1B01	198	G2A01	52	G2E07	62			G4D04	116
G1B02	60	G2A02	53	G2E08	64	**G4 – Amateur Radio**		G4D05	108
G1B03	59	G2A03	52	G2E09	73	**Practices**		G4D06	116
G1B04	78	G2A04	52	G2E10	72	G4A01	115	G4D07	108
G1B05	37	G2A05	51	G2E11	65	G4A02	60	G4D08	48
G1B06	38	G2A06	51	G2E12	66	G4A03	47	G4D09	49
G1B07	38	G2A07	51	G2E13	72	G4A04	110	G4D10	48
G1B08	37	G2A08	46	G2E14	63	G4A05	100	G4D11	48
G1B09	39	G2A09	53			G4A06	177		
G1B10	59	G2A10	49	**G3 – Radio Wave**		G4A07	100	G4E01	184
G1B11	36	G2A11	46	**Propagation**		G4A08	110	G4E02	184
G1B12	36			G3A01	91	G4A09	104	G4E03	141
		G2B01	46	G3A02	93	G4A10	58	G4E04	141
G1C01	29	G2B02	77	G3A03	92	G4A11	49	G4E05	183
G1C02	27	G2B03	48	G3A04	92	G4A12	47	G4E06	184
G1C03	30	G2B04	54	G3A05	92	G4A13	115	G4E07	166
G1C04	28	G2B05	48	G3A06	93	G4A14	100	G4E08	139
G1C05	27	G2B06	45	G3A07	95	G4A15	164	G4E09	140
G1C06	31	G2B07	45	G3A08	94			G4E10	140
G1C07	68	G2B08	32	G3A09	91	G4B01	102	G4E11	141
G1C08	67	G2B09	78	G3A10	91	G4B02	103		
G1C09	68	G2B10	79	G3A11	90	G4B03	103	**G5 – Electrical**	
G1C10	68	G2B11	77	G3A12	92	G4B04	103	**Principles**	
G1C11	68	G2B12	77	G3A13	92	G4B05	138	G5A01	155
				G3A14	95	G4B06	138	G5A02	153
G1D01	24	G2C01	58	G3A15	95	G4B07	102	G5A03	153
G1D02	42	G2C02	57	G3A16	94	G4B08	186	G5A04	154
G1D03	25	G2C03	58			G4B09	186	G5A05	155
G1D04	43	G2C04	57	G3B01	90	G4B10	192	G5A06	154
G1D05	42	G2C05	54	G3B02	85	G4B11	185	G5A07	156
G1D06	24	G2C06	54	G3B03	84	G4B12	185	G5A08	156
G1D07	42	G2C07	55	G3B04	83	G4B13	185	G5A09	153
G1D08	43	G2C08	58	G3B05	83	G4B14	138	G5A10	155
G1D09	23	G2C09	57	G3B06	86	G4B15	101	G5A11	155
G1D10	43	G2C10	57	G3B07	86			G5A12	156
G1D11	24	G2C11	57	G3B08	82			G5A13	156
		G2D01	35	G3B09	81				

COMMON CW ABBREVIATIONS

AA	**All** after	NR	**Number**
AB	**All** before	NW	**Now;** I resume transmission
ABT	**About**	OB	**Old** boy
ADR	**Address**	OM	**Old** man
AGN	**Again**	OP-OPR	**Operator**
ANT	**Antenna**	OT	**Old** timer; old top
AR	**End** of message	PBL	**Preable**
BCI	**Broadcast** interference	PSE-PLS	**Please**
BK	**Break;** break me; break in	PWR	**Power**
BN	**All** between; been	PX	**Press**
B4	**Before**	R	**Received** as transmitted; are
C	**Yes**	RCD	**Received**
CFM	**Confirm;** I confirm	REF	**Refer** to; referring to; reference
CK	**Check**	RPT	**Repeat;** I repeat
CL	**I** am closing my station; call	SED	**Said**
CLD-CLG	**Called;** calling	SEZ	**Says**
CUD	**Could**	SIG	**Signature;** signal
CUL	**See** you later	SKED	**Schedule**
CUM	**Come**	SRI	**Sorry**
CW	**Continuous** Wave	SVC	**Service;** prefix to service message
DLD-DLVD	**Delivered**	TFC	**Traffic**
DX	**Distance**	TMW	**Tomorrow**
FB	**Fine** business; excellent	TNX	**Thanks**
GA	**Go** ahead (or resume sending)	TU	**Thank** you
GB	**Good-by**	TVI	**Television** interference
GBA	**Give** better address	TXT	**Text**
GE	**Good** evening	UR-URS	**Your;** you're; yours
GG	**Going**	VFO-	**Variable-frequency** oscillator
GM	**Good** morning	VY	**Very**
GN	**Good** night	WA	**Word** after
GND	**Ground**	WB	**Word** before
GUD	**Good**	WD-WDS	**Word;** words
HI	**The** telegraphic laugh; high	WKD-WKG	**Worked;** working
HR	**Here;** hear	WL	**Well;** will
HV	**Have**	WUD	**Would**
HW	**How**	WX	**Weather**
KN	**Listening** for specific station(s)	XMTR	**Transmitter**
LID	**A** poor operator	XTAL	**Crystal**
MILS	**Milliamperes**	XYL	**Wife**
MSG	**Message;** prefix to radiogram	YL	**Young** lady
N	**No**	73	**Best** regards
ND	**Nothing** doing	88	**Love** and kisses
NIL	**Nothing;** I have nothing for you		

THREE SIMPLE RULES FOR 60 METERS

When operating 60 meters, it is crucial that you transmit on the correct frequency within the authorized channel. Compliance with the rules when using Single Sideband phone or sound card digital modes is very straightforward. CW operation is slightly different. 60 Meter channels are assigned by the following table, where the frequency represents the VFO display (suppressed carrier) frequency of your transceiver, which is also the low frequency boundary of the channel:

Channel 1: 5330.5 kHz
Channel 2: 5346.5 kHz
Channel 3: 5357.0 kHz
Channel 4: 5371.5 kHz
Channel 5: 5403.5 kHz

If you heed the following three rules, you will be in compliance with the FCC regulations:

(1) Phone Operation: Set your transmitter to Upper Sideband (USB) and your VFO to display the frequency of the chosen channel from the table. Be sure your transmitter is set to limit the bandwidth to 2.8 kHz. Check your operator's manual if you are unsure about how to do this. Most modern rigs default to this setting, but READ THE MANUAL!

(2) Sound Card Digital Modes: Set your transmitter to USB, select the channel frequency on your VFO, and click on 1.5 kHz on your waterfall or spectrum display. This will place your transmitted signal properly in the CENTER of the channel.

(3) CW operation: Place your transmitted signal in the CENTER of the channel, 1.5 kHz above the assigned carrier frequency shown in the table. Depending on your particular transceiver, this MAY OR MAY NOT correspond to your VFO display frequency! READ YOUR OPERATOR'S MANUAL TO BE SURE.

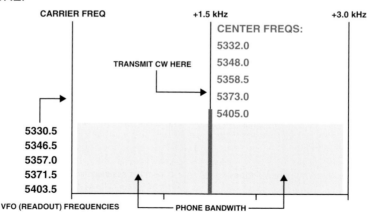

The diagram above shows the position of your transmitted signal within a 60 meter channel.

One final note: If you're using ***non-sound card digital modes***, such as "old school" RTTY with direct FSK modulation, you must assure that your transmitted signal is exactly centered in the channel, using any reliable means at your disposal.

Glossary

Amateur communication: Noncommercial radio communication by or among amateur stations solely with a personal aim and without personal or business interest.

Amateur operator/primary station license: An instrument of authorization issued by the FCC comprised of a station license, and also incorporating an operator license indicating the class of privileges.

Amateur operator: A person holding a valid license to operate an amateur station issued by the FCC. Amateur operators are frequently referred to as ham operators.

Amateur Radio services: The amateur service, the amateur-satellite service, and the radio amateur civil emergency service.

Amateur-satellite service: A radiocommunication service using stations on Earth satellites for the same purpose as those of the amateur service.

Amateur service: A radiocommunication service for the purpose of self-training, intercommunication and technical investigations carried out by amateurs; that is, duly authorized persons interested in radio technique solely with a personal aim and without pecuniary interest.

Amateur station: A station licensed in the amateur service embracing necessary apparatus at a particular location used for amateur communication.

AMSAT: Radio Amateur Satellite Corporation, a nonprofit scientific organization. (P.O. Box #27, Washington, DC 20044)

ANSI: American National Standards Institute. A non-government organization that develops recommended standards for a variety of applications.

APRS: Automatic Position Radio System, which takes GPS (Global Positioning System) information and translates it into an automatic packet of digital information.

ARES: Amateur Radio Emergency Service — the emergency division of the American Radio Relay League. Also see RACES

ARRL: American Radio Relay League, national organization of U.S. Amateur Radio operators. (225 Main Street, Newington, CT 06111)

Audio Frequency (AF): The range of frequencies that can be heard by the human ear, generally 20 hertz to 20 kilohertz.

Automatic control: The use of devices and procedures for station control without the control operator being present at the control point when the station is transmitting.

Automatic Volume Control (AVC): A circuit that continually maintains a constant audio output volume in spite of deviations in input signal strength.

Beam or Yagi antenna: An antenna array that receives or transmits RF energy in a particular direction. Usually rotatable.

Block diagram: A simplified outline of an electronic system where circuits or components are shown as boxes.

Broadcasting: Information or programming transmitted by radio means intended for the general public.

Bulletin No. 65: The Office of Engineering & Technology bulletin that provides specified safety guidelines for human exposure to radiofrequency (RF) radiation.

Business communications: Any transmission or communication the purpose of which is to facilitate the regular business or commercial affairs of any party. Business communications are prohibited in the amateur service.

Call Book: A published list of all licensed amateur operators available in North American and Foreign editions.

Call sign: The FCC systematically assigns each amateur station its primary call sign.

Certificate of Successful Completion of Examination (CSCE): A certificate providing examination credit for 365 days. Both written and code credit can be authorized.

Coaxial cable, Coax: A concentric, two-conductor cable in which one conductor surrounds the other, separated by an insulator.

Controlled Environment: Involves people who are aware of and who can exercise control over radiofrequency exposure. Controlled exposure limits apply to both occupational workers and Amateur Radio operators and their immediate households.

Control operator: An amateur operator designated by the licensee of an amateur station to be responsible for the station transmissions.

Coordinated repeater station: An amateur repeater station for which the transmitting and receiving frequencies have been recommended by the recognized repeater coordinator.

Coordinated Universal Time (UTC): (Also Greenwich Mean Time, UCT or Zulu time.) The time at the zero-degree (0°) Meridian which passes through Greenwich, England. A universal time among all amateur operators.

Crystal: A quartz or similar material which has been ground to produce natural vibrations of a specific frequency. Quartz crystals produce a high degree of frequency stability in radio transmitters.

CW: See Morse code.

Dipole antenna: The most common wire antenna. Length is equal to one-half of the wavelength. Fed by coaxial cable.

Dummy antenna: A device or resistor which serves as a transmitter's antenna without radiating radio waves. Generally used to tune up a radio transmitter.

Duplexer: A device that allows a single antenna to be simultaneously used for both reception and transmission.

Duty cycle: As applies to RF safety, the percentage of time that a transmitter is "on" versus "off" in a 6- or 30-minute time period.

Effective Radiated Power (ERP): The product of the transmitter (peak envelope) power, expressed in watts, delivered to the antenna, and the relative gain of an antenna over that of a half-wave dipole antenna.

Electromagnetic radiation: The propagation of radiant energy, including infrared, visible light, ultraviolet, radiofrequency, gamma and X-rays, through space and matter.

Emergency communication: Any amateur communication directly relating to the immediate safety of life of individuals or the immediate protection of property.

Examination Element: The written theory exam or CW test required for various classes of FCC Amateur Radio licenses. Technician must pass Element 2 written theory; General must pass Element 3 written theory plus Element 1 CW; Extra must pass Element 4 written theory.

Far Field: The electromagnetic field located at a great distance from a transmitting antenna. The far field begins at a distance that depends on many factors, including the wavelength and the size of the antenna. Radio signals are normally received in the far field.

FCC Form 605: The FCC application form used to apply for a new amateur operator/primary station license or to renew or modify an existing license.

Federal Communications Commission (FCC): A board of five Commissioners, appointed by the President, having the power to regulate wire and radio telecommunications in the U.S.

Feedline: A system of conductors that connects an antenna to a receiver or transmitter.

Field Day: Annual activity sponsored by the ARRL to demonstrate emergency preparedness of amateur operators.

Field strength: A measure of the intensity of an electric or magnetic field. Electric fields are measured in volts per meter; magnetic fields in amperes per meter.

Filter: A device used to block or reduce alternating currents or signals at certain frequencies while allowing others to pass unimpeded.

Frequency: The number of cycles of alternating current in one second.

Frequency coordinator: An individual or organization which recommends frequencies and other operating and/ or technical parameters for amateur repeater operation in order to avoid or minimize potential interferences.

Frequency Modulation (FM): A method of varying a radio carrier wave by causing its frequency to vary in accordance with the information to be conveyed.

Frequency privileges: The transmitting frequency bands available to the various classes of amateur operators. The various Class privileges are listed in Part 97.301 of the FCC rules.

Ground: A connection, accidental or intentional, between a device or circuit and the earth or some common body and the earth or some common body serving as the earth.

Ground wave: A radio wave that is propagated near or at the earth's surface.

Handi-Ham system: Amateur organization dedicated to assisting handicapped amateur operators. (3915 Golden Valley Road, Golden Valley, MN 55422)

Harmful interference: Interference which seriously degrades, obstructs or repeatedly interrupts the operation of a radio communication service.

Harmonic: A radio wave that is a multiple of the fundamental frequency. The second harmonic is twice the fundamental frequency, the third harmonic, three times, etc.

Hertz: One complete alternating cycle per second. Named after Heinrich R. Hertz, a German physicist. The number of hertz is the frequency of the audio or radio wave.

High Frequency (HF): The band of frequencies that lie between 3 and 30 Megahertz. It is from these frequencies that radio waves are returned to earth from the ionosphere.

High-Pass filter: A device that allows passage of high frequency signals but attenuates the lower frequencies. When installed on a television set, a high-pass filter allows TV frequencies to pass while blocking lower-frequency amateur signals.

Inverse Square Law: The physical principle by which power density decreases as you get further away from a transmitting antenna. RF power density decreases by the inverse square of the distance.

Ionization: The process of adding or stripping away electrons from atoms or molecules. Ionization occurs when substances are heated at high temperatures or exposed to high voltages. It can lead to significant genetic damage in biological tissue.

Ionosphere: Outer limits of atmosphere from which HF amateur communications signals are returned to earth.

IRC: International Reply Coupon, a method of prepaying postage for a foreign amateur's QSL card.

Jamming: The intentional, malicious interference with another radio signal.

Key clicks, Chirps: Defective keying of a telegraphy signal sounding like tapping or high varying pitches.

Linear amplifier: A device that accurately reproduces a radio wave in magnified form.

Long wire: A horizontal wire antenna that is one wavelength or longer in length.

Low-Pass filter: Device connected to worldwide transmitters that inhibits passage of higher frequencies that cause television interference but does not affect amateur transmissions.

Machine: A ham slang word for an automatic repeater station.

Malicious interference: See jamming.

MARS: The Military Affiliate Radio System. An organization that coordinates the activities of amateur communications with military radio communications.

Maximum authorized transmitting power: Amateur stations must use no more than the maximum transmitter power necessary to carry out the desired communications. The maximum P.E.P. output power levels authorized Novices are 200 watts in the 80-, 40-, 15- and 10-meter bands, 25 watts in the 222-MHz band, and 5 watts in the 1270-MHz bands.

Maximum Permissible Exposure (MPE): The maximum amount of electric and magnetic RF energy to which a person may safely be exposed.

Maximum usable frequency (MFU): The highest frequency that will be returned to earth from the ionosphere.

Medium frequency (MF): The band of frequencies that lies between 300 and 3,000 kHz (3 MHz).

Microwave: Electromagnetic waves with a frequency of 300 MHz to 300 GHz. Microwaves can cause heating of biological tissue.

Mobile operation: Radio communications conducted while in motion or during halts at unspecified locations.

Mode: Type of transmission such as voice, teletype, code, television, facsimile.

Modulate: To vary the amplitude, frequency, or phase of a radiofrequency wave in accordance with the information to be conveyed.

Morse code: The International Morse code, A1A emission. Interrupted continuous wave communications conducted using a dot-dash code for letters, numbers and operating procedure signs.

Near Field: The electromagnetic field located in the immediate vicinity of the antenna. Energy in the near field depends on the size of the antenna, its wavelength and transmission power.

Nonionizing radiation: Electromagnetic waves, or fields, which do not have the capability to alter the molecular structure of substances. RF energy is nonionizing radiation.

Novice operator: An FCC licensed, entry-level amateur operator in the amateur service.

Occupational exposure: See controlled environment.

OET: Office of Engineering & Technology, a branch of the FCC that has developed the guidelines for radiofrequency (RF) safety.

Ohm's law: The basic electrical law explaining the relationship between voltage, current and resistance. The current (I) in a circuit is equal to the voltage (E) divided by the resistance (R), or $I = E/R$.

OSCAR: "Orbiting Satellite Carrying Amateur Radio." A series of satellites designed and built by amateur operators of several nations.

Oscillator: A device for generating oscillations or vibrations of an audio or radiofrequency signal.

Packet radio: A digital method of communicating computer-to-computer. A terminal-node controller makes up the packet of data and directs it to another packet station.

Peak Envelope Power (PEP): 1. The power during one radiofrequency cycle at the crest of the modulation envelope, taken under normal operating conditions. 2. The maximum power that can be obtained from a transmitter.

Phone patch: Interconnection of amateur radio to the public switched telephone network, and operated by the control operator of the station.

Power density: A measure of the strength of an electro-magnetic field at a distance from its source. Usually expressed in milliwatts per square centimeter (mW/cm2). Far-field power density decreases according to the Law of Inverse Squares.

Power supply: A device or circuit that provides the appropriate voltage and current to another device or circuit.

Propagation: The travel of electromagnetic waves or sound waves through a medium.

Public exposure: See "uncontrolled" environment.

Q-signals: International three-letter abbreviations beginning with the letter Q used primarily to convey information using the Morse code.

QSL Bureau: An office that bulk processes QSL (radio confirmation) cards for (or from) foreign amateur operators as a postage-saving mechanism.

RACES (Radio Amateur Civil Emergency Service): A radio service using amateur stations for civil defense communications during periods of local, regional, or national emergencies.

Radiation: Electromagnetic energy, such as radio waves, traveling forth into space from a transmitter.

Radiofrequency (RF): The range of frequencies over 20 kilohertz that can be propagated through space.

Radiofrequency (RF) radiation: Electromagnetic fields or waves having a frequency between 3 kHz and 300 GHz.

Radiofrequency spectrum: The eight electromagnetic bands ranked according to their frequency and wavelength. Specifically, the very-low, low, medium, high, very-high, ultra-high, super-high, and extremely-high frequency bands.

Radio wave: A combination of electric and magnetic fields varying at a radiofrequency and traveling through space at the speed of light.

Repeater operation: Automatic amateur stations that retransmit the signals of other amateur stations.

Routine RF radiation evaluation: The process of determining if the RF energy from a transmitter exceeds the Maximum Permissible Exposure (MPE) limits in a controlled or uncontrolled environment.

RST Report: A telegraphy signal report system of Readability, Strength and Tone.

S-meter: A voltmeter calibrated from 0 to 9 that indicates the relative signal strength of an incoming signal at a radio receiver.

Selectivity: The ability of a circuit (or radio receiver) to separate the desired signal from those not wanted.

Sensitivity: The ability of a circuit (or radio receiver) to detect a specified input signal.

Short circuit: An unintended, low-resistance connection across a voltage source resulting in high current and possible damage.

Shortwave: The high frequencies that lie between 3 and 30 Megahertz that are propagated long distances.

Single-Sideband (SSB): A method of radio transmission in which the RF carrier and one of the sidebands is suppressed and all of the information is carried in the one remaining sideband.

Skip wave, Skip zone: A radio wave reflected back to earth. The distance between the radio transmitter and the site of a radio wave's return to earth.

Sky-wave: A radio wave that is refracted back to earth.

Sometimes called an ionospheric wave.

Specific Absorption Rate (SAR): The time rate at which radiofrequency energy is absorbed into the human body.

Spectrum: A series of radiated energies arranged in order of wavelength. The radio spectrum extends from 20 kilohertz upward.

Spurious Emissions: Unwanted radiofrequency signals emitted from a transmitter that sometimes cause interference.

Station license, location: No transmitting station shall be operated in the amateur service without being licensed by the FCC. Each amateur station shall have one land location, the address of which appears in the station license.

Sunspot Cycle: An 11-year cycle of solar disturbances which greatly affects radio wave propagation.

Technician operator: An Amateur Radio operator who has successfully passed Element 2.

Technician-Plus: An amateur operator who has passed a 5-wpm code test in addition to Technician Class requirements.

Telegraphy: Communications transmission and reception using CW, International Morse code.

Telephony: Communications transmission and reception in the voice mode.

Telecommunications: The electrical conversion, switching, transmission and control of audio video and data signals by wire or radio.

Temporary operating authority: Authority to operate your amateur station while awaiting arrival of an upgraded license.

Terrestrial station location: Any location of a radio station on the surface of the earth including the sea.

Thermal effects: As applies to RF radiation, biological tissue damage resulting because of the body's inability to cope with or dissipate excessive heat.

Third-party traffic: Amateur communication by or under the supervision of the control operator at an amateur station to another amateur station on behalf of others.

Time-averaging: As applies to RF safety, the amount of electromagnetic radiation over a given time. The premise of time-averaging is that the human body can tolerate the thermal load caused by high, localized RF exposures for short periods of time.

Transceiver: A combination radio transmitter and receiver.

Transition region: Area where power density decreases inversely with distance from the antenna.

Transmatch: An antenna tuner used to match the impedance of the transmitter output to the transmission line of an antenna.

Transmitter: Equipment used to generate radio waves. Most commonly, this radio carrier signal is amplitude varied or frequency varied (modulated) with information and radiated into space.

Transmitter power: The average peak envelope power (output) present at the antenna terminals of the transmitter. The term "transmitted" includes any external radiofrequency power amplifier which may be used.

Ultra High Frequency (UHF): Ultra high frequency radio waves that are in the range of 300 to 3,000 MHz.

Uncontrolled environment: Applies to those persons who have no control over their exposure to RF energy in the environment. Residences adjacent to ham radio installations are considered to be in an "uncontrolled" environment.

Upper Sideband (USB): The proper operating mode for sideband transmissions made in the new Novice 10-meter voice band. Amateurs generally operate USB at 20 meters and higher frequencies; lower sideband (LSB) at 40 meters and lower frequencies.

Very High Frequency (VHF): Very high frequency radio waves that are in the range of 30 to 300 MHz.

Volunteer Examiner: An amateur operator of at least a General Class level who prepares and administers amateur operator license examinations.

Volunteer Examiner Coordinator (VEC): A member of an organization which has entered into an agreement with the FCC to coordinate the efforts of volunteer examiners in preparing and administering examinations for amateur operator licenses.

Index

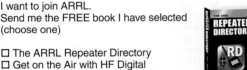

FREE
CQ Mini-Sub!

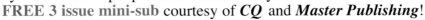

We'd like to introduce you to a Ham Radio magazine that's fun to read, interesting from cover to cover and written so that you can understand it—**FREE**! The magazine is *CQ Amateur Radio*—read and enjoyed by thousands of people each month. Get your **FREE 3 issue mini-sub** courtesy of *CQ* and *Master Publishing*!

CQ is aimed squarely at the **active** ham. You'll find features and columns covering the broad and varied landscape of the amateur radio hobby from contesting and DXing to satellites and the latest digital modes. Equipment reviews, projects and articles on the science as well as the art of radio communications—all in the pages of *CQ Amateur Radio*.

Reserve your FREE 3-issue mini-sub today!
Remove this page, fill in your information below, tape closed with the postage-paid *CQ* address showing and mail today!

Send my FREE 3-issue CQ Mini Sub to:

Name _____

Address _____

City_____ State _____ Zip _____

Email Address _____

Make a great deal even better!

Add a one-year CQ subscription to your FREE mini-sub at a

Special Introductory Rate:

☐ **15 Print issues for only $33.00**

☐ **15 Digital issues for only $25.00**

Email address for digital sub: _____

Yes! I want to take advantage of this special 15-issue offer.

☐ Check/Money Order enclosed
Bill my: ☐ Visa ☐ MasterCard ☐ AMEX ☐ Discover Exp. Date_____

Fax your order to: 516-681-2926
Visit our web site: www.cq-amateur-radio.com

BUSINESS REPLY MAIL
FIRST–CLASS MAIL   PERMIT NO. 2055   HICKSVILLE, NY

POSTAGE WILL BE PAID BY ADDRESSEE

CQ COMMUNICATIONS, INC.
17 WEST JOHN STREET, UNIT 1
HICKSVILLE NY 11801–9962

TAPE

Fill in your address information
on the reverse side of this page, fold in half,
tape closed and mail today!

FREE
CQ Amateur Radio
Mini-Sub!

TAPE

TAPE

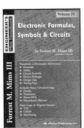

FCC Commercial Radio License Study Materials
General Radiotelephone Operator's License

GROL+RADAR

Get your FCC commercial radio licenses and add valuable credentials to your resume! *GROL+RADAR* includes the new FCC Element 1 question pool for the Marine Radio Operator Permit (MROP), the Element 3 pool for the General Radiotelephone Operator License (GROL), and the Element 8 pool for the RADAR Endorsement. Many employers require these licenses for jobs in marine, aero, safety, and municipal positions. Gordo and his team have written clear explanations for all the Q&A to make studying for these exams educational and fun. If you're an Extra Class ham, many of the technical/math questions will look familiar to you. Fully-illustrated to aid your learning. **GROL $49.95**

GROL+RADAR Book & Software Package Enhance your learning experience using our practice exam software along with the *GROL+RADAR* book. Software includes answer explanations from the book – when you select a wrong answer, the explanation from the book appears to reinforce your learning. **GRSP $79.95**

Learn More With Our 'Basic' Series

Basic Electronics

by Gene McWhorter & Alvis Evans is for anyone who wants to understand the fundamentals of electronics. Explains electronic devices and circuits – how they work and are used. Contains detailed illustrations that support easy-to-read text. Practical, worked-out examples demonstrate circuit applications. **BELC $19.95**

Basic Communications Electronics

by Jack Hudson, W9MU, & Jerry Luecke, KB5TZY. Explains analog electronic devices and circuits – how they work and how they are used to build communications systems. Emphasis on semiconductor devices and integrated circuits (ICs). For anyone who wants to understand analog electronics and wireless communications. **BCOM $19.95**

Basic Digital Electronics

by Alvis Evans. Explains digital system functions and how circuits are used to build them. Discusses the functions required to design digital systems, the circuits used to make decisions, code conversions, data selections, interfacing and storage, and the circuits that keep all operations in time and under control. **BDIG $19.95**